The 200...

Stageco...

Bus Handbook

British Bus Publishing

Body codes used in the Bus Handbook series:

Type:

A   Articulated vehicle
B   Bus, either single-deck or double-deck
BC   Interurban - high-back seated bus
C   Coach
M   Minibus with design capacity of 16 seats or less
N   Low-floor bus (*Niederflur*), either single-deck or double-deck
O   Open-top bus (CO = convertible - PO = partial open-top)

Seating capacity is then shown. For double-decks the upper deck quantity is followed by the lower deck.

Door position:-

C   Centre entrance/exit
D   Dual doorway.
F   Front entrance/exit
R   Rear entrance/exit (no distinction between doored and open)
T   Three or more access points

Equipment:-

L   Lift for wheelchair   TV   Training vehicle.
M   Mail compartment   RV   Used as tow bus or engineers vehicle.
T   Toilet

Allocation:-

t   Training bus
u   out of service - maintenance or seasonal requirement
w   Vehicle is withdrawn and awaiting disposal.

e.g. - B32/28F is a double-deck bus with thirty-two seats upstairs, twenty-eight down and a front entrance/exit.
      N43D is a low-floor bus with two or more doorways.

Re-registrations:-

Where a vehicle has gained new index marks the details are listed at the end of each fleet showing the current mark, followed in sequence by those previously carried starting with the original mark.

Regional books in the series:

The Scottish Bus Handbook
The Ireland & Islands Bus Handbook
The North East Bus Handbook
The Yorkshire Bus Handbook
The Lancashire, Cumbria and Manchester Bus Handbook
The Merseyside and Cheshire Bus Handbook
The East Midlands Bus Handbook
The West Midlands Bus Handbook
The Welsh Bus Handbook
The Eastern Bus Handbook
The South East Bus Handbook
The South West Bus Handbook

Annual books are produced for the major groups:

The Stagecoach Bus Handbook
The First Bus Handbook
The Arriva Bus Handbook
The National Express Handbook
Some editions for earlier years are available. Please contact the publisher.

Associated series:

The Hong Kong Bus Handbook
The Leyland Lynx Handbook
The Model Bus Handbook
The Postbus Handbook
The Overall Advertisment Bus Handbook - Volume 1
The Toy & Model Bus Handbook - Volume 1 - Early Diecasts
The Fire Brigade Handbook (fleet list of each local authority fire brigade)
The Fire Brigade Handbook - Special Appliances Volume 1
The Fire Brigade Handbook - Special Appliances Volume 2
The Police Range Rover Handbook

The 2003 Stagecoach Bus Handbook

The 2003 Stagecoach Bus Handbook is the eighth edition of this volume dedicated to the various bus fleets of Stagecoach Holdings, both within the United Kingdom and its overseas operations outside the Americas.

Although this book has been produced with the encouragement of, and in co-operation with, Stagecoach management, it is not an official Stagecoach fleet list and the vehicles included are subject to variation, particularly as new vehicle deliveries lead to older vehicles being 'cascaded' to other subsidiaries. Some vehicles listed are no longer in regular use on service but are retained for special purposes or preserved by the company. The services operated and the allocation of vehicles to subsidiary companies are subject to variation at any time, although accurate at the time of going to print. The contents are correct to December 2002.

Quality photographs for inclusion in the series are welcome, for which a fee is payable. The publishers unfortunately cannot accept responsibility for any loss and request you show your name on each picture or slide.

To keep the fleet information up to date we recommend the Ian Allan publication, Buses, published monthly, or for more detailed information, the PSV Circle monthly news sheets. The writer and publisher would be glad to hear from readers should any information be available which corrects or enhances that given in this publication.

Principal Editors: Stuart Martin; Bill Potter and David Donati.

Acknowledgments:
We are grateful to Keith Grimes, Nigel Hunt, Mark Jameson, Malcolm Jones, Steve Sanderson, Malcolm Tranter, Tony Wilson, the PSV Circle and the Management and officials of Stagecoach Group and their operating companies for their kind assistance and co-operation in the compilation of this book.

The front cover photo is by Mark Doggett and the fronticepiece by Mark Lyons. Rear cover pictures are by Ken Mackenzie and Richard Godfrey.

ISBN 1 897990 83 9
Published by British Bus Publishing Ltd
16 St Margaret's Drive, Wellington, Telford, TF1 3PH

Telephone: 01952 255669 - Facsimile 01952 222397 - www.britishbuspublishing.co.uk
© British Bus Publishing Ltd, January 2003

Contents

During the course of a vehicles life there are many occasions when, for a variety or reasons, it is considered desirable to move vehicles from one depot to another, and from one fleet to another. The Bus Handbook series is interested primarily in vehicles and features bus fleets, irrespective of the operators disc that may be displayed. To aid the management of Stagecoach vehicles the identification of the vehicles was consolidated into a single series in January 2003.   While many options were considered, the most appropriate seemed to organise the numbers to allow vehicles of similar type to be numbered together. To avoid input errors with leading zeros, no vehicle has been numbered below 10000.   Leyland and Volvo Ollympians have been separated as have low and standard floor vehicles. The result will allow the transfer of vehicles between depot to be undertaken more easily. Buses will be allocated numbers as they are ordered, the number being retained thought the vehicle's life. The scheme has allowed fragmented batches to be reunited in series. Latterly carrying number one in the South East fleet, R119KRG now carries number 33119. It is seen in Durrington. *Richard Godfrey*

Stagecoach

Stagecoach Group plc is a leading operator of buses, trains in the UK and overseas. This Bus Handbook details the bus and coach fleets of UK Bus and Overseas Bus though, for Coach USA, only the operation centres are listed.

Stagecoach can trace its roots back to a small self-drive caravan and caravanette rental business that was formed in Perth in 1976. Trading as Gloagtrotter (later GT Coaches), the business expanded a couple of years later to include minibus private hire under the original partnership of Ann Gloag, now one of the Non-Executive Directors of Stagecoach Group, and her husband, Robin. Her brother, Brian Souter, now Executive Chairman (an accountant by profession), joined the fledgling organisation in 1980 just prior to its starting regular long distance services at which time the Stagecoach name, suggested jointly by Ann and David, their brother, was adopted. This move into regular services was made possible by coach deregulation, introduced in the 1980 Transport Act.

Stagecoach was born out of deregulation and matured through privatisation. The freedom of deregulation and the opportunities of privatisation have facilitated the rapid growth of Stagecoach.

The first service began in October 1980, an overnight run from Dundee to London. Subsequently further legs were added that brought in Aberdeen and Glasgow to form a network of coach services within Scotland and running south of the border to London via Manchester and Birmingham. The quality of vehicle provided on these services quickly improved, exotic foreign double deck coaches in a bright livery becoming the norm from 1982 onwards in marked contrast to the traditional single deck coaches with a rather dowdy image used by their main competitor - Scottish Bus Group.

In December 1982 Mrs Gloag's husband left the business and set up his own company trading as Highwayman Coaches at Errol, near Perth. In tandem with the coach service expansion, a number of school contracts had been secured. These were operated primarily with second hand Bristol Lodekkas and, by the mid 1980s, Stagecoach was the largest operator of that type, with a fleet of over twenty. In December 1980 Stagecoach took its first step into regular bus service operation when the Perth to Errol route of A & C McLennan of Spittalfield was taken over. It was this route, which five years later, was to see the birth of the 'Provincial Routemaster Revival', that Stagecoach started when it introduced Routemasters between Perth and Errol in the spring of 1985. In the early 1980s a number of other Scottish coach operations were absorbed into Stagecoach including Adamson & Low of Edinburgh and Bennetts of Kilwinning in Ayrshire, although both were subsequently disposed of. After a period of consolidation, a further expansion into local bus services was achieved when, in November 1985, the remaining business of McLennan's of Spittalfield was purchased. This gave the Stagecoach company a significant presence in the Tayside region and, most importantly, McLennan's extensive workshops and engineering facilities at Spittalfield which were needed to maintain the ever-growing express coach fleet.

The 1985 Transport Act resulted in the deregulation of bus services outside of London. As implementation of the Act drew near, Stagecoach prepared its plans for a major expansion in the bus market. A new company was formed called Magicbus, and on 26th October 1986 it commenced operating a number of services in Glasgow. The vehicles used were primarily Routemasters and these vehicles brought back conductor operation to the city. At the same time there was some expansion of services in Tayside, with Stagecoach taking over commercially a number of rural routes left for the tendering process by Strathtay Scottish, including the routes north of Perth to Aberfeldy and Pitlochry.

With established operations in Tayside and Glasgow, and an extensive network of express services, the Stagecoach team considered for the first time acquiring operators outside its native Scotland, and took an interest in the pending privatisation of National Bus Company's subsidiaries. An unsuccessful bid for City of Oxford did not deter the directors who turned their attention to Hampshire Bus. Directors Brian Souter and Ann Gloag together with their uncle Fraser McColl and the General Manager of Hampshire Bus formed a new holding company, Skipburn Limited. Hampshire Bus, together with Pilgrim Coaches, was successfully purchased on 2nd April 1987. The new owners did not waste time in rationalising their new acquisition, with Pilgrim Coaches, which had been loss-making from the outset, closing down on 26th April 1987. By 3rd October, the Southampton area operations had been sold to Southern Vectis who formed a new company, trading as Solent Blue Line, to operate the routes. The residual Hampshire Bus operation continues as part of the Stagecoach South company with depots at Andover, Basingstoke and Winchester.

In 1987 Derek Scott joined the board as Finance Director, and subsequently played a key role in shaping the growth of the group before taking a back seat in the post of company secretary since 1996. While still digesting Hampshire Bus, the Stagecoach board turned its attention to the acquisition of a second NBC subsidiary. This time Cumberland was the target and, following a successful offer, Stagecoach took control of Cumberland Motor Services on 23rd July 1987. The Cumberland operations were based at Whitehaven with depots in Carlisle, Penrith, Keswick, Workington and Millom. The new owners quickly recast the Carlisle city network and introduced crew-operated Routemasters. The Cumberland company acquired a number of its competitors during 1988 including Yeowart's of Whitehaven and Kirkpatrick of Brigham, near Cockermouth.

In July 1987 the McColl interests in Skipburn were acquired by the then Stagecoach Holdings. However, further expansion of the group was still being sought. Under the NBC privatisation rules any purchaser could acquire only three subsidiaries. However, Hampshire Bus and Pilgrim Coaches had been classed as one unit, Cumberland a second and, therefore, Stagecoach was able to acquire United Counties as its third NBC company. The area of operation encompassed Bedford, Corby, Huntingdon, Kettering and Northampton and was the group's first presence in the Midlands. As with Cumberland, it was not long before the potential of Routemasters was realised and the Corby and Bedford networks received a fleet of these vehicles soon after the Stagecoach acquisition.

During 1988 Professor Ewan Brown CBE joined the board of directors in a non-executive capacity. Being a Merchant Banker by profession, and a former non-executive director of the Scottish Transport Group, he brought valuable skills and knowledge to the management team.

Up to this point the Stagecoach Group had acquired three NBC companies. All were operating a typical mix of National Bus Company standard vehicles that primarily consisted of Leyland Nationals and Leopards, and Bristol VRTs. Additionally, the fleet in Scotland was mainly secondhand Routemasters and Bristol Lodekkas together with Volvo B58 and Neoplan coaches for the express network. Vehicles in Scotland were in the then standard Stagecoach livery of white with blue, red and mustard (later to become orange) stripes and it was decided that in order to provide flexibility and enable vehicles to be transferred between fleets, all vehicles in the group would be painted in this corporate style. Very quickly the new livery began to appear on all three English fleets.

New vehicle purchases had to be made in order that the bus companies could maintain and develop their business into the 1990s and early purchases of Alexander-bodied Mercedes 709 minibuses and Olympians were to be a portent of large numbers of vehicles of these types in years to come. The importance of investing in new vehicles, and its consequent increase in patronage and reduction of maintenance costs, has continued.

The most significant event of 1988 was the private placing of a quantity of Stagecoach shares with institutional investors. This raised £5 million and set the financial scene for Stagecoach to develop into a major force within the bus industry. It was also a sign of things to come, that is the planned Stock Market flotation five years later.

1989 saw the first Stagecoach acquisition overseas when, in March of that year, it purchased a 51% share in United Transport Malawi Limited from United Transport International, a British Electric Traction (BET) subsidiary.

The vehicles operated in Africa were somewhat strange to British eyes with large numbers of ERF Trailblazer and Leyland Victory single deckers, all built to meet the rough African conditions where much mileage is run on dirt roads. Full details of the vehicles with pictures can be found in the mid 1990s editions of this Handbook. Stagecoach sold the operation in 1997 though some of the double-deck buses were returned for operation in Greater Manchester.

Having ventured into Africa, Stagecoach soon returned to the acquisition trail in England. East Midland Motor Services had been sold to its management by NBC, but in April 1989 the management decided to sell its entire share holding, Stagecoach being the purchaser. The operation was conducted under East Midland, Mansfield & District, and Rainworth Travel names in the East Midlands area, and in addition there were two Frontrunner operations, one based in Essex and the other in north west Derbyshire and eastern Greater Manchester. The Frontrunner South East operation was quickly sold on to Ensign Bus of Purfleet while Ribble absorbed the Derbyshire/Manchester operation. This left the East Midland management to concentrate on its own territory and soon its coaching operations were consolidated into Rainworth Travel which was renamed Midland Travel. The bus operations were based in Worksop, Chesterfield and Mansfield and, as with other acquisitions, former London Routemasters were again tried, this time in Mansfield where Routemaster operation lasted until 1991. In May 1993 the Midland Travel coaching operation was sold to Skills of Nottingham.

Only a matter of days after the East Midland acquisition, a further company was acquired from its management. Ribble Motor Services Limited, based in the north west of England, had also been bought by its management team and had subsequently purchased, from United Transport, the Bee Line Buzz Company - a large minibus operation based in Manchester, together with the Zippy minibus operation based in Preston.

Having added two major bus companies in North West England to one it already owned, Stagecoach embarked upon a reorganisation and rationalisation of its interests in the area. The Barrow-in-Furness municipal undertaking had been in financial difficulties for some time, following heavy competition with Ribble, and its services and depot were acquired in May 1989. For operational control reasons, and to align with county boundaries, Ribble's South Cumbrian and Lake District operations were transferred to Cumberland Motor Services, which also took control in Barrow. In September of 1989 Ribble sold its Bee Line Buzz subsidiary and some of its own Ribble Manchester operations to the Drawlane Group though it retained the Preston-based Zippy minibuses. Ribble remained to concentrate on the central Lancashire area and Bolton.

Despite the activity in England there were still changes taking place in Scotland during 1989. On 19th June new bus services in and around the cities of Perth and Dundee were introduced, primarily in competition with Strathtay Scottish, whose managing director, Neil Renilson was recruited by the group at the same time. This new network was branded Perth Panther and, after a prolonged period of competition, in which both operators used Routemasters on Perth City services, Strathtay closed their Crieff depot and operations in 1991 and their Perth depot and operations in the summer of 1993.

Perhaps the most surprising development of 1989 was the decision by Stagecoach to sell the express coach operations that had been the genesis of the company. On 4th August

1989 the company announced the sale of its express network to National Express who re-branded the operation as Caledonian Express. With this sale Stagecoach clearly indicated that it was to concentrate on local bus operations in future. The Scottish operations saw further expansion when Inverness Traction was purchased from receivership in November. Inverness Traction had been competing with Highland Scottish on town services in Inverness since 1987. Stagecoach placed this Inverness operation under the Magicbus and Perth Panther management, and renamed the Magicbus company Stagecoach Scotland Ltd as the holding company. All of these operations were carving out their market through head to head competition with established state-owned operators, whereas in England established operators had been purchased, and competitive pressures were the other way round.

The south coast of England was not neglected either. In August 1989 the management of Southdown decided to sell out to Stagecoach. This brought a sixth former NBC subsidiary into the fold and Stagecoach then acquired, in October, the operations of Portsmouth City Bus from Southampton City Bus who held 75% and a workers' co-operative which owned the remaining 25%. In December 1989 Hastings and District was added when the management sold the company, which it had bought from NBC.

In 1990 there was expansion overseas with the purchase of Gray Coach Lines of Toronto, Canada. This brought to the Stagecoach Group an extensive network of express coach services throughout eastern Canada together with Niagara Falls sightseeing tours and the Toronto City/Airport express coach service. The venture proved to be unsuccessful in financial terms and the Group's interest in Gray Coach Lines was sold to Greyhound Lines of Canada in December 1992, but not before a number of Stagecoach Scotland Bristol FLFs had been transferred for sightseeing tour work.

One result of the large expansion on the south coast of England was an inquiry by the Monopolies and Mergers Commission. The DTI subsequently instructed Stagecoach to divest themselves of Portsmouth City Bus, and this operation was later sold to Transit Holdings in January 1991. The South of England subsidiaries that remained were then restructured and consolidated in April 1992 when a new company, Stagecoach South Limited, was given overall control of Hastings Buses, Southdown and Hampshire Bus. As part of the reorganisation Southdown was split into two operating companies, Sussex Coastline Buses and South Coast Buses, the latter also taking in Hastings Buses. The Southdown name was discontinued, and South Coast Buses operating from Eastbourne and Hastings with Coastline Buses trading from Chichester, Havant and Worthing.

Following on from the privatisation of NBC the Government decided to extend privatisation to the Scottish Bus Group. It was decreed that any one purchaser could acquire only two companies and Stagecoach completed its quota with the purchase of Bluebird Northern and Fife Scottish during the first half of 1991. Bluebird was acquired in March and its archaic legal company name of Northern Scottish Omnibuses Ltd was quickly changed to Bluebird Buses Ltd. Bluebird was placed under common management with Stagecoach Scotland Ltd and its fleet renumbered into a single series.

By July of 1991 the Fife company was also under the Stagecoach umbrella, and in the autumn of 1991 Stagecoach Scotland further expanded when it took over the remaining Inverness and Easter Ross area operations from Highland, adding some 30 extra buses to the Inverness Traction fleet, plus the former Highland depot at Tain.

With two former SBG companies now under its wing, plus the Perth and Inverness operations, Stagecoach had established a strong presence on the eastern side of Scotland. In line with Stagecoach policy the corporate colours started to appear on the newly-acquired fleets and fleet renewal commenced, primarily involving Alexander-bodied Mercedes minibuses and Leyland Olympians. There were also transfers north of the border of vehicles from the English companies, which resulted in some unfamiliar types of vehicle being introduced into Scotland, especially ECW-bodied Bristol VRTs. The VRT had been despised by SBG with all its initial examples being exchanged for NBC-owned Bristol FLFs.

November 1991 saw further expansion in Africa following BET's decision to divest itself of local bus operations throughout the world and Stagecoach saw potential in acquiring its Kenya operations to add to those of Malawi though all the African interests have now been sold. There is one company in the Stagecoach Group that plays a not insignificant part in the UK transport system as a whole, but operates no buses. National Transport Tokens was formed in the 1970s to manufacture and distribute concessionary travel tokens to various bodies, mostly local authorities and a minority shareholding came to Stagecoach with the purchase of Ribble in April 1989. The aluminium tokens produced by National Transport Tokens are accepted by a variety of operators in lieu of cash fares, including bus companies, taxi firms and rail services. Stagecoach bought a controlling interest in the company in March 1992 and its headquarters were moved from Manchester to Preston and, more recently, Blackburn.

It came as a significant surprise in April 1992 when Stagecoach decided to sell another of its initial operations. Having disposed of the express network the deal was now to sell the Glasgow-based Magicbus operation to recently privatised Kelvin Central Buses. The vehicles transferred included some newly-delivered Dennis Darts and a substantial number of Bristol VRTs and Routemasters, and Kelvin also acquired the Glasgow depot. The Magicbus name and Stagecoach livery continued in use with Kelvin Central until 1993 as part of the deal.

1992 also saw further expansion of the southern fleet when Stagecoach acquired Alder Valley's operations based at depots in Aldershot, Alton and Hindhead. Alder Valley had been through a particularly disturbed time having had a number of owners since privatisation from NBC and suffering from subsequent fragmentation. The operation acquired by Stagecoach was placed under the Stagecoach South umbrella and is operated under the brand name Hants & Surrey.

Having seen the deregulation and privatisation process in the United Kingdom the Wellington municipal authority in New Zealand decided to embark on a similar course of action. In October 1992 the Wellington City Transport undertaking was privatised and Stagecoach was the successful bidder. There are three companies involved: Wellington City Transport, with a depot at Kilbirnie and an outstation at Karori; Cityline Auckland based at Papakura and Cityline Hutt Valley with depots at Lower Hutt and Stokes Valley. With its new undertaking, Stagecoach gained experience of operating MAN and Hino vehicles but, more interestingly, also operating electric traction. The Wellington City Transport fleet contains over seventy Volvo trolleybuses while Wellington City Transport's share in Harbour City Cable Car Limited resulted in Stagecoach having an operating interest in this funicular railway for a short time.

Overseas developments in 1992 were not confined to Africa and New Zealand. For some time Stagecoach had held a stake in Speedybus Enterprises Limited of Hong Kong, whose primary functions were to sell advertising space on double deckers it supplied to Chinese municipal bus companies, and to import vehicles to China through Hong Kong. Speedybus also supplied Hong Kong double deckers to Stagecoach Malawi. In 1992 Stagecoach Hong Kong Ltd was formed to tender for bus services in Hong Kong, and to gain an operating base in the colony. (Speedybus was primarily a bus dealer and bus advertising contractor rather than an operator, and Stagecoach's 50% interest was disposed of in 1993). In 1994 the company commenced operating services on two commuter routes with five Volvo B10Ms. These vehicles were almost the same as the Stagecoach standard Alexander PS-bodied Volvo B10Ms except for their length and that they were fitted with air conditioning to cope with the humid Hong Kong climate. In 1995 six tri-axle Volvo Olympians joined the operation and a second residents' route was introduced. The Hong Kong operations were sold in the summer of 1996 after attempts to enlarge the business through the tendering/franchising process had been unsuccessful.

In the spring of 1993 Lancaster City Council expressed an intention to sell its municipal bus undertaking, much of the network comprising joint services with Ribble. As Ribble already had a substantial presence in Lancaster and the surrounding area, Stagecoach was not expected to be a bidder for the operation. However, in order to protect its interests in the area, Ribble registered many of Lancaster City's routes and subsequently the City Council decided to liquidate their undertaking, selling the depot and some twelve buses to Ribble during 1993. As a result of this acquisition Ribble was able to close its own, smaller, depot in Morecambe and move into the former council depot in Heysham, which it retained until new facilities were opened in 2000.

Expansion in the south of England continued in 1993 when the management of East Kent sold their company. This is yet another former NBC subsidiary that was originally purchased by a management team. Again the new acquisition was placed under the control of Stagecoach South. In 1994 four Dennis low-floor vehicles with Berkhof bodies were allocated to South's fleet for the Canterbury Park and Ride service, these being the first such vehicles in the Stagecoach Group with more of the type delivered during 1996 for a Greater Manchester PTE contract.

While the Government had not legislated for the privatisation of municipal bus companies, a number of councils took the opportunity to sell before the end of 1993 to allow all of the income from the sale to be used on other projects. (The proportion for reallocation was later reduced to 75% if sold before 31st March 1997).

Grimsby Cleethorpes Transport was jointly owned by the Boroughs of Grimsby and Cleethorpes and the two councils decided to sell the undertaking through a competitive tendering process and Stagecoach were the successful bidder. The deal was completed in November 1993 and brought the Stagecoach livery to South Humberside. The vehicles acquired were of a typical municipal nature and included substantial numbers of Dennis Dominators and Lances. The last of the five Lances delivered in 1993 was painted into Stagecoach livery before delivery.

The 1000th new bus to join Stagecoach was handed over to Ann Gloag and Brian Souter on the opening day of Coach & Bus 93; this was a Volvo B6 destined for United Counties. The order for new vehicles for delivery in 1995 was the largest annual order for buses in the UK since privatisation began in the 1980s. Purchasing policy continued to be based on Volvo double deck and single deck chassis together with Mercedes-Benz minibuses, though during 1995 Dennis started to supply their Dart and Javelin in significant numbers. Alexander, with assembly plants in Scotland and Northern Ireland, were the preferred bus body builder with Plaxton as the coach body supplier. Some vehicles were bodied by Northern Counties when destined to be for the Group's provincial operations.

December 1993 saw a further major acquisition by Stagecoach. Western Travel Ltd was formed on the privatisation of the Cheltenham and Gloucester company from NBC. Cheltenham and Gloucester operates in both the cities in its title together with services in Swindon and the Cotswolds based on Stroud. Western Travel itself went on the acquisition trail as part of the NBC privatisation process and acquired the Midland Red South company which brought with it operations in Leamington Spa, Nuneaton, Rugby, Stratford-upon-Avon and Warwick. Western Travel had also secured the eastern part of the National Welsh operation trading as Red & White, adding operations around the Red & White historical base of Monmouthshire and the eastern valleys of South Wales. A further 650 vehicles were added to the Stagecoach Group with this purchase, the first being painted into corporate colours in December 1993.

1993 also saw the company become listed on the London Stock Exchange. The successful share flotation attracted much publicity and the proceeds gave the group access to considerable additional funds with which to expand. Some 20,000 (over 90%) of Stagecoach's UK employees became shareholders. A significant addition to the management team in 1993 was Keith Cochrane, who was appointed company secretary and group financial controller. He later became group finance director in 1996 and in February 2000 he succeeded Mike Kinski as group chief executive. At 35, Keith Cochrane was one of the youngest CEOs of larger listed UK companies.

1994 saw the bus industry's consolidation accelerate and Stagecoach's development move into the larger metropolitan markets in which it previously had limited operations. The year opened with the launch of Stagecoach Manchester at the end of January. Although a division of Ribble, it traded separately under its own brand name on the long established 192 route from central Manchester to Hazel Grove south of Stockport. Originally set up as a unit with sixteen B6s, rapid passenger growth called for more and larger vehicles, and the year finished with 23 B10Ms allocated to the route. In the autumn of 1995 this operation, with the vehicles, was sold to EYMS Group Ltd who also operated south Manchester services through their Finglands subsidiary.

The first full scale acquisition of 1994 was Western Scottish, a former SBG company, which was owned by its management and employees. Western is based at Ayr with other depots at Cumnock, Dumfries, Kilmarnock and Stranraer, and a number of sub-depots both on the mainland and on the Isle of Arran. Shortly after acquisition the legal company name was changed to Western Buses Limited.

In July 1994 Busways Travel Services Ltd became a subsidiary company of Stagecoach. Busways Travel Services Ltd was a private limited company established by the Transport Act 1985 to acquire the bus undertaking of Tyne and Wear Passenger Transport Executive.

Busways commenced trading in October 1986 under the ownership of the PTA, though its origins can be found in the municipal transport undertakings in Newcastle upon Tyne, South Shields and Sunderland, and also the private companies acquired in 1973 (Armstrong Galley) and 1975 (Economic). In May 1989 a management/employee buyout was successfully completed. The management of ten purchased 51% of the shares while 49% were purchased for employees through an ESOP. The Tyne and Wear Omnibus Company Ltd was acquired in November 1989 and in August 1993 Busways acquired a majority shareholding in Wellcome Passenger Transport Ltd.

With a fleet of 590 buses and coaches Busways provided mainly urban local bus services in the Newcastle upon Tyne, South Shields and Sunderland areas whose combined population is approximately a million. Because of the strength of the Busways brand names in the local market the group agreed that Busways should retain its distinctive liveries once Busways joined the group and the presentation of trading names was revised to include reference to group membership. However, during 1995 corporate livery was introduced following a local employee decision after market research showed the group livery to have a more modern image.

Also in the summer of 1994, Stagecoach announced its intention to buy a 20% share in Mainline, the former South Yorkshire PTE bus operation based on Sheffield, Doncaster and Rotherham. In October, however, the Office of Fair Trading decided to investigate this purchase the result being a requirement for Stagecoach to divest its interest. While a sale to FirstGroup was agreed, an appeal against the principle of forced divestment was made but subsequently lost in the London courts.

The breakthrough into London bus operation was achieved in September 1994 with the purchase of London Buses' subsidiaries East London and Selkent as part of the privatisation of the capital's red bus fleets. In the case of East London this returned Stagecoach operations to that area of the city following the disposal of East Midland's

Frontrunner South East in 1989 to Ensign Bus of Purfleet. Both companies run local suburban services in their respective areas of London as well as trunk routes into the central area. East London's fleet comprised 600 buses operating out of depots at Leyton, Barking, East Ham and Stratford, while Selkent's had 450 buses operating from depots at Bromley, Catford, Plumstead and Orpington, the latter since closed as a result of the Roundabout network tender losses.

Further expansion in the urban areas of the north east of England followed a few weeks later with the acquisition of Cleveland Transit early in the month of October, and along with it 51% of the share capital of formerly troubled Kingston upon Hull City Transport. The remaining 49% of Kingston upon Hull City transport owned by the ESOP was also acquired. Days later, Darlington City Transport, which had been experiencing financial problems for some time, ceased trading after Busways established a competing network of services in the town, and with it the birth of Stagecoach Darlington. In the middle of the following month Hartlepool Transport joined Stagecoach in an agreed sale. Hartlepool, also based in the county of Cleveland, employed some 145 staff and operated 68 vehicles. In 1995 the management of the Darlington operation was transferred from Busways to Cleveland Transit.

November 1994 was planned to see the return of Stagecoach into Glasgow with the introduction of Stagecoach Glasgow, a 60-vehicle quality operation, in similar fashion to the Manchester unit. However, two days before Stagecoach Glasgow was due to commence operations, Strathclyde Buses announced they would sell 20% of their shares to Stagecoach in a similar style deal to the Mainline share exchange, and the Stagecoach Glasgow operation, staff and 18 Volvo B10Ms passed to SBL. Like the Mainline operation, this holding attracted the attention of the Monopolies and Mergers Commission who, after investigation, instructed divestment. A legal appeal was lost in July 1996, although the DTI agreed in an out of court settlement not to seek any undertakings against Stagecoach in Strathclyde (apart from separate undertakings in respect of A1 services in Ayrshire) or South Yorkshire.

Further expansion in 1995 commenced in January with the acquisition of A1 Service. This was a complex sale in that Ayrshire Bus Owners was the last Scottish co-operative bus company and was owned by nine separate family members. Stagecoach took 75 vehicles with the purchase, not all constituent members sold all their vehicles, and Stagecoach declined to purchase some of the most elderly vehicles. As a result of this and an urgent need to replace many of those acquired, Leyland Titans and Bristol VRs were transferred from other companies to ensure operational needs were met. During the year no less than 21 new Volvo Olympians and many modern mid-life vehicles were placed with this operation to replace the very elderly A1 fleet, which had been the subject of a Traffic Commissioner's maintenance hearing and warning shortly prior to the sale to Stagecoach.

Despite the small scale of this operation the Secretary of State for Trade and Industry directed the Monopolies and Mergers Commission to inquire into the purchase. Much criticism of the MMC was voiced over this inquiry as each investigation costs the taxpayer a considerable amount of money and consumes valuable management time and energy. It was widely commented on at the time that often larger acquisitions by other groups were being cleared without referral. In November the report was published allowing the retention of the operation providing certain conditions on fares and service levels were adhered to.

June 1995 saw the announcement of a joint venture with Montagu Private Equity to buy part of Rodoviária de Lisboa, the main operator in and around the Portuguese capital. The main towns served are Cascais, Estoril and Sintra, with the 900mm gauge Sintra tram operation included though this has subsequently returned to municipal operation. In 2001 the Portuguese operations was sold. In New Zealand Stagecoach acquired the operations of Cesta Travel in Wellington, which brought one additional vehicle to the fleet and Stokes Valley Coaches of Upper Hutt. The Runcimans Motors business was also acquired with bus services taken into the Cityline Hutt Valley operation initially while the remaining contract and hire business was acquired subsequently, retaining a local identity.

In July 1995 Stagecoach confirmed the acquisition of ailing Chesterfield Transport following an Extraordinary General Meeting at which 99% of Chesterfield's employees voted in favour of the take over. The Chesterfield operation was placed under East Midland management, who moved its local depot to the former municipal's Stonegravels depot. This acquisition too became the subject of a Monopolies and Mergers Commission enquiry with vehicle repainting delayed pending the outcome. Meanwhile ten much-travelled B10Ms were transferred in from Ribble. This purchase was found to be in the public interest and cleared during 1996 allowing the fleet to be renumbered and brought together.

October brought Coach and Bus 95 at which four Stagecoach buses were exhibited by various suppliers. Mercedes-Benz displayed the 800th 709D for the group, destined for Cumberland. On the Northern Counties stand was the last of 52 Volvo Olympians destined for Selkent, all of which are now in provincial fleets. Also in red livery was an Alexander-bodied Dennis Dart for East London but the main Stagecoach attraction was the Volvo B10L demonstrator for the group. After the show it operated in the Fife fleet for a year alongside new B10Ms and featured the Säffle-designed body built by Alexander as its Ultra model.

The investment in new vehicles continued during 1995 with some 627 new vehicles delivered in the year ending 30th April, and at Coach and Bus 95 substantial corporate orders were announced totaling over 1000 buses for delivery during 1996. 1996 was another year of outstanding growth with pre-tax profits up 34% despite adverse weather and fuel duty increases. In Scotland, Bluebird was granted the Royal Warrant for services to the Royal Family with vehicles at Ballater now displaying the Royal Coat of Arms. Western Buses saw the greatest change with many services revised and new routes introduced, including several Stagecoach Express inter-urban services providing links from the centres of operation to Glasgow and Edinburgh. Fife introduced the first articulated coaches on its service from Glasgow and further articulated coaches built by Plaxton entered service with other fleets. In November 1996 Bluebird won the prestigious Bus Company of the year award, at a ceremony in London where the Managing Director, Neil Renilson, received the award from the then Minister of Transport, John Watts.

The north west of England saw the acquisition of GM Buses South (now Stagecoach Manchester) in February after several months of speculation. Also in the north west, Ribble secured the Hyndburn operations during September; the services to be provided from several Ribble depots as the purchase did not include the Hyndburn operation buildings in Accrington.

The Midlands fleets were joined by Cambus in 1995 and the administration of Cambus and Chesterfield Transport were integrated into East Midland at Chesterfield. The MMC report presented to Parliament in 1996 noted that Chesterfield Transport could have collapsed if Stagecoach had not made the merger offer. Following the merger with Cambus undertakings were agreed with the Department of Trade that the divestment of the Huntingdon depot and Milton Keynes operations of Cambus would be made and this took place the following year.

In the west of England two operations units were in operation, Stagecoach West and Stagecoach Devon the latter acquired from Transit Holdings in February 1996. All three divisions of Stagecoach West (Cheltenham & Gloucester, Midland Red South and Red & White) received new single deck buses and minibuses during the year with the Volvo B10Ms being devoted to the important corridors of Nuneaton-Coventry,

Cheltenham-Gloucester and Newport-Tredegar. The Devon operation was formed by the amalgamation into one company with two operational divisions of Exeter and Torbay, the latter acquiring open-top Bristol VRs to re-instate regular big-bus services in the Torquay area. 185 vehicles were delivered to Stagecoach South in 1996, some 25% of the fleet strength. Stagecoach South also received Titans from Selkent as part of a group policy to cascade urban vehicles to lighter duties at mid-life and help minimise whole-life costs.

During March 1996 the small Hong Kong operation was sold, the B10Ms moving to New Zealand while the Olympians remained on the colony, passing to Citybus.

The group was awarded a seven-year franchise for South West Trains in December 1995 and took over operations in February 1996. SWT operates urban and main line passenger rail services from London Waterloo to over 200 stations principally in south west London, Surrey, Hampshire and Dorset using 1022 vehicles, mainly electric multiple units and all the Class 159 diesel rail cars. One of the early developments was the introduction of bus/rail feeder services between Romsey-Winchester and Bordon-Liphook using buses initially provided by East London though operated by Stagecoach South. The Isle of Wight rail line franchise was also awarded to Stagecoach during 1996.

August 1996 saw the acquisition of Porterbrook Leasing Company MEBO Limited, one of three railway rolling stock leasing operators (ROSCO). Control of this operation was sold in 1999 at a substantial profit to the group.

Swebus was acquired on 2nd October, though the announcement that Stagecoach was the preferred bidder was made several weeks earlier though this operations was sold in 1999 to help fund other projects. The Swebus fleet was detailed in the 1999 edition of this book.

Some 625 vehicles were ordered for 1997 delivery for Stagecoach's British fleets In the year to April 1998 turnover increased by 20% to £1,381 million, the results reflecting the first full year contributions from Porterbrook and Swebus, an improved performance from South West Trains as well as further growth within the UK bus division. This growth was attributed to organic passenger growth of 1.6% achieved mostly through ticket initiatives and innovative network planning. On 30th April 1998, Stagecoach announced Mike Kinski's appointment as Group Chief Executive with Brian Souter continuing as Executive Chairman. The 1998 vehicle delivery for the UK bus division included the first from MAN with Oxford (acquired from Transit Holdings in July the previous year) and Manchester introducing the low floor examples, while Jonckheere became the preferred supplier of coach bodywork supplying examples for both luxury and inter-urban duties.

1998 also saw Stagecoach focus on improving customer service and the development of integrated public transport, particularly around Prestwick airport, the Supertram services in Sheffield and to connect with Virgin Trains (where Stagecoach acquired a 49% interest in October).

The Overseas Bus Division saw expansion in New Zealand when the 600-vehicle Yellow Bus Company and Fuller's Ferries were acquired. These were consolidated into the existing operations. Fuller's Ferries operate nine vessels on routes between Auckland and surrounding islands.

As 1998 drew towards its close the South China Morning Post reported that Stagecoach had commenced negotiations to purchase a substantial holding in Hong Kong Citybus from China Paint, acquiring control in March 1999. Citybus operate approximately 110 franchised routes with more than 950 buses. The network is governed by two franchises. The Hong Kong island franchise covers the routes within Hong Kong island and cross harbour routes to Kowloon. The Chek Lap Kok airport franchise covers routes to the airport from Hong Kong island and Tung Chung, a new town on Lantau Island. The company also operates non-franchised services on residential routes and when acquired ran five long-haul routes between Hong Kong and the southern part of Guangdong province, though these ceased in 2000. On 7th May, the group acquired 45% of Hong Kong Kwoon Chung (Chongqing) Bus Investments which has been placed under Citybus control. This operation, involves three metropolitan routes in mainland China.

Turnover grew a further 15% across all the business in 1999 and the new vehicle programme for 1999 included 16 Volvo B10M coaches for National Express contracts with Jonckheere bodywork; 2 Plaxton MPDs for Western Scottish; 100 10-metre Dennis Dart SLF bodied by Plaxton (66) and Alexander; 106 MAN 18.220 low floor buses with Alexander ALX300 bodywork and a further 172 Dennis Tridents with Alexander bodywork, the majority to 'London' specification. The continued investment in new buses brought the average age of the fleet to seven years, one of the lowest in the industry.

On 14th June 1999 the group announced it proposed to acquire Coach USA. At the time of purchase, Coach USA was the largest provider of motorcoach charter and sightseeing services and one of the largest non-municipal providers of commuter and transit services in USA. This purchase introduced the North American Bus Division into the group structure. Coach USA conducts operations throughout the United States and parts of Canada with operating locations in over 120 cities. Coach USA operates approximately 9500 buses, coaches and taxicabs. Since May 1996 the company had increased its size through the purchase of over 70 motorcoach and taxicab businesses.

To partly fund Coach USA it was decided to sell the Swebus operation during 1999, thus reducing the group's European presence in favour of North America.

To end the 20th Century the UK Bus Division took in 731 buses during the year 2000. These comprised a further 60 MAN/Alexander ALX300 buses, 158 Dennis Trident/Alexander ALX400 and 5 Dennis Tridents/Plaxton President. The rest were Dennis Darts with 29 receiving ALX200 bodywork, 66 being the SPD variant supplied by Plaxton with the balance of 53 being supplied in varying lengths of the Plaxton Pointer.

In April 2000 the group sold the rail leasing company Porterbrook to Abbey National. Much time was spent on the rail division during the year with new proposals for the extension of the South West Trains franchise along with Virgin-Stagecoach proposals for the East Coast Main Line. Brian Hinkley left the Board in July 2000 being replaced by Graham Eccles from the rail industry.

Brian Cox, an Executive Director of Stagecoach Group was appointed full time Executive Chairman of the UK Bus division with Les Warneford as Managing Director for the whole division. The new structure includes twelve operating companies reduced from nineteen. The new structure was to deliver both a stronger centre based in Perth, with the companies supported by a new information technology system for the division. Fuel Saver tickets aimed at moving people from cars onto buses is one of the main initiatives of the launch. The group used the opportunity to introduce a new corporate styling, its first change in twenty years, which started to appear on new buses from 2001. Changes to styling involved a new interior scheme and the introduction of Lazzerini Practico seats with a new mid blue moquette that incorporates the new logo. A 'London' version of the scheme was adapted to meet the tendering requirements though it retains the family look all aimed at a new drive to attract people onto the buses.

In 2001 the bus operations at four depots in East Lancashire were sold to Blazefield Holdings, while contract renewals in London have taken the share of TfL routes to 16%.

New vehicle deliveries for 2001 and 2002 were mostly destined for the London operations with planned cascades to the provinces. In 2001 these comprised 176 Alexander-bodied Dennis Tridents along with 110 Dennis Darts with Alexander bodywork of varying lengths with more of the same types for 2002. The provincial needs met by a further fifty MAN 18.220 buses with ALX300 bodywork in 2001 and a further fifty are expected soon. Optare Solo minibuses for Midland Red and Lancashire and Excel midibuses for East Midlands were a new departure and these joined a single 8.5 metre Dart for Devon.

The new millennium saw much change to the UK rail network. Consequent to the accident at Hatfield, major disruption occurred to the whole service network. Stagecoach remained firmly committed to rebuilding the confidence of passengers to deliver a modern, efficient and safe railway though the liquidation of Railtrack has caused further uncertainly. Its two principal operations, South West Trains and Virgin Rail Group have seen much investment in new units. Stagecoach was granted preferred bidder status for a franchise for South West Trains and placed a £1 billion order for new rolling stock the first of which are now arriving in the UK having been built and tested on the continent before delivery to the UK through the tunnel. At Virgin the new Voyager and Pendelino trains are now in service.

Stagecoach believe their Kick Start proposal for targeted funding, successfully implemented in New Zealand and trialed in our home town of Perth in Scotland, can benefit communities across the country, delivering more comprehensive bus services, reduced congestion, better value for the taxpayer, with important environmental and social inclusion benefits.

Kick Start is now being promoted to the UK Government. Both partners recognised that bus priority measures alone were insufficient to develop rapid organic passenger growth. The New Zealand system incorporates, Transfund, a government established central funding body, which makes payments to regional councils to enable authorities to contract bus operators to introduce service increases short-term investment over three years to fund public transport improvements until they attract sufficient new passengers to make these services sustainable. The majority of Kick Start projects have arisen from ideas for service improvements developed by bus operators and then submitted to regional councils.

As a result the New Zealand fleet has been increased significantly and a further sixty buses are on order. For UK Bus, 2003 sees the new fleet numbers applied to the vehicles. The new scheme has taken an intellegent approach to the single fleet scheme and will allow geater flexablity in fleet management and swifter transfers between operations. Most types may be identified from their first two digits with last three reflecting their number or index mark where possible. In future numbers will be allocated as vehicles are ordered, thus the 2003 planned deliveries are shown.

More and more services are being operated on behalf of local authorities, either as tendered services or direct contracts Occasionally these require the use of specific buses with promotional liveries. Three Tridents carry the Canterbury Park and Ride livery seen here on 17690, X602VDY features single-door bodywork.
Richard Godfrey

Stagecoach UK Depots

East Scotland:	ES
Aberdeen	AN
Aberhill	AL
Banchory	BJ
Buckie (Elgin, Moray)	BQ
Cowdenbeath	CJ
Dunfermline	DE
Glenrothes	GS
Inverness	IS
Kirkcaldy	KY
Perth	PH
Peterhead (Buchan)	FH
St Andrews	SA

West Scotland:	WS
Ardrossan	AS
Arran	AA
Ayr	AY
Cumnock	CC
Dumfries	DS
Dunoon	DU
Glasgow	GW
Kilmarnock	KK
Rothesay	RO
Stranraer	SR

North East:	NE
Byker, Newcastle	BY
Darlington	DA
Hartlepool	HP
Slatyford, Newcastle	SY
South Shields	SS
Stockton	SC
Sunderland	SU

North West:	NW
Barrow	BA
Carlisle	CE
Chorley	CY
Kendal	KL
Lillyhall	LL
Morecambe	ME
Preston	PR

Manchester:	MA
Glossop	GP
Hyde Road, Manchester	HE
Princess Road, Manchester	PS
Charles Street, Stockport	CS
Stockport (Daw Bank)	ST

East Midlands:	EM
Chesterfield	CH
Grimsby	GY
Hull	HL
Mansfield	MD
Worksop	WP

East:	EA
Bedford	BD
Cambridge	CB

	CX
Corby	CX
Kettering	KG
Northampton	NN
Peterborough	PE

South Midlands:	SM
Banbury	BB
Leamington	LE
Nuneaton	NU
Oxford	OX
Rugby	RU
Witney	WY

London:	LN
Barking	BK
Bow	BW
Bromley	TB
Catford	TL
Leyton,	T
Plumstead	PD
North Street, Romford	NS
Stratford	SD
Upton Park	U

South East:	SE
Aldershot	AT
Andover	AR
Ashford	AD
Basingstoke	BE
Canterbury	CA
Chichester	CR
Chichester (Sussex Bus)	SB
Dover	DO
Folkestone	FO
Hastings	HS
Lewes	LS
Portsmouth	PM
Thanet	TH
Winchester	WI
Worthing	WG

South West:	SW
Exeter	EX
Exmouth	EH
Torquay	TQ

Wales & West:	WW
Aberdare	AE
Brynmawr	BR
Caerphilly	CL
Cheltenham	CT
Chepstow	CW
Cirencester	CI
Cwmbran	CN
Gloucester	GR
Merthyr Tydfil	MR
Porth	PT
Ross-on-Wye	RY
Stroud	SZ
Swindon	SN

Stagecoach UK *Depot Codes - code order*

Arran	AA	Morecambe	ME
Aberdare	AE	Merthyr Tydfil	MR
Ashford	AD	Mansfield	MD
Abcrhill	AL	Northampton	NN
Aberdeen	AN	North Street, Romford	NS
Andover	AR	Nuneaton	NU
Ardrossan	AS	Oxford	OX
Aldershot	AT	Plumstead	PD
Ayr	AY	Peterborough	PE
Barrow	BA	Perth	PH
Bedford	BD	Portsmouth	PM
Basingstoke	BE	Princess Road, Manchester	PS
Banchory	BJ	Porth	PT
Barking	BK	Preston	PR
Brynmawr	BR	Rothesay	RO
Buckie / Elgin	BQ	Rugby	RU
Bow	BW	Ross-on-Wye	RY
Banbury	BB	St Andrews	SA
Byker, Newcastle	BY	Sussex Bus	SB
Canterbury	CA	Stockton	SC
Cambridge	CB	Stratford	SD
Cumnock	CC	Swindon	SN
Carlisle	CE	Stranraer	SR
Chesterfield	CH	South Shields	SS
Cowdenbeath	CJ	Stockport (Daw Bank)	ST
Caerphilly	CL	Slatyford, Newcastle	SY
Cwmbran	CN	Sunderland	SU
Chichester	CR	Stroud	SZ
Charles Street, Stockport	CS	Leyton	T
Cheltenham	CT	Bromley	TB
Chepstow	CW	Thanet	TH
Corby	CX	Catford	TL
Chorley	CY	Torquay	TQ
Darlington	DA	Upton Park	U
Dunfermline	DE	Worthing	WG
Dover	DO	Winchester	WI
Dumfries	DS	Worksop	WP
Dunoon	DU	Witney	WY
Exmouth	EH		
Exeter	EX		
Peterhead	FH		
Folkestone	FO		
Glossop	GP		
Gloucester	GR		
Glenrothes	GS		
Glasgow	GW	**Company codes:**	
Grimsby	GY		
Hyde Road, Manchester	HE	East Midlands	EM
Hull	HL	East Scotland	ES
Hartlepool	HP	East	EA
Hastings	HS	London	LN
Inverness	IS	Manchester	MA
Kettering	KG	North East	NE
Kilmarnock	KK	North West	NW
Kendal	KL	South East	SE
Kirkcaldy	KY	South Midlands	SM
Leamington	LE	South West	SW
Lillyhall	LL	West Scotland	WS
Lewes	LS	Wales & West	WW

While the Titans have been all but eliminated from the London operation many are still in use with provincial fleets. Using five digits allows for much flexibility, thus all Titans have had 10000 added their original London number. The original example, 10001, THX401S, remains at North Street depot in Romford where it is now used as a special event vehicle. It is seen at the North Weald bus rally in April 2002. *Richard Godfrey*

10001	NS	THX401S	Leyland Titan TNLXB2RRSp	Park Royal			B44/26D	1978			

10003-10056			Leyland Titan TNLXB2RRSp	Park Royal			B44/26D	1978-80			
10003	SUu	WYV3T	**10005**	AY	WYV5T	**10029**	AY	WYV29T	**10056**	ME	WYV56T

10180-10246			Leyland Titan TNLXB2RRSp	Park Royal			B44/26D	1978-80			
10179	ME	CUL179V	**10197**	RO	CUL197V	**10209**	AY	CUL209V	**10244**	SEw	EYE244V
10180	SEw	CUL180V	**10208**	KK	CUL208V	**10236**	KK	EYE236V	**10246**	DS	EYE246V
10190	SEw	CUL190V									

10252	AY	GYE252W	Leyland Titan TNLXB2RR	PR/Leyland	B44/29D	1981
10254	ME	GYE254W	Leyland Titan TNLXB2RR	PR/Leyland	B44/29D	1981
10273	RO	GYE273W	Leyland Titan TNLXB2RR	PR/Leyland	B44/29D	1981
10281	ME	GYE281W	Leyland Titan TNLXB2RR	PR/Leyland	B44/29D	1981
10285	ME	KYN285X	Leyland Titan TNLXB2RR	Leyland	B44/29D	1981

10311-10542			Leyland Titan TNLXB2RR	Leyland			B44/27F*	1981-82	*10512 is O44/27F		
10311	ME	KYV311X	**10410**	SR	KYV410X	**10469**	EHw	KYV469X	**10511**	SEw	KYV511X
10334	CE	KYV311X	**10444**	EHw	KYV444X	**10473**	EHw	KYV473X	**10512**	KL	KYV512X
10340	ME	KYV340X	**10462**	EX	KYV462X	**10492**	CN	KYV492X	**10542**	CN	KYV542X
10348	SEw	KYV348X									

As well as conversions to single-door, several of the Titans are now open-top. In Lakeland, they operate along-side Olympians and have now displaced former Southdown VRs. Pictured at Bowness is 11091, which is one of several vehicles dedicated to the Grasmere - Bowness service. *Bob Downham*

10555-10675

Leyland Titan TNLXB2RR   Leyland   B44/27F   1982

10555	KY	NUW555Y	10582	KY	NUW582Y	10602	CW	NUW602Y	10649	DA	NUW649Y
10556	CX	NUW556Y	10584	CX	NUW584Y	10605	CW	NUW605Y	10651	CN	NUW651Y
10558	KY	NUW558Y	10585	EX	NUW585Y	10615	KY	NUW615Y	10654	AL	NUW654Y
10559	CX	NUW559Y	10586	CJ	NUW586Y	10619	CN	NUW619Y	10659	SC	NUW659Y
10560	AL	NUW560Y	10587	AL	NUW587Y	10622	GS	NUW622Y	10660	EXw	NUW660Y
10562	KY	NUW562Y	10588	CX	NUW588Y	10623	GS	NUW623Y	10662	CN	NUW662Y
10565	CX	NUW565Y	10589	CN	NUW589Y	10626	CJ	NUW626Y	10664	SC	NUW664Y
10566	DE	NUW566Y	10590	CX	NUW590Y	10634	DA	NUW634Y	10665	CN	NUW665Y
10569	CX	NUW569Y	10591	CJ	NUW591Y	10643	SC	NUW643Y	10666	SC	NUW666Y
10571	CJ	NUW571Y	10592	CW	NUW592Y	10645	SSw	NUW645Y	10668	NEw	NUW668Y
10572	ESu	NUW572Y	10593	AL	NUW593Y	10646	CN	NUW646Y	10670	CA	NUW670Y
10574	AL	NUW574Y	10596	ASw	NUW596Y	10647	CAw	NUW647Y	10673	SC	NUW673Y
10576	CX	NUW576Y	10601	CJ	NUW601Y	10648	SC	NUW648Y	10675	SC	NUW675Y
10577	AL	NUW577Y									

10684-10820

Leyland Titan TNLXB2RR   Leyland   B44/27F   1982-83

10684	ME	OHV684Y	10719	CW	OHV719Y	10762	SR	OHV762Y	10802	GS	OHV802Y
10686	CWu	OHV686Y	10728	ME	OHV728Y	10789	GS	OHV789Y	10809	ME	OHV809Y
10699	CWu	OHV699Y	10729	ME	OHV729Y	10791	KY	OHV791Y	10819	KY	RYK819Y
10700	DS	OHV700Y	10738	ME	OHV738Y	10801	CJ	OHV801Y	10820	CJ	RYK820Y
10702	CW	OHV702Y	10751	AL	OHV751Y						

10824-10999

Leyland Titan TNLXB2RR   Leyland   B44/29F   1983-84

10824	RO	A824SUL	10840	SC	A840SUL	10866	KK	A866SUL	10935	GS	A935SYE
10825	CJ	A825SUL	10843	KK	A843SUL	10867	AL	A867SUL	10944	AL	A944SYE
10826	SC	A826SUL	10846	SCw	A846SUL	10873	AL	A873SUL	10945	KY	A945SYE
10827	STw	A827SUL	10849	SC	A849SUL	10874	CC	A874SUL	10950	KK	A950SYE
10830	CX	A830SUL	10854	RY	A854SUL	10902	CJ	A902SYE	10976	EHu	A976SYE
10832	GS	A832SUL	10855	ME	A855SUL	10905	CN	A905SYE	10996	KY	A996SYE
10834	GS	A834SUL	10858	CJ	A858SUL	10921	DE	A921SYE	10999	AY	A999SYE
10838	SN	A838SUL	10859	SWw	A859SUL	10922	DE	A922SYE			

The one Titan to have been painted into the new scheme is 10589, NUW589Y which is based at Cwmbran. It is seen in Chepstow while working the Newport service. *Richard Godfrey*

11007-11076 Leyland Titan TNLXB2RR Leyland B44/29F 1984

11007	SA	A607THV	11026	BYw	A626THV	11045	KK	A645THV
11013	AL	A613THV	11032	EH	A632THV	11050	AL	A650THV
11022	DA	A622THV	11034	CX	A634THV	11066	SA	A66THX

11067	EHu	A67THX
11076	AY	A76THX

11079	WSu	B79WUV	Leyland Titan TNLXB2RR	Leyland	O44/26F	1984
11081	WSu	B81WUV	Leyland Titan TNLXB2RR	Leyland	O44/26F	1984
11083	WSu	B83WUV	Leyland Titan TNLXB2RR	Leyland	O44/26F	1984
11084	CJ	B84WUV	Leyland Titan TNLXB2RR	Leyland	B44/29F	1984
11091	KL	B91WUV	Leyland Titan TNLXB2RR	Leyland	O44/26F	1984
11092	WSu	B92WUV	Leyland Titan TNLXB2RR	Leyland	O44/26F	1984
11093	SA	NIB5233	Leyland Titan TNLXB2RR	Leyland	O44/26F	1984
11096	CX	B96WUV	Leyland Titan TNLXB2RR	Leyland	B44/29F	1984
11097	CJ	B97WUV	Leyland Titan TNLXB2RR	Leyland	B44/29F	1984
11099	CX	B99WUV	Leyland Titan TNLXB2RR	Leyland	B44/29F	1984
11100	KL	NIB5232	Leyland Titan TNLXB2RR	Leyland	O44/29F	1984
11106	PH	NIB5455	Leyland Titan TNLXB2RR	Leyland	B44/29F	1984
11108	SNw	B108WUV	Leyland Titan TNLXB2RR	Leyland	B44/29F	1984
11110	KL	RIB4309	Leyland Titan TNLXB2RR	Leyland	B44/29F	1984
11112	SN	B112WUV	Leyland Titan TNLXB2RR	Leyland	B44/29F	1984
11114	PH	NIB4138	Leyland Titan TNLXB2RR	Leyland	B44/29F	1984
11116	GS	B116WUV	Leyland Titan TNLXB2RR	Leyland	B44/29F	1984
11117	CX	B117WUV	Leyland Titan TNLXB2RR	Leyland	B44/29F	1984
11119	CJ	B119WUV	Leyland Titan TNLXB2RR	Leyland	B44/29F	1984
11121	CA	B121WUV	Leyland Titan TNLXB2RR	Leyland	B44/29F	1984
11122	SA	B122WUV	Leyland Titan TNLXB2RR	Leyland	B44/29F	1984
11124	SEw	B124WUV	Leyland Titan TNLXB2RR	Leyland	B44/29F	1984
11125	CA	B125WUV	Leyland Titan TNLXB2RR	Leyland	B44/29F	1984

In London, Routemasters operate for Stagecoach from Upton Park and Bow garages. The vehicles are turned out in excellent condition and, to keep with tradition, retain an all-red livery. The vehicles provided by Transport for London have been supplemented by others brought back from the provinces. An interesting vehicle is 12156, LFF875, which was once 456CLT in the Green Line RMC class and still retains its rear doors. It is seen in Trafalgar Square. The initial plan to add 12000 to the Routemaster number was changed to allow the RMLs to be kept in approximate age sequence and so the third digit became significant 0 for those below RM1000, 1 for the 1000s etc. *Mark Lyons*

12013	U	WLT613	AEC Routemaster R2RH	Park Royal	B36/28R	1960
12060	WSu	EDS50A	AEC Routemaster R2RH	Park Royal	B36/28R	1960
12080	U	USK625	AEC Routemaster R2RH	Park Royal	B36/28R	1961
12086	U	WLT886	AEC Routemaster R2RH	Park Royal	B36/28R	1962
12090	U	XFF814	AEC Routemaster R2RH	Park Royal	B36/28R	1962
12098	BW	XFF813	AEC Routemaster R2RH	Park Royal	B36/28R	1962
12107	ESu	LDS201A	AEC Routemaster 2R2RH	Park Royal	B36/24R	1963
12127	U	527CLT	AEC Routemaster 2R2RH	Park Royal	B36/28R	1963
12156	U	LFF875	AEC Routemaster 2R2RH	Park Royal	B32/25RD	1962
12161	U	461CLT	AEC Routemaster 2R2RH	Park Royal	B32/25RD	1962
12185	U	485CLT	AEC Routemaster 2R2RH	Park Royal	B32/25RD	1962
12189	U	XSL596A	AEC Routemaster 2R2RH	Park Royal	B36/28R	1962
12199	U	YTS820A	AEC Routemaster 2R2RH	Park Royal	B36/28R	1963

12272-12456   AEC Routemaster R2RH1   Park Royal   B40/32R   1965-66   Owned by TfL.

12272	U	CUV272C	12392	BW	JJD392D	12429	BW	JJD429D	12445	U	JJD445D
12286	U	CUV286C	12399	BW	JJD399D	12435	BW	JJD435D	12450	BW	JJD450D
12300	BW	CUV300C	12402	BW	JJD402D	12437	BW	JJD437D	12451	BW	JJD451D
12303	U	CUV303C	12415	BW	JJD415D	12444	BW	JJD444D	12456	U	JJD456D
12311	U	CUV311C									

12462-12592   AEC Routemaster R2RH1   Park Royal   B40/32R   1966   Owned by TfL.

12462	BW	JJD462D	12493	BW	JJD493D	12527	BW	JJD527D	12565	U	JJD565D
12470	BW	JJD470D	12495	BW	JJD495D	12541	U	JJD541D	12581	U	JJD581D
12481	BW	JJD481D	12496	U	JJD496D	12550	U	JJD550D	12592	BW	JJD592D
12488	BW	JJD488D	12497	U	JJD497D						

12607-12760   AEC Routemaster R2RH1   Park Royal   B40/32R   1967-68   Owned by TfL.

12607	BW	NML607E	12642	U	NML642E	12671	U	SMK671F	12738	BW	SMK738F
12610	U	NML610E	12657	BW	NML657E	12696	BW	SMK696F	12743	BW	SMK743F
12616	U	NML616E	12661	U	SMK661F	12705	U	SMK705F	12748	U	SMK748F
12624	BW	NML624E	12665	BW	SMK665F	12709	BW	SMK709F	12749	BW	SMK749F
12639	U	NML639E	12668	BW	SMK668F	12719	BW	SMK719F	12760	U	SMK760F
12641	U	NML641E	12670	U	SMK670F	12723	U	SMK723F			

Stagecoach inherited from Manchester a significant number of Leyland Olympians, some of which have now moved around the group. These have gained 13000 to their original numbers. Early examples of the type are painted into MagicBus livery for the cut-price operations aimed primarily at the University population on the Wilmslow Road corridor. Now numbered 13024, A24HNC is seen heading for Ashton which plies the busy Old Road corridor. *Richard Godfrey*

13020-13025

Leyland Olympian ONLXCT/1R   Northern Counties   B43/30F   1983-84

| 13020 | HE | A585HDB | 13022 | HE | A22HNC | 13024 | HE | A24HNC | 13025 | HE | A25HNC |
| 13021 | HE | A21HNC | 13023 | HE | A23HNC | | | | | | |

13026-13033

Leyland Olympian ONLXB/1R   Northern Counties   B43/30F   1984

| 13026 | HE | A26ORJ | 13028 | HE | A28ORJ | 13030 | HE | A30ORJ | 13032 | HE | A32ORJ |
| 13027 | HE | A27ORJ | 13029 | HE | A29ORJ | 13031 | HE | A31ORJ | 13033 | HE | A33ORJ |

13034-13236

Leyland Olympian ONLXB/1R   Northern Counties   B43/30F*   1984-86   *13198/214 are BC43/26F
*13117 is O43/30F

13034	HE	B34PJA	13088	HE	B88SJA	13147	ST	B147XNA	13185	ST	C185YBA
13035	HE	B35PJA	13089	HE	B89SJA	13149	ST	B149XNA	13191	PS	C191YBA
13036	HE	B36PJA	13091	PS	B91SJA	13150	HE	B150XNA	13193	ST	C193YBA
13039	HE	B39PJA	13094	HE	B94SJA	13153	ST	B153XNA	13195	HE	C195YBA
13049	HE	B49PJA	13095	HE	B95SJA	13154	HEu	B154XNA	13196	HE	C196YBA
13053	HE	B53PJA	13110	PS	B110SJA	13155	ST	B155XNA	13197	ST	C197YBA
13055	HE	B55PJA	13114	HE	B114SJA	13156	ST	C156YBA	13198	ST	C198YBA
13056	HE	B56PJA	13117	KL	B117TVU	13158	ST	C158YBA	13199	HE	C199YBA
13057	HE	B57PJA	13118	HE	B118TVU	13164	ST	C164YBA	13205	ST	C205CBU
13058	HE	B58PJA	13119	HE	B119TVU	13165	HE	C165YBA	13207	HE	C207CBU
13060	HE	B60PJA	13121	HE	B121TVU	13166	HE	C166YBA	13208	ST	C208CBU
13065	HE	B65PJA	13122	HE	B122TVU	13167	ST	C167YBA	13210	ST	C210CBU
13067	PS	B67PJA	13124	GP	B124TVU	13169	HE	C169YBA	13212	ST	C212CBU
13069	PS	B69PJA	13125	GP	B125TVU	13170	HE	C170YBA	13213	PR	C213CBU
13070	HE	B70PJA	13126	GP	B126WNB	13172	ST	C172YBA	13214	HE	C214CBU
13072	HE	B72PJA	13132	GP	B132WNB	13173	ST	C173YBA	13215	ST	C215CBU
13074	HE	B74PJA	13133	GP	B133WNB	13174	ST	C174YBA	13216	HE	C216CBU
13077	HE	B77PJA	13135	GP	B135WNB	13175	ST	C175YBA	13221	ST	C221CBU
13080	GP	B80PJA	13137	HE	B137WNB	13176	ST	C176YBA	13224	HE	C224CBU
13082	HE	B82PJA	13138	GP	B138WNB	13178	PS	C178YBA	13226	PS	C226ENE
13084	HE	B84SJA	13143	GP	B143WNB	13179	HE	C179YBA	13230	HEw	C230ENE
13086	PS	B86SJA	13145	GP	B145WNB	13181	PS	C181YBA	13234	ST	C234ENE
13087	HE	B87SJA	13146	HE	B146XNA	13184	ST	C184YBA	13236	PS	C236EVU

Now carrying the new livery is one of the Olympian prototypes. 14100 was the second prototype and supplied to the National Bus Company for evaluation who allocated it to the, then, large Ribble operation. Carrying Stagecoach in Lancashire names it was seen at Haigh Hall for the centenary of transport in Wigan.
Bob Downham

13255-13277

Leyland Olympian ONLXB/1R Northern Counties BC43/26F 1986-87

| 13255 | GP | C255FRJ | 13268 | PS | D268JVR | 13272 | ST | D272JVR | 13277 | ST | D277JVR |
| 13260 | GP | D260JVR | 13269 | GP | D269JVR | | | | | | |

13282-13304

Leyland Olympian ONLXB/1RZ Northern Counties B43/30F* 1988-89 *13291 is BC43/25F

13282	ST	F282DRJ	13291	ST	F291DRJ	13296	BA	F296DRJ	13300	ST	F300DRJ
13283	ST	F283DRJ	13294	ST	F294DRJ	13297	BA	F297DRJ	13301	ST	F301DRJ
13285	ST	F285DRJ	13295	ST	F295DRJ	13298	ST	F298DRJ	13304	ST	F304DRJ
13289	ST	F289DRJ									

| 14000 | BD | F110NES | Leyland Olympian ON6LXCT/5RZ | Alexander RL | | B66/44F | 1989 |

14001-14011

Leyland Olympian ONLXB/1R Eastern Coach Works B45/32F* 1981 *14001 is BC45/27F
*14002/6 are BC41/27F

14001	BD	ARP601X	14005	NN	ARP605X	14008	NN	ARP608X	14010	NN	ARP610X
14002	KG	ARP602X	14006	NN	ARP606X	14009	NN	ARP609X	14011	NN	ARP611X
14004	NN	ARP604X	14007	NN	ARP607X						

14020-14049

Leyland Olympian ONLXB/2RZ Alexander RL B51/36F* 1988-89 *14035-44 are B51/34F
*14045-9 are BC51/31F

14020	KG	F620MSL	14028	KG	F628MSL	14036	BD	F636YRP	14043	KG	G643EVV
14021	KG	F621MSL	14029	KG	F629MSL	14037	BD	F637YRP	14044	BD	G644EVV
14022	BD	F622MSL	14030	BD	F630MSL	14038	BD	F638YRP	14045	KG	G645EVV
14023	BD	F623MSL	14031	BD	F631MSL	14039	BD	G639EVV	14046	BD	G646EVV
14024	BD	F624MSL	14032	BD	F632MSL	14040	BD	G640EVV	14047	PE	G647EVV
14025	KG	F625MSL	14033	KG	F633MSL	14041	BD	G641EVV	14048	BD	G648EVV
14026	KG	F626MSL	14034	BD	F634MSP	14042	BD	G642EVV	14049	BD	G649EVV
14027	KG	F627MSL	14035	BD	F635YRP						

| 14054 | KG | H654VVV | Leyland Olympian ON2R56G13Z4 | Alexander RL | | B51/34F | 1990 |

14055-14070   Leyland Olympian ON2R50G13Z4   Northern Counties Palatine   B47/29F   1992

14055	BD	K655UNH	14059	KG	K659UNH	14063	BD	K663UNH	14068	KG	K668UNH
14056	BD	K656UNH	14060	KG	K660UNH	14064	BD	K664UNH	14069	KG	K669UNH
14057	KG	K657UNH	14061	BD	K661UNH	14065	BD	K665UNH	14070	KG	K670UNI I
14058	KG	K658UNH	14062	BD	K662UNH	14067	KG	K667UNH			

14100	CY	DBV100W	Leyland Olympian B45.02	Eastern Coach Works	B45/33F	1980
14102	KLw	JFR2W	Leyland Olympian ONLXB/1R	Eastern Coach Works	O45/32F	1981
14116	PR	OFV16X	Leyland Olympian ONLXB/1R	Eastern Coach Works	B45/32F	1982
14117	CY	OFV17X	Leyland Olympian ONLXB/1R	Eastern Coach Works	B45/32F	1982
14129	KL	VRN829Y	Leyland Olympian ONLXBT/1R	Eastern Coach Works	O45/32F	1982
14134	PR	DBV134Y	Leyland Olympian ONLXB/1R	Eastern Coach Works	B45/32F	1983
14138	CY	A138MRN	Leyland Olympian ONLXB/1R	Eastern Coach Works	B45/32F	1984

14170-14179   Leyland Olympian ONLXB/1R   Eastern Coach Works   BC42/30F   1985

| 14170 | PR | C170ECK | 14175 | KL | C175ECK | 14177 | BA | C177ECK | 14179 | CY | C179ECK |
| 14174 | ME | C174ECK | 14176 | PR | C176ECK | | | | | | |

14180-14189   Leyland Olympian ON2R56G16Z4   Alexander RL   BC51/31F   1989

14180	SC	G180JHG	14183	SU	G183JHG	14186	BY	G186JHG	14188	PR	G188JHG
14181	BY	G181JHG	14184	BY	G184JHG	14187	PR	G187JHG	14189	DA	G189JHG
14182	SU	G182JHG	14185	SC	G185JHG						

14191-14197   Leyland Olympian ON2R56G16Z4   Alexander RL   BC51/36F*   1990   *14193/5-7 are B51/34F

| 14191 | HP | H191WFR | 14193 | PR | H193WFR | 14195 | PR | H195WFR | 14197 | CY | H197WFR |
| 14192 | BY | H192WFR | 14194 | BY | H194WFR | 14196 | PR | H196WFR | | | |

14198-14210   Leyland Olympian ON2R56G13Z4   Alexander RL   BC43/27F   1991

14198	CY	J198HFR	14202	ME	J202HFR	14205	ME	J205HFR	14208	ME	J208HFR
14199	PR	J199HFR	14203	CE	J203HFR	14206	ME	J206HFR	14209	ME	J209HFR
14201	PR	J201HFR	14204	ME	J204HFR	14207	ME	J207HFR	14210	ME	J210HFR

14216-14223   Leyland Olympian ONLXB/1R   Alexander RL   B45/32F   1984-85

| 14216 | CY | B892UAS | 14219 | CY | B895UAS | 14220 | PR | B896UAS | 14223 | PR | B899UAS |
| 14217 | PR | B893UAS | | | | | | | | | |

14228-14235   Leyland Olympian ON2R50G13Z4   Alexander RL   BC43/27F   1992

| 14228 | CE | K128DAO | 14230 | CE | K130DAO | 14232 | CE | K132DAO | 14234 | LL | K134DAO |
| 14229 | CE | K129DAO | 14231 | CE | K131DAO | 14233 | LL | K133DAO | 14235 | ME | K135DAO |

14239	PS	F201FHH	Leyland Olympian ONLXCT/3RZ	Alexander RL	BC55/41F	1989
14240	PS	F202FHH	Leyland Olympian ONLXCT/3RZ	Alexander RL	BC55/41F	1989
14241	BA	URM801Y	Leyland Olympian ONLXB/1R	Eastern Coach Works	BC45/30F	1982
14242	BA	URM802Y	Leyland Olympian ONLXB/1R	Eastern Coach Works	B45/32F	1982

14243-14251   Leyland Olympian ONLXB/2RZ   Alexander RL   B51/36F   1988

14243	BA	F803FAO	14246	BA	F806FAO	14248	KL	F808FAO	14250	CY	F810FAO
14244	CY	F804FAO	14247	CY	F807FAO	14249	CY	F809FAO	14251	KL	F811FAO
14245	BA	F805FAO									

14252-14259   Leyland Olympian ON2R56G13Z4   Alexander RL   B51/34F   1990

| 14252 | KL | H112SAO | 14254 | LL | H114SAO | 14256 | PR | H116SAO | 14258 | LL | H118SAO |
| 14253 | LL | H113SAO | 14255 | LL | H115SAO | 14257 | LL | H117SAO | 14259 | PR | H119SAO |

14260-14267   Leyland Olympian ON2R56G13Z4   Alexander RL   BC47/27F   1991

| 14260 | CY | J120AAO | 14262 | CY | J122AAO | 14264 | CY | J124XHH | 14266 | ME | J126XHH |
| 14261 | CY | J121AAO | 14263 | CY | J123XHH | 14265 | PR | J125XHH | 14267 | ME | J127XHH |

14271-14275 — Leyland Olympian ONLXB/2RZ — Alexander RL — B51/36F — 1990

14271	SN	G101AAD	14273	GR	G103AAD	14274	SZ	G104AAD	14275	SZ	G105AAD
14272	SN	G102AAD									

14278	PR	CUB72Y	Leyland Olympian ONLXB/1R	Roe		B47/29F	1983	A1 Service, 1995
14279	GSu	EWY74Y	Leyland Olympian ONLXB/1R	Roe		Publicity	1983	Allisons, Dunfermline, 2000
14280	DE	EWY75Y	Leyland Olympian ONLXB/1R	Roo		B47/29F	1983	Allisons, Dunfermline, 2000
14281	GR	UWW3X	Leyland Olympian ONLXB/1R	Roe		B47/29F	1982	

14282-14294 — Leyland Olympian ONLXB/1R — Roe — B47/29F — 1982-83

14282	SZ	JHU899X	14286	SZ	LWS34Y	14289	GR	LWS37Y	14292	GR	LWS40Y
14283	GR	UWW7X	14287	GR	LWS35Y	14290	GRw	LWS38Y	14293	SZ	LWS41Y
14284	GR	JHU912X	14288	SZ	LWS36Y	14291	GR	LWS39Y	14294	GR	NTC132Y
14285	GR	LWS33Y									

14303-14325 — Leyland Olympian ONLXB/1R — Eastern Coach Works — B45/32F — 1981-84

14303	HL	NHL303X	14316	CH	A316XWG	14320	CHw	A320YWJ	14323	WP	A323AKU
14314	HL	A314XWG	14318	CH	A318XWG	14321	CHw	A321YWJ	14324	MD	A324AKU
14315	MD	A315XWG	14319	MD	A319XWG	14322	HL	A322AKU	14325	MD	A325AKU

14326-14336 — Leyland Olympian ONLXB/1R — Eastern Coach Works — B45/32F* — 1986 — *14326/7/9 are BC42/30F

14326	MD	C326HWJ	14331	MD	C331HWJ	14333	WP	C333HWJ	14335	MD	C335HWJ
14327	CH	C327HWJ	14332	MD	C332HWJ	14334	CH	C334HWJ	14336	MD	C336HWJ
14329	CH	C329HWJ									

14337-14343 — Leyland Olympian ON6LXB/2RZ — Alexander RL — BC51/31F — 1989

14337	KY	G337KKW	14339	HL	G339KKW	14341	HL	G341KKW	14343	MD	G343KKW
14338	PH	G338KKW	14340	MD	G340KKW	14342	MD	G342KKW			

14344-14353 — Leyland Olympian ON2R56G13Z4 — Alexander RL — BC51/31F* — 1990-91 — *14349-53 are BC47/27F

14344	MD	H344SWA	14347	CH	H347SWA	14350	MD	J350XET	14352	MD	J352XET
14345	MD	H345SWA	14348	CH	H348SWA	14351	MD	J351XET	14353	MD	J353XET
14346	MD	H346SWA	14349	MD	J349XET						

14354-14358 — Leyland Olympian ON2R50G13Z4 — Northern Counties Palatine — B47/29F — 1992

14354	MD	K354DWJ	14356	MD	K356DWJ	14357	MD	K357DWJ	14358	MD	K358DWJ
14355	MD	K355DWJ									

14359-14363 — Leyland Olympian ON2R50G13Z4 — Alexander RL — BC43/27F — 1992

14359	WP	K359DWJ	14361	WP	K361DWJ	14362	HL	K362DWJ	14363	HL	K363DWJ
14360	WP	K360DWJ									

14364-14392 — Leyland Olympian ONLXB/1RH — Eastern Coach Works — B42/29F — 1986

14364	HL	C114CHM	14372	CR	C122CHM	14377	LE	D127FYM	14382	NU	D132FYM
14365	LE	C115CHM	14373	LE	D123FYM	14378	LE	D128FYM	14384	ATu	D134FYM
14367	HL	C116CHM	14374	LE	D124FYM	14379	HL	D129FYM	14386	NU	D136FYM
14369	LE	C119CHM	14375	LE	D125FYM	14380	HL	D130FYM	14387	RU	D137FYM
14370	AT	C120CHM	14376	AT	D126FYM	14381	RU	D131FYM	14392	LE	D142FYM
14371	RU	C121CHM									

14402	BY	SSA2X	Leyland Olympian ONLXB/1R	Alexander RL	B45/32F	1981	
14403	BY	SSA3X	Leyland Olympian ONLXB/1R	Alexander RL	B45/32F	1981	
14404	KY	SSA4X	Leyland Olympian ONLXB/1R	Alexander RL	B45/32F	1981	
14405	SC	SSA5X	Leyland Olympian ONLXB/1R	Alexander RL	B45/32F	1981	
14408	PH	K508ESS	Leyland Olympian ON2R50G13Z4	Alexander RL	BC43/27F	1992	
14409	AN	K509ESS	Leyland Olympian ON2R50G13Z4	Alexander RL	BC43/27F	1992	
14410	AN	K510ESS	Leyland Olympian ON2R50G13Z4	Alexander RL	BC43/27F	1992	
14411	AN	K511ESS	Leyland Olympian ON2R50G13Z4	Alexander RL	BC43/27F	1992	
14412	GW	C800HCS	Leyland Olympian ONLXB/1R	Eastern Coach Works	B45/32F	1986	A1 Service, 1995
14415	AN	K515ESS	Leyland Olympian ON2R50G13Z4	Alexander RL	BC43/27F	1992	
14418	AN	K518ESS	Leyland Olympian ON2R50G13Z4	Alexander RL	BC43/27F	1992	

Leamington Spa is the new home to Leyland Olympian 14381, D131FYM. This batch carry Eastern Coach Works bodywork, and was new to London Buses. They were one of the first batches Stagecoach chose to cascade from London to the provinces after the Titans. Now numbered back as a batch they can be found from across the group from Winchester to Hull. *Richard Godfrey*

14434-14460

			Leyland Olympian ONLXB/1R			Alexander RL			B45/32F*	1983-85	*14444 is BC41/29F
14434	BY	YSO34Y	14450	KY	B350LSO	14454	WS	B354LSO	14457	PH	B357LSO
14435	BY	YSO35Y	14451	AN	B351LSO	14455	PH	B355LSO	14458	PH	B358LSO
14444	PH	A44FRS	14452	PH	B352LSO	14456	IS	B356LSO	14460	DE	B360LSO
14448	KY	B348LSO									

14461	IS	C461SSO	Leyland Olympian ONLXB/1RV	Alexander RL	BC43/27F	1986	
14462	DE	C462SSO	Leyland Olympian ONLXB/1RV	Alexander RL	BC43/27F	1986	
14463	FH	C463SSO	Leyland Olympian ONLXB/1RV	Alexander RL	BC43/27F	1986	
14464	SN	MHS4P	Leyland Olympian ONLXB/1RV	Alexander RL	BC43/27F	1986	
14465	SN	MHS5P	Leyland Olympian ONLXB/1RV	Alexander RL	BC43/27F	1986	
14466	GW	C466SSO	Leyland Olympian ONLXB/1RV	Alexander RL	BC43/27F	1986	

14467-14474

			Leyland Olympian ONLXB/1RV			Alexander RL			B47/30F	1986	
14467	PH	C467SSO	14469	PH	C469SSO	14471	PH	GSO1V	14473	BA	C383SAO
14468	PH	C468SSO	14470	PH	C470SSO	14472	BD	C472SSO	14474	BA	C384SAO

14475-14489

			Leyland Olympian ONLXB/1RV			Alexander RL			BC43/27F	1987	
14475	BA	D384XAO	14479	BD	D379XRS	14483	BD	D383XRS	14487	PH	D387XRS
14476	BD	GSO6V	14480	BA	D380XRS	14484	BD	D384XRS	14488	FH	D388XRS
14477	BD	GSO7V	14481	BA	D381XRS	14485	FH	D385XRS	14489	AN	D389XRS
14478	MD	GSO8V	14482	BD	D382XRS	14486	PH	D386XRS			

14490	IS	J120XHH	Leyland Olympian ON2R56G13Z4	Alexander RL	BC47/27F	1991	
14491	IS	J121XHH	Leyland Olympian ON2R56G13Z4	Alexander RL	BC47/27F	1991	
14492	IS	J122XHH	Leyland Olympian ON2R56G13Z4	Alexander RL	BC47/27F	1991	
14493	BD	J620GCR	Leyland Olympian ON2R56G13Z4	Alexander RL	B51/34F	1991	
14494	BD	J621GCR	Leyland Olympian ON2R56G13Z4	Alexander RL	B51/34F	1991	
14495	BD	J622GCR	Leyland Olympian ON2R56G13Z4	Alexander RL	B51/34F	1991	

14496-14499
Leyland Olympian ON2R56G13Z4   Alexander RL   BC47/27F   1992

14496	AN	J196YSS	14497	AN	J197YSS	14498	AN	J198YSS	14499	IS	J199YSS

14500	GR	E500LFL	Leyland Olympian ONLXCT/1RH	Optare	BC43/27F	1988
14501	GR	E501LFL	Leyland Olympian ONLXCT/1RH	Optare	BC43/27F	1988
14502	SZ	E502LFL	Leyland Olympian ONLXCT/1RH	Optare	BC43/27F	1988

14506-14517
Leyland Olympian ONLXB/1RZ   Northern Counties   B45/30F   1989

14506	PE	F506NJE	14509	BD	F509NJE	14512	BD	F512NJE	14515	LE	F515NJE
14507	PE	F507NJE	14510	BD	F510NJE	14513	CB	F513NJE	14516	LE	F516NJE
14508	BD	F508NJE	14511	BD	F511NJE	14514	CB	F514NJE	14517	LE	F517NJE

14520	BY	F41XCS	Leyland Olympian ONCL10/1RZ	Leyland	B47/31F	1989	A1 Service, 1995
14521	GW	F524WSJ	Leyland Olympian ONCL10/1RZ	Leyland	B47/31F	1989	A1 Service, 1995
14522	AS	F149XCS	Leyland Olympian ONCL10/1RZ	Leyland	B47/31F	1989	A1 Service, 1995
14523	PE	H473CEG	Leyland Olympian ON2R50G13Z4	Leyland	B47/31F	1990	
14524	PE	H474CEG	Leyland Olympian ON2R50G13Z4	Leyland	B47/31F	1990	
14525	PE	H475CEG	Leyland Olympian ON2R50G13Z4	Leyland	B47/31F	1990	

14601-14665
Leyland Olympian ONLXB/1R   Alexander RH   B45/31F   1985-86

14601	KK	C601LFT	14619	GW	C619LFT	14635	HL	C635LFT	14650	SN	C650LFT
14602	GW	C602LFT	14621	HL	C621LFT	14636	HL	C636LFT	14651	HP	C651LFT
14603	CC	C603LFT	14622	GW	C622LFT	14637	HL	C637LFT	14652	DA	C652LFT
14604	GW	C604LFT	14623	GW	C623LFT	14638	GW	C638LFT	14653	GW	C653LFT
14605	BY	C605LFT	14624	SN	C624LFT	14639	HP	C639LFT	14654	GW	C654LFT
14608	GW	C608LFT	14625	GW	C625LFT	14640	GW	C640LFT	14655	DA	C655LFT
14609	CT	C609LFT	14626	GW	C626LFT	14641	SN	C641LFT	14656	GW	C656LFT
14610	SZ	C610LFT	14627	GW	C627LFT	14642	BY	C642LFT	14657	GW	C657LFT
14611	BY	C611LFT	14628	GW	C628LFT	14643	HL	C643LFT	14658	DA	C658LFT
14612	GW	C612LFT	14629	GW	C629LFT	14644	HL	C644LFT	14659	SN	C659LFT
14613	HE	C613LFT	14630	HL	C630LFT	14645	BY	C645LFT	14661	SC	C661LFT
14614	BY	C614LFT	14631	HE	C631LFT	14646	BY	C646LFT	14662	GW	C662LFT
14615	SC	C615LFT	14632	HL	C632LFT	14647	GW	C647LFT	14663	GW	C663LFT
14616	GW	C616LFT	14633	HL	C633LFT	14648	HP	C648LFT	14664	HL	C664LFT
14617	SC	C617LFT	14634	HL	C634LFT	14649	HL	C649LFT	14665	HL	C665LFT
14618	SC	C618LFT									

14667-14676
Leyland Olympian ON2R50C13Z4   Northern Counties Palatine   B47/30F   1990-91

14667	SU	H667BNL	14670	SU	H670BNL	14673	SU	H673BNL	14675	SU	H675BNL
14668	BY	H668BNL	14671	SU	H671BNL	14674	SU	H674BNL	14676	SU	H676BNL
14669	BY	H669BNL	14672	SU	H672BNL						

14701-14708
Leyland Olympian ON2R50G13Z4   Alexander RL   B47/32F   1992

14701	KY	J801WFS	14703	KY	J803WFS	14705	KY	J805WFS	14707	DE	J807WFS
14702	KY	J802WFS	14704	KY	J804WFS	14706	DE	J806WFS	14708	BD	J808WFS

14709-14725
Leyland Olympian ON2R50G13Z4   Alexander RL   B47/32F   1992

14709	BD	K709ASC	14715	TH	K715ASC	14719	DE	K719ASC	14723	DE	K723ASC
14710	BD	K710ASC	14716	TH	K716ASC	14720	DE	K720ASC	14724	DE	K724ASC
14713	BD	K713ASC	14717	AR	K717ASC	14721	DE	K721ASC	14725	DE	K725ASC
14714	CA	K714ASC	14718	DE	K718ASC	14722	DE	K722ASC			

14801-14810
Leyland Olympian ON2R56C16Z4   Northern Counties   B51/34F   1990

14801	HS	H801BKK	14804	HS	H804BKK	14807	CA	H807BKK	14809	CA	H809BKK
14802	HS	H802BKK	14805	HS	H805BKK	14808	CA	H808BKK	14810	TH	H810BKK
14803	AD	H803BKK	14806	AD	H806BKK						

14811	FO	J811NKK	Leyland Olympian ON2R50C13Z4	Northern Counties	B47/30F	1992	East Kent, 1993
14812	FO	J812NKK	Leyland Olympian ON2R50C13Z4	Northern Counties	B47/30F	1992	East Kent, 1993
14813	FO	J813NKK	Leyland Olympian ON2R50C13Z4	Northern Counties	B47/30F	1992	East Kent, 1993
14814	FO	J814NKK	Leyland Olympian ON2R50C13Z4	Northern Counties	B47/30F	1992	East Kent, 1993

East Kent chose Northern Counties bodywork for the batch of Leyland Olympians delivered in 1990. Now numbered 14805, H805BKK illustrates the original Palatine body and short curved windscreen. The batch all remain in the East Kent area. *Martin Smith*

14815-14819

Leyland Olympian ON2R56G13Z4   Alexander RL   B51/34F   1990

14815	TH	H815CBP	**14817**	WG	H817CBP	**14818**	CR	H818CBP	**14819**	TH	H819CBP
14816	WI	H816CBP								

14821-14830

Leyland Olympian ON2R50C13Z4   Northern Counties   B47/30F   1993

14821	FO	K821TKP	**14824**	TH	K824TKP	**14827**	TH	L827BKK	**14829**	AD	L829BKK
14822	AD	K822TKP	**14825**	TH	K825TKP	**14828**	AS	L828BKK	**14830**	AD	L830BKK
14823	TH	K823TKP	**14826**	TH	L826BKK					

14871	GY	A71GEE	Leyland Olympian ONTL11/1R	Eastern Coach Works	B45/31F	1983

14901-14927

Leyland Olympian ONLXB/1RH   Northern Counties   B43/30F   1988

14901	HL	E901KYR	**14910**	HL	E910KYR	**14917**	HL	E917KYR	**14922**	HL	E922KYR
14905	HL	E905KYR	**14911**	HL	E911KYR	**14918**	HL	E918KYR	**14923**	HL	E923KYR
14906	HL	E906KYR	**14912**	HL	E912KYR	**14919**	HL	E919KYR	**14924**	HL	E924KYR
14907	HL	E907KYR	**14914**	HL	E914KYR	**14920**	HL	E920KYR	**14925**	HL	E925KYR
14908	HL	E908KYR	**14915**	HL	E915KYR	**14921**	HL	E921KYR	**14927**	HL	E927KYR
14909	HL	E909KYR								

14930	RU	B910ODU	Leyland Olympian ONLXB/1R	Eastern Coach Works	B45/32F	1984
14931	RU	B911ODU	Leyland Olympian ONLXB/1R	Eastern Coach Works	B45/32F	1984
14932	RU	B912ODU	Leyland Olympian ONLXB/1R	Eastern Coach Works	B45/32F	1984
14933	OXw	B960ODU	Leyland Olympian ONLXB/1R	Eastern Coach Works	BC42/30F	1984
14935	RU	C962XVC	Leyland Olympian ONLXB/1RH	Eastern Coach Works	BC42/29F	1985
14936	BB	C963XVC	Leyland Olympian ONLXB/1RH	Eastern Coach Works	BC42/29F	1985
14937	OXw	C964XVC	Leyland Olympian ONLXB/1RH	Eastern Coach Works	BC42/29F	1985

14942-14947

Leyland Olympian ONLXB/1R   Eastern Coach Works   B45/32F*   1983   *14945 is O45/32F

14942	RU	A542HAC	**14944**	RU	A544HAC	**14946**	KG	A546HAC	**14947**	KG	A547HAC
14943	RU	A543HAC	**14945**	KL	A545HAC					

14948	BD	A561KWY	Leyland Olympian ONLXB/1R	Eastern Coach Works	B45/32F	1983
14949	BD	A681KDV	Leyland Olympian ONLXB/1R	Eastern Coach Works	B45/32F	1983
14950	BD	A683KDV	Leyland Olympian ONLXB/1R	Eastern Coach Works	B45/32F	1983

The picturesque route from Keswick to Seatoller gained Olympian 14945, A545HAC following its transfer from Midland Red where it sustained accident damage to the roof. *Bob Downham*

14951-14956

Leyland Olympian ON2R56G13Z4   Alexander RL   B51/36F   1988

14951	BE	F601MSL	**14953**	WI	F603MSL	**14955**	WI	F605MSL	**14956**	WI	F606MSL
14952	BE	F602MSL	**14954**	BE	F604MSL						

14957-14964

Leyland Olympian ON2R56G13Z4   Alexander RL   BC51/31F   1989

14957	AR	G807RTS	**14959**	WI	G809RTS	**14961**	WI	G211SSL	**14963**	AN	G213SSL
14958	BE	G808RTS	**14960**	WI	G210SSL	**14962**	AN	G212SSL	**14964**	AN	G214SSL

14970	CR	J720GAP	Leyland Olympian ON2R56G13Z4	Alexander RL	BC47/27F	1992
14971	CR	J721GAP	Leyland Olympian ON2R56G13Z4	Alexander RL	BC47/27F	1992
14972	CR	J722GAP	Leyland Olympian ON2R56G13Z4	Alexander RL	BC47/27F	1992
14973	PM	J623GCR	Leyland Olympian ON2R56G13Z4	Alexander RL	B47/30F	1991
14974	AR	J624GCR	Leyland Olympian ON2R56G13Z4	Alexander RL	B47/30F	1991

14975-14984

Leyland Olympian ON2R56G13Z4   Alexander RL   B51/34F   1990

14975	CR	G705TCD	**14978**	CA	G708TCD	**14981**	DO	G701TCD	**14983**	DO	G703TCD
14976	CA	G706TCD	**14979**	DO	G709TCD	**14982**	CA	G702TCD	**14984**	DO	G704TCD
14977	CA	G707TCD	**14980**	CA	G710TCD						

14985-14990

Leyland Olympian ON2R50G13Z4   Alexander RL   BC43/27F   1992

14985	AT	K235NHC	**14987**	AT	K237NHC	**14989**	AT	K239NHC	**14990**	WI	K240NHC
14986	AR	K236NHC	**14988**	AT	K238NHC						

Dennis Dominators are confined to the Manchester and East Midland fleets. Buses at Hull depot are part of the latter fleet though at the moment they share the Transit operators licence discs. Pictured in the city once noted for its massive trawler fleet is 15061, C221WAJ which has Northern Counties bodywork. Many of the buses new to Manchester are retained for immediate use elsewhere within the group should the need arise.
Richard Godfrey

15001-15030

Dennis Dominator DDA1003			Northern Counties			B43/32F		1985		

15001	PSw	B901TVR	15009	GY	B909TVR	15017	HEu	B917TVR	15024	PS	B24TVU
15002	GY	B902TVR	15010	HEu	B910TVR	15018	HLw	B918TVR	15025	PSw	B25TVU
15003	GY	B903TVR	15011	HEu	B911TVR	15019	PS	B919TVR	15026	PS	B26TVU
15004	GY	B904TVR	15012	PS	B912TVR	15020	PS	B920TVR	15027	HEu	B27TVU
15005	HEw	B905TVR	15013	HEw	B913TVR	15021	PS	B21TVU	15028	HEu	B28TVU
15006	PSw	B906TVR	15014	HEu	B914TVR	15022	PSw	B22TVU	15029	PS	B29TVU
15007	GY	B907TVR	15015	HEu	B915TVR	15023	HEt	B23TVU	15030	PS	B30TVU
15008	GY	B908TVR	15016	HEu	B916TVR						

15031-15040

Dennis Dominator DDA2033			Northern Counties Palatine			B43/29F		1991		

15031	PS	H131GVM	15034	PS	H134GVM	15037	PS	H137GVM	15039	PS	H139GVM
15032	PS	H132GVM	15035	PS	H135GVM	15038	PS	H138GVM	15040	PS	H140GVM
15033	PS	H133GVM	15036	PS	H136GVM						

15041	HL	E140SAT	Dennis Dominator DDA1014			East Lancashire (1992)		B45/32F		1987	

15042-15051

Dennis Dominator DDA1016			East Lancashire			B45/31F		1988		

15042	HLw	F142BKH	15046	HL	F146BKH	15048	HL	F148BKH	15050	HLw	F150BKH
15043	HL	F143BKH	15047	HL	F147BKH	15049	HL	F149BKH	15051	HL	F151BKH
15044	HLu	F144BKH									

15052	HL	E132SAT	Dennis Dominator DDA1014	East Lancashire (1992)	B45/21D	1987
15059	HL	C219WAJ	Dennis Dominator DD1009	Northern Counties	B43/31F	1985
15060	HL	C220WAJ	Dennis Dominator DD1009	Northern Counties	B43/31F	1985
15061	HL	C221WAJ	Dennis Dominator DD1009	Northern Counties	B43/31F	1985
15062	HL	C222WAJ	Dennis Dominator DD1009	Northern Counties	B43/31F	1985

In 1995 Stagecoach took delivery of twenty new Dennis Dragons for its Kenya operation, but as the operating conditions declined the buses were brought back to the UK for further use. These buses are long tri-axle vehicles more commonly supplied to Hong Kong operators. The type are now based at Princess Road depot and mostly used on Magic Bus services that link the University of Manchester's with students accomodation in the suburbs. Seen in Oxford Street is 15184, M684TDB. *Gerry Mead*

15075	GY	F75TFU	Dennis Dominator DDA1021	Alexander RH	B45/33F	1989	
15076	GY	F76TFU	Dennis Dominator DDA1021	Alexander RH	B45/33F	1989	
15077	GY	F77TFU	Dennis Dominator DDA1021	Alexander RH	B45/33F	1989	
15079	GY	G79VFW	Dennis Dominator DDA1028	Alexander RH	B45/33F	1990	
15080	GY	G80VFW	Dennis Dominator DDA1028	Alexander RH	B45/33F	1990	
15081	GY	G81VFW	Dennis Dominator DDA1029	Alexander RH	B45/33F	1990	
15084	GY	H484BEE	Dennis Dominator DDA1034	East Lancashire	B45/33F	1991	
15085	GY	H485BEE	Dennis Dominator DDA1034	East Lancashire	B45/33F	1991	
15092	GY	J92DJV	Dennis Dominator DDA1036	East Lancashire	B45/33F	1992	
15093	GY	J93DJV	Dennis Dominator DDA1036	East Lancashire	B45/33F	1992	
15094	GY	J94DJV	Dennis Dominator DDA1036	East Lancashire	B45/33F	1992	

15180-15199

Dennis Dragon DDA1820 — Duple Metsec/AVA — B51/37F — 1995-96 — Stagecoach Kenya, 1998-99

15180	PS	M680TDB	15185	PS	M685TDB	15190	PS	M690TDB	15195	PS	M695TDB
15181	PS	M681TDB	15186	PS	M686TDB	15191	PS	M691TDB	15196	PS	M696TDB
15182	PS	M682TDB	15187	PS	M687TDB	15192	PS	M692TDB	15197	PS	M379TJA
15183	PS	M683TDB	15188	PS	M688TDB	15193	PS	M693TDB	15198	PS	L392LNA
15184	PS	M684TDB	15189	PS	M689TDB	15194	PS	M694TDB	15199	PS	M699TDB

15201-15212

Volvo Citybus B10M-50 — Northern Counties — BC43/33F — 1989

15201	SB	F301MYJ	15204	PM	F304MYJ	15207	HS	F307MYJ	15210	AL	F310MYJ
15202	PM	F302MYJ	15205	HS	F305MYJ	15208	HS	F308MYJ	15211	AL	F311MYJ
15203	PM	F303MYJ	15206	SB	F306MYJ	15209	HS	F309MYJ	15212	DE	F312MYJ

15246	CC	B24CGA	Volvo Citybus B10M-50	Alexander RV	B47/37F	1985	A1 Service, 1995
15247	AY	E864RCS	Volvo Citybus B10M-50	Alexander RV	BC41/29F	1987	
15248	AL	E865RCS	Volvo Citybus B10M-50	Alexander RV	BC41/29F	1987	
15249	AY	E866RCS	Volvo Citybus B10M-50	Alexander RV	BC45/33F	1987	
15250	AL	E867RCS	Volvo Citybus B10M-50	Alexander RV	BC45/33F	1987	
15258	GS	B108CCS	Volvo Citybus B10M-50	Alexander RV	BC45/35F	1987	
15259	AL	E909KSG	Volvo Citybus B10M-50	Alexander RV	BC45/35F	1986	
15260	AL	E910KSG	Volvo Citybus B10M-50	Alexander RV	BC45/35F	1986	

New numbers for Stagecoach's Scania double-decks commence 153xx and can be seen in service in Newcastle, Manchester and the East Kent area. Showing the version of the Palatine body with the deeper windscreen is 15330, J230XKY, which was new to London Buses. *Martin Smith*

15269-15276

Volvo Citybus B10M-50   Alexander RV   BC45/35F*   1986   *15272-4 are B47/37F

| 15269 | KY | C807USG | 15271 | AL | C801USG | 15273 | GS | C803USG | 15275 | CJ | C805USG |
| 15270 | SA | C800USG | 15272 | GS | C802USG | 15274 | GS | C804USG | 15276 | AL | C806USG |

15277-15299

Volvo Citybus B10M-50   Alexander RV   B47/37F   1985-86   *15294/5/8/9 are BC45/35F

15277	SA	B177FFS	15284	GS	B184FFS	15290	DE	C790USG	15295	GS	C795USG
15279	KY	B179FFS	15285	CJ	B185FFS	15291	GS	C791USG	15296	CJ	C796USG
15280	GS	B180FFS	15286	CJ	B186FFS	15292	DE	C792USG	15297	CJ	C797USG
15281	KY	B181FFS	15287	CJ	C787USG	15293	SA	C793USG	15298	AL	C798USG
15282	CJ	B182FFS	15288	SA	C788USG	15294	AL	C794USG	15299	CJ	C799USG
15283	GS	B183FFS	15289	GS	C789USG						

15301-15310

Scania N113DRB   Alexander RH   B47/29F   1990

15301	BY	H421BNL	15304	BY	H424BNL	15307	BY	H427BNL	15309	BY	H429BNL
15302	BY	H422BNL	15305	BY	H425BNL	15308	BY	H428BNL	15310	BY	H430BNL
15303	BY	H423BNL	15306	BY	H426BNL						

| 15311 | CA | F781KKP | Scania N113DRB | Alexander RH | B47/33F | 1989 |
| 15312 | CA | F782KKP | Scania N113DRB | Alexander RH | B47/33F | 1989 |

15313-15317

Scania N113DRB   Northern Counties Palatine   B47/28F   1991

| 15313 | HE | H463GVM | 15315 | HE | H465GVM | 15316 | HE | H466GVM | 15317 | HE | H467GVM |
| 15314 | HE | H464GVM | | | | | | | | | |

15322-15329

Scania N113DRB   Alexander RH   O47/31F*   1991   *15324/5/9 are B47/31F

| 15322 | EX | J822HMC | 15324 | TQ | J824HMC | 15326 | EX | J826HMC | 15328 | EX | J828HMC |
| 15323 | EX | J823HMC | 15325 | EX | J825HMC | 15327 | TQ | J827HMC | 15329 | EX | J829HMC |

15330	TH	J230XKY	Scania N113DRB			Northern Counties Palatine	B47/33F	1991
15331	TH	J231XKY	Scania N113DRB			Northern Counties Palatine	B47/33F	1991

15332-15345

			Scania N113DRB			Northern Counties Palatine	B41/27F	1991

15332	TH	J132HMT	15336	TH	J136HMT	15340	CA	J140HMT	15343	CA	J143HMT
15333	TH	J133HMT	15337	CA	J137HMT	15341	TH	J141HMT	15344	TH	J144HMT
15334	TH	J134HMT	15338	TH	J138HMI	15342	IH	J142HMT	15345	CA	J145HMT
15335	CA	J135HMT	15339	TH	J139HMT						

15346-15371

			Scania N113DRB			Northern Counties Palatine	B41/27F	1991-92

15346	TH	K846LMK	15353	CA	K853LMK	15360	HS	K860LMK	15366	TH	K866LMK
15347	TH	K847LMK	15354	TH	K854LMK	15361	CA	K861LMK	15367	TH	K867LMK
15348	TH	K848LMK	15355	TH	K855LMK	15362	CA	K862LMK	15368	CA	K868LMK
15349	TH	K849LMK	15356	CA	K856LMK	15363	CA	K863LMK	15369	TH	K869LMK
15350	TH	K850LMK	15357	CA	K857LMK	15364	CA	K864LMK	15370	TH	K870LMK
15351	TH	K851LMK	15358	CA	K858LMK	15365	CA	K865LMK	15371	TH	K871LMK
15352	TH	K852LMK	15359	CA	K859LMK						

15513	GY	MBE613R	Leyland Fleetline FE30AGR	Roe	O45/29D	1976
15514	GY	BJV103L	Daimler Fleetline CRG6LX	Roe	O45/29D	1973
15724	MEu	DBV24W	Bristol VRT/SL3/6LXB	Eastern Coach Works	B43/31F	1980
15731	MEu	KRM431W	Bristol VRT/SL3/6LXB	Eastern Coach Works	B43/31F	1980
15735	MEu	KRM435W	Bristol VRT/SL3/6LXB	Eastern Coach Works	B43/31F	1980
15741	SEu	MFN41R	Bristol VRT/SL3/6LXB	Eastern Coach Works	B43/31F	1976
15760	BE	JOU160P	Bristol VRT/SL3/501 (6LXB)	Eastern Coach Works	B43/28F	1975
15761	BE	EWS746W	Bristol VRT/SL3/680 (6LXB)	Eastern Coach Works	BC43/31F	1981
15762	BE	EWS748W	Bristol VRT/SL3/680 (6LXB)	Eastern Coach Works	BC43/31F	1981
15763	BE	EWS751W	Bristol VRT/SL3/680 (6LXB)	Eastern Coach Works	BC43/31F	1981
15808	HPu	EJR108W	Leyland Atlantean AN68A/2R	Alexander AL	B49/37F	1980
15810	SC	EJR110W	Leyland Atlantean AN68A/2R	Alexander AL	B49/37F	1980
15811	SC	EJR111W	Leyland Atlantean AN68A/2R	Alexander AL	B49/37F	1980
15818	DA	EJR118W	Leyland Atlantean AN68A/2R	Alexander AL	B49/37F	1980
15822	DA	AKV142V	Leyland Atlantean AN68A/2R	Alexander AL	B49/37F	1980
15824	HP	SCN249S	Leyland Atlantean AN68A/2R	Alexander AL	B49/37F	1978
15825	SC	AKV135V	Leyland Atlantean AN68A/2R	Alexander AL	B49/37F	1980
15826	DA	AKV156V	Leyland Atlantean AN68A/2R	Alexander AL	B49/37F	1980
15827	HP	AKV147V	Leyland Atlantean AN68A/2R	Alexander AL	B49/37F	1980
15828	HP	AKV148V	Leyland Atlantean AN68A/2R	Alexander AL	B49/37F	1980
15830	SC	AKV180V	Leyland Atlantean AN68A/2R	Alexander AL	B49/37F	1980
15855	HEt	SND455X	Leyland Atlantean AN68A/1R	Northern Counties	TV	1982
15869	SA	ABV669A	Leyland Atlantean PDR1/1	Metro Cammell	O44/31F	1961

The demise of the Bristol VR has reduced the type to just Morecambe and Basingstoke while the only remaining Fleetlines are the seasonal open-tops at Grimsby.
Pictured on School duties in Lancaster is Morecambe's VR 15727, FAO427V which, in January 2003, has just been placed into store.
Bob Downham

16001	NS	P801GMU	Volvo Olympian YN2RV18Z4	Northern Counties Palatine	B49/31D	1996
16002	NS	P802GMU	Volvo Olympian YN2RV18Z4	Northern Counties Palatine	B49/31D	1996
16003	NS	P803GMU	Volvo Olympian YN2RV18Z4	Northern Counties Palatine	B49/31D	1996

16004-16026   Volvo Olympian YN2RV18Z4   Northern Counties Palatine   B49/31F   1996

16004	CB	P804GMU	16010	CB	P810GMU	16016	EX	P816GMU	16022	CB	P822GMU
16005	CB	P805GMU	16011	CB	P811GMU	16017	EX	P817GMU	16023	CB	P823GMU
16006	CB	P806GMU	16012	CB	P812GMU	16018	CB	P818GMU	16024	CB	P824GMU
16007	CB	P807GMU	16013	CB	P813GMU	16019	CB	P819GMU	16025	CB	P825GMU
16008	CB	P808GMU	16014	CB	P814GMU	16020	CB	P820GMU	16026	CB	P826GMU
16009	CB	P809GMU	16015	CB	P815GMU	16021	CB	P821GMU			

16027-16043   Volvo Olympian YN2RV18Z4   Northern Counties Palatine   B49/31D*   1996-97   *B49/30F in provincial fleets

16027	LE	P527HMP	16032	LE	P532HMP	16036	DE	P536HMP	16040	DS	P540HMP
16028	LE	P528HMP	16033	LE	P533HMP	16037	DS	P537HMP	16041	NS	P541HMP
16029	LE	P529HMP	16034	LE	P534HMP	16038	DS	P538HMP	16042	NS	P542HMP
16030	LE	P530HMP	16035	DE	P535HMP	16039	CC	P539HMP	16043	NS	P543HMP
16031	LE	P531HMP									

16044-16081   Volvo Olympian   Alexander RL   B51/28D   1997

16044	BW	P644SEV	16054	BW	R154VPU	16064	BW	R164VPU	16073	BW	R173VPU
16045	BW	P645SEV	16055	BW	R155VPU	16065	BW	R165VPU	16074	AS	R174VPU
16046	BW	P646SEV	16056	BW	R156VPU	16066	BW	R166VPU	16075	BW	R175VPU
16047	BW	R747XAR	16057	BW	R157VPU	16067	BW	R167VPU	16076	OX	R176VPU
16048	BW	R148VPU	16058	BW	R158VPU	16068	AS	R168VPU	16077	BW	R177VPU
16049	BW	R149VPU	16059	BW	R159VPU	16069	BW	R169VPU	16078	OXu	R178VPU
16050	BW	R150VPU	16060	BW	R160VPU	16070	PD	R170VPU	16079	OX	R179VPU
16051	BW	R151VPU	16061	BW	R161VPU	16071	BW	R171VPU	16080	WWu	R180VPU
16052	BW	R152VPU	16062	BW	R162VPU	16072	OXu	R172VPU	16081	BW	R181VPU
16053	BW	R153VPU	16063	BW	R163VPU						

16082-16100   Volvo Olympian   Northern Counties Palatine   B45/23D   1997

16082	PD	R82XNO	16087	TL	R87XNO	16092	TL	R92XNO	16097	TL	R97XNO
16083	PD	R83XNO	16088	PD	R188XNO	16093	PD	R93XNO	16098	PD	R98XNO
16084	TL	R84XNO	16089	PD	R89XNO	16094	PD	R94XNO	16099	TL	R207XNO
16085	TL	R85XNO	16090	TL	R190XNO	16095	PD	R95XNO	16100	PD	R210XNO
16086	TL	R86XNO	16091	PD	R91XNO	16096	TL	R96XNO			

With the arrival of new Tridents into London the provincial fleets are gaining Volvo Olympians that have undergone conversion. Recent recipients from the plan are West Scotland with six, South Midlands taking seven and Cheltenham five. Currently in service ar Bow is 16053, R153VPU, shown here operating route 8 in Piccadilly.
Gerry Mead

Stagecoach London took delivery of vehicles with both Alexander and Northern Counties bodywork while retaining a single number series with VA or VN prefix as appropriate. Following renumbering, the class code is now associated with the duty information on the side of the vehicle. From the 1998 intake, 16115 shows the latter styling as it heads for Romford rail station in June 2002. *Gerry Mead*

16101-16121   Volvo Olympian   Northern Counties Palatine   B45/23D   1998

16101	PD	R101XNO	16107	PD	R107XNO	16112	NS	R112XNO	16117	NS	R117XNO
16102	PD	R102XNO	16108	PD	R108XNO	16113	PD	R113XNO	16118	NS	R118XNO
16103	TL	R103XNO	16109	PD	R109XNO	16114	PD	R114XNO	16119	NS	R119XNO
16104	TL	R104XNO	16110	TL	S110SHJ	16115	NS	R115XNO	16120	NS	R120XNO
16105	PD	R105XNO	16111	NS	R311XNO	16116	NS	R116XNO	16121	NS	R121XNO
16106	TL	R206XNO									

16122-16148   Volvo Olympian   Alexander RL   B45/23D   1998

16122	TB	R122EVX	16129	SD	R129EVX	16136	PD	R136EVX	16143	PD	R143EVX
16123	TB	R123EVX	16130	TB	R130EVX	16137	PD	R137EVX	16144	SMu	R144EVX
16124	TB	R124EVX	16131	PD	R131EVX	16138	PD	R138EVX	16145	PD	R145EVX
16125	TB	R125EVX	16132	PD	R132EVX	16139	PD	R139EVX	16146	BW	R146EVX
16126	TB	R126EVX	16133	TB	R133EVX	16140	OXu	R140EVX	16147	PD	R147EVX
16127	WWu	R127EVX	16134	PD	R134EVX	16141	SMu	R141EVX	16148	BW	R148EVX
16128	SD	R128EVX	16135	PD	R135EVX	16142	WWu	R142EVX			

16149-16178   Volvo Olympian   Northern Counties Palatine   B49/27D*   1998   *16164 is B49/31F

16149	PD	R149HHK	16157	TB	R157HHK	16165	PD	R165HHK	16172	PD	R172HHK
16150	PD	R150HHK	16158	PD	R158HHK	16166	PD	R166HHK	16173	PD	R173HHK
16151	PD	R151HHK	16159	PD	R159HHK	16167	PD	R167HHK	16174	PD	R174HHK
16152	PD	R152HHK	16160	PD	R160HHK	16168	PD	R168HHK	16175	TB	R175HHK
16153	NS	R153HHK	16161	PD	R161HHK	16169	PD	R169HHK	16176	PD	R176HHK
16154	NS	R154HHK	16162	PD	R162HHK	16170	PD	R170HHK	16177	PD	R177HHK
16155	PD	R155HHK	16163	PD	R163HHK	16171	PD	R171HHK	16178	TB	R178HHK
16156	NS	R156HHK	16164	TQ	R164HHK						

Clarence Esplanade in Southsea provides the background for this view of 16306, S306CCD. This batch carry Alexander bodies fitted with high-back seating, suitable for the longer interurban routes on which they are used. *Tony Wilson*

16198	AN	L26JSA	Volvo Olympian YN2RV18Z4	Northern Counties Palatine	BC43/25F	1993
16199	AN	L27JSA	Volvo Olympian YN2RV18Z4	Northern Counties Palatine	BC43/25F	1993
16200	IS	L28JSA	Volvo Olympian YN2RV18Z4	Northern Counties Palatine	BC43/25F	1993
16201	IS	L101JSA	Volvo Olympian YN2RV18Z4	Northern Counties Palatine	BC43/25F	1993
16202	IS	L102JSA	Volvo Olympian YN2RV18Z4	Northern Counties Palatine	BC43/25F	1993

16203-16208
Volvo Olympian   Alexander RL   B47/32F   1998

16203	RY	R203DHB	16205	RY	R205DHB	16207	RY	R207DHB	16208	RY	R208DHB
16204	RY	R204DHB	16206	RY	R206DHB						

16209-16232
Volvo Olympian   Alexander RL   BC45/32F*   1997   *16221/2 are B51/36F

16209	KG	83CBD	16215	KG	R565DRP	16223	NN	S753DRP	16228	NN	S758DRP
16210	KG	R560DRP	16216	KG	R566DRP	16224	NN	S754DRP	16229	NN	S759DRP
16211	KG	R561DRP	16217	KG	R567DRP	16225	NN	S755DRP	16230	NN	S760DRP
16212	KG	R562DRP	16218	KG	R568DRP	16226	NN	S756DRP	16231	NN	S761DRP
16213	KG	R563DRP	16221	NN	R701DNH	16227	NN	S757DRP	16232	PE	S762DRP
16214	KG	R564DRP	16222	NN	R702DNH						

16241-16250
Volvo Olympian YN2RV18Z4   Northern Counties Palatine   BC43/25F   1993

16241	TH	L241SDY	16244	ME	L244SDY	16247	TH	L247SDY	16249	AN	L249SDY
16242	TH	L242SDY	16245	ME	L245SDY	16248	AN	L248SDY	16250	AN	L250SDY
16243	ME	L243SDY	16246	TH	L246SDY						

16260-16290
Volvo Olympian   Alexander RL   B51/36F*   1996-98   *16260-3 are B51/32F
*16288-90 are BC47/32F

16260	WI	P260WPN	16268	BE	P268VPN	16276	WI	P276VPN	16284	CA	P284VPN
16261	WI	P261WPN	16269	BE	P269VPN	16277	WI	P277VPN	16285	FO	P285VPN
16262	BE	P262WPN	16270	CA	S270CCD	16278	PM	P278VPN	16286	TH	P286VPN
16263	WI	P263WPN	16271	CA	S271CCD	16279	AN	P279VPN	16287	FO	P287VPN
16264	CA	P264VPN	16272	CA	S272CCD	16281	CR	P281VPN	16288	WI	P288VPN
16265	CA	P265VPN	16273	CA	S273CCD	16282	CR	P282VPN	16289	WI	P289VPN
16266	CA	P266VPN	16274	CA	S274CCD	16283	CA	P283VPN	16290	WI	P290VPN
16267	CA	P267VPN	16275	CA	S275CCD						

In 1996 several buses initially intended for the South fleet were delivered to Preston for use in the Lancashire area. Many have now moved to Kendal who provide the buses on the popular 555 *lakes link* service between Keswick and Lancaster. Seen entering the Windermere rail interchange is 16339, N339NPN. *Bob Downham*

16291-16305 Volvo Olympian Alexander RL B51/36F 1998

16291	WI	R291HCD	16295	AR	R295HCD	16299	CA	R299HCD
16292	WI	R292HCD	16296	CA	R296HCD	16301	TH	R301HCD
16293	AR	R293HCD	16297	CA	R297HCD	16302	PM	S302CCD
16294	AR	R294HCD	16298	CA	R298HCD			

16303	WI	S303CCD
16304	WI	S304CCD
16305	AL	S305CCD

16306-16324 Volvo Olympian Alexander RL BC43/36F 1998

16306	PM	S306CCD	16311	WG	S311CCD	16316	HS	S316CCD	16320	AT	S320CCD
16307	PM	S307CCD	16312	WG	S312CCD	16317	HS	S317CCD	16322	PM	S322CCD
16308	WG	S308CCD	16313	LS	S313CCD	16318	HS	S318CCD	16323	PM	S323CCD
16309	WG	S309CCD	16314	LS	S314CCD	16319	AT	S319CCD	16324	PM	S324CCD
16310	WG	S310CCD	16315	HS	S315CCD						

16325-16340 Volvo Olympian YN2RC16V3 Alexander RL B47/32F 1996

16325	PR	N325NPN	16329	PR	N329NPN	16334	KL	N334NPN	16338	KL	N338NPN
16326	PR	N326NPN	16330	KL	N330NPN	16335	KL	N335NPN	16339	KL	N339NPN
16327	PR	N327NPN	16331	KL	N331NPN	16336	KL	N336NPN	16340	KL	N340NPN
16328	PR	N328NPN	16332	KL	N332NPN	16337	KL	N337NPN			

16341-16359 Volvo Olympian YN2RC16V3 Alexander RL BC47/28F 1996

16341	PM	N341MPN	16346	WG	N346MPN	16351	AT	N351MPN	16356	LS	N356MPN
16342	PM	N342MPN	16347	WG	N347MPN	16352	AT	N352MPN	16357	LS	N357MPN
16343	PM	N343MPN	16348	WG	N348MPN	16353	AT	N353MPN	16358	LS	N358MPN
16344	PM	N344MPN	16349	WG	N349MPN	16354	LS	N354MPN	16359	LS	N359MPN
16345	WG	N345MPN	16350	WG	N350MPN	16355	LS	N355MPN			

16360-16380 — Volvo Olympian YN2RC16V3 — Alexander RL — B47/32F — 1995

16360	CA	N360LPN	16366	BE	N366LPN	16371	FO	N371LPN	16376	FO	N376LPN
16361	CA	N361LPN	16367	BE	N367LPN	16372	FO	N372LPN	16377	FO	N377LPN
16362	CA	N362LPN	16368	DO	N368LPN	16373	LS	N373LPN	16378	FO	N378LPN
16363	DO	N363LPN	16369	DO	N369LPN	16374	LS	N374LPN	16379	BE	N379LPN
16364	DO	N364LPN	16370	DO	N370LPN	16375	FO	N375LPN	16380	BE	N380LPN
16365	FO	N365LPN									

16381-16399 — Volvo Olympian YN2RC16V3 — Alexander RL — BC47/28F — 1995-96

16381	TH	N381LPN	16386	DO	N386LPN	16391	AT	N391LPN	16396	WI	N396LPN
16382	HS	N382LPN	16387	DO	N387LPN	16392	LS	N392LPN	16397	PM	N397LPN
16383	HS	N383LPN	16388	HS	N388LPN	16393	AR	N393LPN	16398	WI	N398LPN
16384	HS	N384LPN	16389	DO	N389LPN	16394	AR	N394LPN	16399	PM	N399LPN
16385	HS	N385LPN	16390	DO	N390LPN	16395	PM	N395LPN			

16401-16420 — Volvo Olympian YN2RV18Z4 — Northern Counties Palatine — B45/23D — 1995

16401	EX	M301DGP	16406	TQ	M306DGP	16411	TQ	M311DGP	16416	TQ	M316DGP
16402	EX	M302DGP	16407	TQ	M307DGP	16412	TQ	M312DGP	16417	TQ	M317DGP
16403	EX	M303DGP	16408	TQ	M308DGP	16413	TQ	M313DGP	16418	TQ	M318DGP
16404	TQ	M304DGP	16409	TQ	M309DGP	16414	TQ	M314DGP	16419	TQ	M319DGP
16405	TQ	M305DGP	16410	TQ	M310DGP	16415	TQ	M315DGP	16420	TQ	M320DGP

16421-16430 — Volvo Olympian YN2RV18Z4 — Northern Counties Palatine — B45/23D — 1995

16421	AL	N321HGK	16424	AL	N325HGK	16427	AL	N327HGK	16429	AL	N329HGK
16422	AL	N322HGK	16425	AL	N324HGK	16428	AL	N328HGK	16430	SA	N330HGK
16423	AL	N323HGK	16426	AL	N326HGK						

16431-16437 — Volvo Olympian YN2RV18Z4 — Northern Counties Palatine — B45/26F — 1995

16431	CB	VLT255	16433	CB	WLT528	16435	CB	WLT908	16437	CB	685DYE
16432	CB	WLT512	16434	CB	WLT682	16436	CB	647DYE			

16438-16451 — Volvo Olympian YN2RV18Z4 — Northern Counties Palatine — B45/23D — 1995

16438	OX	N338HGK	16442	GR	N342HGK	16446	CN	N346HGK	16450	SN	N350HGK
16439	OX	N339HGK	16443	SN	N343HGK	16447	CN	N347HGK	16451	SN	N351HGK
16440	OX	N340HGK	16444	CN	N344HGK	16448	TQ	N348HGK	16452	SNu	N352HGK
16441	RY	N341HGK	16445	CN	N345HGK	16449	SN	N349HGK			

16453-16460 — Volvo Olympian — Alexander RL — B51/35F — 1996-97

16453	CH	P153KWJ	16455	CH	P151KWJ	16457	CH	P157KWJ	16459	CH	P159KAK
16454	CH	P154KWJ	16456	CH	P156KWJ	16458	CH	P158KWJ	16460	CH	P160KAK

16461-16469 — Volvo Olympian — Alexander RL — B51/36F — 1998

16461	HL	S161RET	16464	WP	S164RET	16466	WP	S166RET	16468	WP	S168RET
16462	HL	S162RET	16465	WP	S165RET	16467	WP	S167RET	16469	WP	S169RET
16463	HL	S163RET									

16471-16479 — Volvo Olympian YN2RV18Z4 — Northern Counties Palatine — B47/29F — 1993

16471	MD	K101JWJ	16474	MD	K104JWJ	16476	MD	K106JWJ	16478	MD	L108LHL
16472	MD	K102JWJ	16475	MD	K105JWJ	16477	MD	K107JWJ	16479	MD	L109LHL
16473	MD	K103JWJ									

16480-16494 — Volvo Olympian YN2RV18Z4 — Alexander RL — B47/32F — 1995

16480	MD	N130AET	16484	CH	N134AET	16488	CH	N138AET	16492	CH	N142AET
16481	MD	N131AET	16485	CH	N135AET	16489	CH	N139AET	16493	CH	N143AET
16482	CH	N132AET	16486	CH	N136AET	16490	CH	N140AET	16494	CH	N144AET
16483	CH	N133AET	16487	CH	N137AET	16491	CH	N141AET			

16495-16500 — Volvo Olympian — Alexander RL — B51/35F — 1996-97

16495	CH	P145KWJ	16497	CH	P152KWJ	16499	HL	P149KWJ	16500	CH	P150KWJ
16496	CH	P146KWJ	16498	HL	P148KWJ						

To celebrate 75 years of East Midland, Volvo Olympian 16487, N137AET carries the traditional yellow and chocolate colour scheme. It is seen in St Mary's Gate, Chesterfield. *Tony Wilson*

16501-16513

Volvo Olympian | Alexander RL | B51/36F | 1997

16501	HE	R501UWL	16505	HE	R505UWL	16508	ST	R508UWL	16511	HE	R511UWL
16502	HE	R502UWL	16506	ST	R506UWL	16509	ST	R509UWL	16512	HE	R512UWL
16503	HE	R503UWL	16507	ST	R507UWL	16510	ST	R510UWL	16513	HE	R513UWL
16504	HE	R504UWL									

16514-16526

Volvo Olympian | Alexander RL | B51/32D | 1998

16514	WY	R414XFC	16518	WY	R418XFC	16521	WY	R421XFC	16524	OX	R424XFC
16515	WY	R415XFC	16519	WY	R419XFC	16522	WY	R422XFC	16525	WY	R425XFC
16516	WY	R416XFC	16520	WY	R420XFC	16523	WY	R423XFC	16526	WY	R426XFC
16517	WY	R417XFC									

16527-16579

Volvo Olympian YN2RV18V3 | Northern Counties Palatine | B49/33F | 1996

16527	BD	P527EFL	16540	PE	P540EFL	16553	CB	P553EFL	16567	CB	P567EFL
16528	PE	P528EFL	16541	CB	P541EFL	16554	CB	P554EFL	16568	PE	P568EFL
16529	PE	P529EFL	16542	CB	P542EFL	16555	NN	P526EFL	16569	BD	P569EFL
16530	PE	P530EFL	16543	CB	P543EFL	16556	CB	P556EFL	16570	BD	P570EFL
16531	PE	P531EFL	16544	CB	P544EFL	16557	PE	P557EFL	16571	BD	P571EFL
16532	PE	P532EFL	16545	CB	P545EFL	16558	PE	P558EFL	16572	CB	P572EFL
16533	CB	P533EFL	16546	PE	P546EFL	16559	PE	P559EFL	16573	CB	P573EFL
16534	PE	P534EFL	16547	PE	P547EFL	16561	PE	P561EFL	16574	CB	P574EFL
16535	PE	P535EFL	16548	PE	P548EFL	16562	PE	P562EFL	16575	CB	P575EFL
16536	PE	P536EFL	16549	PE	P549EFL	16563	CB	P563EFL	16576	CB	P576EFL
16537	PE	P537EFL	16550	PE	P550EFL	16564	CB	P564EFL	16577	CB	P577EFL
16538	PE	P538EFL	16551	CB	P551EFL	16565	CB	P565EFL	16578	CB	P578EFL
16539	PE	P539EFL	16552	CB	P552EFL	16566	CB	P566EFL	16579	CB	P579EFL

16580-16586

Volvo Olympian | Alexander RL | B45/27F | 1998

16580	PE	R580JVA	16582	PE	R582JVA	16584	BD	R584JVA	16586	BD	R586JVA
16581	PE	R581JVA	16583	BD	R583JVA	16585	BD	R585JVA			

Provincial buses supplied new with dual doors are unusual though thirteen entered service from South Midland's Witney depot in 1998. These carry Alexander bodywork and provide links into Oxford. Now numbered 16523, R423XFC is seen in its home town. *Richard Godfrey*

16587-16593

| | | | | | | | Volvo Olympian | Alexander RL | BC47/32F | 1998 |

16587	PE	S587BCE	16589	PE	S589BCE	16591	PE	S591BCE	16593	PE	S593BCE
16588	PE	S588BCE	16590	PE	S590BCE	16592	PE	S592BCE			

16598	LE	N518XER	Volvo Olympian YN2RV18Z4	Northern Counties Palatine	BC45/31F	1995
16599	LE	N519XER	Volvo Olympian YN2RV18Z4	Northern Counties Palatine	BC45/31F	1995
16600	LE	N520XER	Volvo Olympian YN2RV18Z4	Northern Counties Palatine	BC45/31F	1995
16601	TQ	R901FDV	Volvo Olympian	Alexander RL	B45/27F	1997
16602	EX	R902JDV	Volvo Olympian	Alexander RL	B51/36F	1998
16603	EX	R903JDV	Volvo Olympian	Alexander RL	B51/36F	1998
16604	EX	R904JDV	Volvo Olympian	Alexander RL	B51/36F	1998
16610	IS	L100JLB	Volvo Olympian YN2RV18Z4	Northern Counties Palatine	BC43/25F	1993

16614-16620

| | | | | | | | Volvo Olympian | Alexander RL | BC47/32F | 1999 |

16614	LE	S914ANH	16616	LE	S916ANH	16618	LE	S918ANH	16620	LE	S920ANH
16615	LE	S915ANH	16617	LE	S917ANH	16619	LE	S919ANH			

16624-16635

| | | | | | | | Volvo Olympian YN2RV18Z4 | Northern Counties Palatine | B49/33F | 1996 |

16624	LL	P224VCK	16627	LL	P227VCK	16630	ME	P230VCK	16633	PR	P233VCK
16625	LL	P225VCK	16628	ME	P228VCK	16631	ME	P231VCK	16634	CY	P234VCK
16626	LL	P226VCK	16629	PR	P229VCK	16632	PR	P232VCK	16635	CY	P235VCK

16636-16645

| | | | | | | | Volvo Olympian YN2RV18Z4 | Alexander RL | B45/27F | 1996 |

16636	CY	P260VPN	16639	CY	P263VPN	16642	PR	P272VPN	16644	PR	P274VPN
16637	CY	P261VPN	16640	PR	P270VPN	16643	PR	P273VPN	16645	PR	P275VPN
16638	CY	P262VPN	16641	PR	P271VPN						

16646-16668

| | | | | | | | Volvo Olympian | Alexander RL | B51/36F | 1997 |

16646	CY	R246NBV	16652	CY	R252NBV	16658	CY	R258NBV	16664	ME	R264NBV
16647	CY	R247NBV	16653	CY	R253NBV	16659	CY	R259NBV	16665	ME	R265NBV
16648	CY	R248NBV	16654	CY	R254NBV	16660	CY	R260NBV	16666	ME	R266NBV
16649	CY	R249NBV	16655	CY	R255NBV	16661	CY	R261NBV	16667	ME	R267NBV
16650	CY	R250NBV	16656	CY	R256NBV	16662	ME	R262NBV	16668	ME	R268NBV
16651	CY	R251NBV	16657	CY	R257NBV	16663	ME	R263NBV			

16669	PR	S903JHG	Volvo Olympian	Alexander RL	BC43/26F	1998
16670	PR	S904JHG	Volvo Olympian	Alexander RL	BC43/26F	1998

16671-16685   Volvo Olympian YN2RV18Z4   Northern Counties Palatine   B47/29F   1993

16671	NN	L671HNV	16675	NN	L675HNV	16679	NN	L679HNV	16683	NN	L683HNV
16672	NN	L672HNV	16676	NN	L676HNV	16680	NN	L680HNV	16684	NN	L684HNV
16673	NN	L673HNV	16677	NN	L677HNV	16681	NN	L681HNV	16685	NN	L685JBD
16674	NN	L674HNV	16678	NN	L678HNV	16682	NN	L682HNV			

16686-16692   Volvo Olympian YN2RV18Z4   Alexander RL   B51/36F   1996

16686	NN	P686JBD	16688	NN	P688JBD	16690	NN	P690JBD	16692	NN	P692JBD
16687	NN	P687JBD	16689	NN	P689JBD	16691	NN	P691JBD			

16693-16699   Volvo Olympian   Alexander RL   B51/36F   1997

16693	NN	R693DNH	16695	NN	R695DNH	16697	NN	R697DNH	16699	NN	R699DNH
16694	NN	R694DNH	16696	NN	R696DNH	16698	NN	R698DNH			

16701-16740   Volvo Olympian YN2RV18Z4   Alexander RL   B47/28F   1995

16701	SS	N701LTN	16711	BY	N711LTN	16721	BY	N721LTN	16731	SS	N731LTN
16702	BY	N702LTN	16712	BY	N712LTN	16722	BY	N722LTN	16732	SS	N732LTN
16703	SS	N703LTN	16713	BY	N713LTN	16723	BY	N723LTN	16733	SS	N733LTN
16704	SS	N704LTN	16714	BY	N714LTN	16724	BY	N724LTN	16734	SS	N734LTN
16705	SS	N705LTN	16715	BY	N715LTN	16725	BY	N725LTN	16735	SS	N735LTN
16706	BY	N706LTN	16716	BY	N716LTN	16726	BY	N726LTN	16736	SS	N736LTN
16707	BY	N707LTN	16717	BY	N717LTN	16727	BY	N727LTN	16737	SS	N737LTN
16708	BY	N708LTN	16718	BY	N718LTN	16728	BY	N728LTN	16738	SS	N738LTN
16709	BY	N709LTN	16719	BY	N719LTN	16729	BY	N729LTN	16739	SS	N739LTN
16710	BY	N710LTN	16720	BY	N720LTN	16730	BY	N730LTN	16740	SS	N740LTN

16744-16782   Volvo Olympian   Alexander RL   B51/36F   1998

16744	HE	R744DRJ	16755	HE	R755DRJ	16764	HE	S764SVU	16773	PS	S773RVU
16745	HE	R745DRJ	16756	HE	R756DRJ	16765	HE	R765DRJ	16774	PS	S774RVU
16746	HE	R746DRJ	16757	HE	R757DRJ	16766	HE	S766SVU	16775	PS	S775RVU
16747	HE	R747DRJ	16758	HE	R758DRJ	16767	PS	S767SVU	16776	PS	S776RVU
16748	HE	R748DRJ	16759	HE	R759DRJ	16768	PS	S768SVU	16778	PS	S778RVU
16749	HE	R749DRJ	16760	HE	R760DRJ	16769	PS	S769RVU	16779	PS	S779RVU
16751	HE	R751DRJ	16761	HE	R761DRJ	16770	PS	S770RVU	16780	PS	S780RVU
16752	HE	R752DRJ	16762	HE	R762DRJ	16771	PS	S771RVU	16781	PS	S781RVU
16753	HE	R753DRJ	16763	HE	R763DRJ	16772	PS	S772RVU	16782	PS	S782RVU
16754	HE	R754DRJ									

16786-16800   Volvo Olympian   Alexander RL   B51/36F   1996

16786	PS	P716GND	16790	PS	P720GND	16794	PS	P724GND	16798	PS	P728GND
16787	PS	P717GND	16791	PS	P721GND	16795	PS	P725GND	16799	PS	P729GND
16788	PS	P718GND	16792	PS	P722GND	16796	PS	P726GND	16800	PS	P730GND
16789	PS	P719GND	16793	PS	P723GND	16797	PS	P727GND			

16817-16827   Volvo Olympian YN2RC16V3   Northern Counties Palatine   B47/29F   1995

16817	HL	M817KRH	16819	HL	M819KRH	16824	HL	M224SVN	16826	HL	M226SVN
16818	HL	M818KRH	16823	HL	M223SVN	16825	HL	M225SVN	16827	HL	M227SVN

16828	HL	P828FEF	Volvo Olympian	Northern Counties Palatine	B49/33F	1997
16829	HL	P829FEF	Volvo Olympian	Northern Counties Palatine	B49/33F	1997
16830	HL	P830FEF	Volvo Olympian	Northern Counties Palatine	B49/33F	1997

16831-16840   Volvo Olympian   Alexander RL   B51/36F   1998

16831	SC	R831OVN	16834	SC	R834OVN	16837	SC	R837OVN	16839	SC	R839OVN
16832	SC	R832OVN	16835	SC	R835OVN	16838	SC	R838OVN	16840	SC	R640OVN
16833	SC	R833OVN	16836	SC	R836OVN						

16846-16866   Volvo Olympian YN2RC16V3   Alexander RL   B47/32F   1995

16846	AS	M490ASW	16852	KK	N852VHH	16857	DS	N857VHH	16862	KK	N862VHH
16847	AS	M491ASW	16853	KK	N853VHH	16858	AS	N858VHH	16863	KK	N863VHH
16848	AS	M492ASW	16854	AS	N854VHH	16859	KK	N859VHH	16864	KK	N864VHH
16849	AS	N849VHH	16855	AS	N855VHH	16860	AS	N860VHH	16865	KK	N865VHH
16850	AS	N850VHH	16856	AS	N856VHH	15861	KK	N861VHH	16866	KK	N866VHH
16851	AS	N851VHH									

Two lengths of Dennis Trident are used by Stagecoach in London, 10.5 m and 9.9 m. Generally, both types are built to the higher 4.4m body though the initial batch and some planned for provincial use are 4.2m. One of the lower variant is 17096, T696KPU seen in the Golden Jubilee colours at Paddington. *Dave Heath*

17001-17098

		Dennis Trident 10.5m			Alexander ALX400 4.2m		N51/22D	1999		

17001	T	S801BWC	17026	T	S826BWC	17050	T	T650KPU	17075	BK	T675KPU
17002	T	S802BWC	17027	T	S827BWC	17051	T	T651KPU	17076	BK	T676KPU
17003	T	S803BWC	17028	T	S828BWC	17052	T	T652KPU	17077	BK	T677KPU
17004	T	S804BWC	17029	T	S829BWC	17053	T	T653KPU	17078	BK	T678KPU
17005	T	S805BWC	17030	T `	S830BWC	17054	T	T654KPU	17079	BK	T679KPU
17006	T	S806BWC	17031	T	S831BWC	17055	T	T655KPU	17080	BK	T680KPU
17007	T	S807BWC	17032	T	S832BWC	17056	T	T656KPU	17081	U	T681KPU
17008	T	S808BWC	17033	T	S833BWC	17057	T	T657KPU	17082	U	T682KPU
17009	T	S809BWC	17034	T	S834BWC	17058	T	T658KPU	17083	U	T683KPU
17010	T	S810BWC	17035	T	S835BWC	17069	T	T659KPU	17084	U	T684KPU
17011	T	S811BWC	17036	T	S836BWC	17060	T	T660KPU	17085	U	T685KPU
17012	T	S812BWC	17037	T	S837BWC	17061	T	T661KPU	17086	U	T686KPU
17013	T	S813BWC	17038	T	S838BWC	17062	T	T662KPU	17087	U	T687KPU
17014	T	S814BWC	17039	BW	S839BWC	17063	BK	T663KPU	17088	U	T688KPU
17015	T	S815BWC	17040	BW	T640KPU	17064	BK	T664KPU	17089	U	T689KPU
17016	T	S816BWC	17041	BW	T641KPU	17065	BK	T665KPU	17090	U	T690KPU
17017	T	S817BWC	17042	BW	T642KPU	17066	BK	T699KVX	17091	U	T691KPU
17018	T	S818BWC	17043	BW	T643KPU	17067	BK	T667KPU	17092	U	T692KPU
17019	T	S819BWC	17044	BW	T644KPU	17068	BK	T668KPU	17093	U	T693KPU
17020	T	S820BWC	17045	BW	T645KPU	17069	BK	T669KPU	17094	U	T694KPU
17021	T	S821BWC	17046	BW	T646KPU	17070	BK	T670KPU	17095	U	T695KPU
17022	T	S822BWC	17047	BW	T647KPU	17071	BK	T671KPU	17096	U	T696KPU
17023	T	S823BWC	17048	BW	T648KPU	17072	BK	T672KPU	17097	U	T697KPU
17024	T	S824BWC	17049	BW	T649KPU	17073	BK	T673KPU	17098	U	T698KPU
17025	T	S825BWC									

Stagecoach chose a more rear-ward position for the exit door. Showing the nearside styling is 17067, T667KPU, seen working route 87 in Romford. *Gerry Mead*

17099-17222

		Dennis Trident 10.5m			Alexander ALX400 4.4m		N47/24D	1999-2000		

17099	PD	VLT14	17130	PD	V130MEV	17161	PD	V161MEV	17192	BW	V192MEV
17100	PD	WLT491	17131	PD	V131MEV	17162	PD	V162MEV	17193	PD	V193MEV
17101	PD	WLT461	17132	NS	V132MEV	17163	PD	V163MEV	17194	BW	V194MEV
17102	PD	V102MEV	17133	PD	V133MEV	17164	PD	V164MEV	17195	PD	V195MEV
17103	PD	V103MEV	17134	PD	V134MEV	17165	U	V165MEV	17196	SD	V196MEV
17104	PD	V104MEV	17135	NS	V135MEV	17166	PD	V166MEV	17197	SD	V197MEV
17105	PD	V105MEV	17136	NS	V136MEV	17167	U	V167MEV	17198	SD	V198MEV
17106	NS	V106MEV	17137	NS	V137MEV	17168	U	V168MEV	17199	SD	V199MEV
17107	PD	V107MEV	17138	PD	V138MEV	17169	U	V169MEV	17200	SD	V363OWC
17108	PD	V108MEV	17139	TL	V139MEV	17170	SD	V170MEV	17201	SD	V201MEV
17109	PD	V109MEV	17140	PD	V140MEV	17171	SD	V171MEV	17202	SD	V202MEV
17110	PD	V476KJN	17141	PD	V141MEV	17172	SD	V172MEV	17203	U	V203MEV
17111	SD	V477KJN	17142	PD	V142MEV	17173	SD	V173MEV	17204	U	V204MEV
17112	PD	V112MEV	17143	TL	V143MEV	17174	SD	V174MEV	17205	U	V205MEV
17113	PD	V113MEV	17144	NS	V144MEV	17175	SD	V175MEV	17206	U	V206MEV
17114	NS	V114MEV	17145	PD	V145MEV	17176	SD	V176MEV	17207	U	V207MEV
17115	PD	V115MEV	17146	BW	V146MEV	17177	SD	V177MEV	17208	U	V208MEV
17116	PD	V116MEV	17147	U	V147MEV	17178	SD	V178MEV	17209	U	V209MEV
17117	PD	V117MEV	17148	TL	V148MEV	17179	SD	V179MEV	17210	U	V210MEV
17118	PD	V118MEV	17149	PD	V149MEV	17180	T	W187CNO	17211	NS	V211MEV
17119	PD	V119MEV	17150	TL	V150MEV	17181	T	V181MEV	17212	NS	V212MEV
17120	PD	V120MEV	17151	TL	V151MEV	17182	T	V182MEV	17213	NS	V213MEV
17121	PD	V478KJN	17152	TL	V152MEV	17183	T	V183MEV	17214	PD	V214MEV
17122	PD	V122MEV	17153	TL	V153MEV	17184	T	V184MEV	17215	PD	V215MEV
17123	PD	V479KJN	17154	TL	V154MEV	17185	T	V185MEV	17216	PD	V216MEV
17124	NS	V124MEV	17155	TL	V155MEV	17186	T	V186MEV	17217	PD	V217MEV
17125	PD	V125MEV	17156	TL	V156MEV	17187	T	V362OWC	17218	PD	V218MEV
17126	PD	V126MEV	17157	TL	V157MEV	17188	T	V188MEV	17219	PD	V219MEV
17127	PD	V127MEV	17158	TL	V158MEV	17189	T	V189MEV	17220	PD	V220MEV
17128	PD	V128MEV	17159	PD	V159MEV	17190	T	V190MEV	17221	PD	V221MEV
17129	U	V129MEV	17160	TL	V160MEV	17191	T	V191MEV	17222	PD	V364OWC

The majority of the buses purchased are the standard length, 10.5metre Trident though Transport for London have requested the shorter on some routes. Pictured in Lewisham is standard 17319, X319NNO. As the previous DVLA system of issuing marks retained a considerable quantity of reserved numbers the opportunity to match both fleet and registration numbers reduced, a problem eliminated with the new scheme. *Richard Godfrey*

17223-17260   Dennis Trident 9.9m   Alexander ALX400 4.4m   N43/21D   2000

17223	TL	X361NNO	17233	TB	X233NNO	17243	U	X243NNO	17252	U	X252NNO
17224	TL	X362NNO	17234	TB	X234NNO	17244	BW	X369NNO	17253	U	X253NNO
17225	TL	X363NNO	17235	TB	X235NNO	17245	BW	X371NNO	17254	U	X254NNO
17226	TL	X364NNO	17236	TB	X236NNO	17246	BW	X246NNO	17255	U	X373NNO
17227	TL	X365NNO	17237	BW	X237NNO	17247	U	X247NNO	17256	U	X256NNO
17228	TL	X366NNO	17238	BW	X238NNO	17248	U	X248NNO	17257	U	X257NNO
17229	TL	X229NNO	17239	BW	X239NNO	17249	U	X249NNO	17258	U	X258NNO
17230	TB	X367NNO	17240	BW	X368NNO	17250	U	X372NNO	17259	U	X259NNO
17231	TB	X231NNO	17241	BW	X241NNO	17251	U	X251NNO	17260	U	WLT575
17232	TB	X232NNO	17242	BW	X242NNO						

17261-17358   Dennis Trident 10.5m   Alexander ALX400 4.4m   N47/24D   2000

17261	PD	X261NNO	17286	TB	X286NNO	17311	PD	X311NNO	17335	TB	X335NNO
17262	PD	X262NNO	17287	TB	X287NNO	17312	PD	X312NNO	17336	TB	X336NNO
17263	PD	X263NNO	17288	TB	X288NNO	17313	PD	X313NNO	17337	TB	X337NNO
17264	PD	X264NNO	17289	TB	X289NNO	17314	PD	X314NNO	17338	TB	X338NNO
17265	PD	X265NNO	17290	TB	X379NNO	17315	PD	X315NNO	17339	TB	X339NNO
17266	PD	X266NNO	17291	U	X291NNO	17316	PD	X385NNO	17340	TB	X395NNO
17267	PD	X267NNO	17292	NS	X292NNO	17317	TL	X317NNO	17341	TB	X341NNO
17268	NS	X268NNO	17293	NS	X293NNO	17318	TL	X386NNO	17342	TB	X342NNO
17269	PD	X269NNO	17294	NS	X294NNO	17319	TL	X319NNO	17343	TB	X343NNO
17270	PD	X376NNO	17295	NS	X295NNO	17320	TL	X387NNO	17344	TB	X344NNO
17271	PD	X271NNO	17296	NS	X296NNO	17321	TL	X388NNO	17345	TB	X396NNO
17272	PD	X272NNO	17297	NS	X297NNO	17322	TL	X322NNO	17346	TB	X346NNO
17273	PD	X273NNO	17298	NS	X298NNO	17323	TL	X389NNO	17347	TB	X347NNO
17274	PD	X274NNO	17299	NS	X299NNO	17324	TB	X324NNO	17348	TB	X348NNO
17275	PD	X377NNO	17300	NS	X381NNO	17325	TL	X391NNO	17349	TB	X349NNO
17276	PD	X276NNO	17301	NS	X301NNO	17326	TL	X326NNO	17350	TL	X397NNO
17277	PD	X277NNO	17302	PD	X302NNO	17327	TL	X327NNO	17351	TB	X351NNO
17278	PD	X278NNO	17303	PD	X303NNO	17328	TL	X392NNO	17352	TB	X352NNO
17279	TB	X279NNO	17304	PD	X304NNO	17329	TL	X329NNO	17353	TB	X353NNO
17280	TB	X378NNO	17305	PD	X382NNO	17330	TL	X393NNO	17354	TB	X354NNO
17281	TB	X281NNO	17306	PD	X383NNO	17331	TL	X331NNO	17355	TB	X398NNO
17282	TB	X282NNO	17307	PD	X307NNO	17332	TL	X332NNO	17356	TB	X356NNO
17283	TB	X283NNO	17308	PD	X308NNO	17333	TL	X394NNO	17357	TB	X357NNO
17284	TB	X284NNO	17309	PD	X309NNO	17334	TB	X334NNO	17358	TB	X358NNO
17285	TB	X285NNO	17310	PD	X384NNO						

17359-17435 Dennis Trident 10.5m Alexander ALX400 4.4m N45/23D* 2001 *17402 is N45/27F

17359	BK	Y359NHK	17379	BK	Y379NHK	17398	SD	Y368NHK	17417	T	LX51FJE
17360	BK	Y508NHK	17380	BK	Y512NHK	17399	SD	LX51FHP	17418	T	LX51FJF
17361	BK	Y361NHK	17381	BK	Y381NHK	17400	SD	Y514NHK	17419	T	LX51FJJ
17362	BK	Y362NHK	17382	BK	Y382NHK	17401	SD	Y401NHK	17420	T	LX51FJK
17363	BK	Y363NHK	17383	BK	LX51FPF	17402	CA	Y103GHC	17421	T	LX51FJN
17364	BK	Y364NHK	17384	BK	Y384NHK	17403	SD	LX51FHS	17422	T	LX51FJO
17365	BK	Y365NHK	17385	BK	Y385NHK	17404	SD	Y404NHK	17423	T	LX51FJP
17366	BK	Y366NHK	17386	BK	Y386NHK	17405	SD	LX51FHT	17424	T	LX51FJV
17367	BK	Y367NHK	17387	BK	LX51FPC	17406	SD	Y517NHK	17425	T	LX51FJY
17368	BK	Y368NHK	17388	BK	Y388NHK	17407	SD	Y407NHK	17426	T	LX51FJZ
17369	BK	Y369NHK	17389	BK	Y389NHK	17408	SD	LX51FHU	17427	T	LX51FKA
17370	BK	Y509NHK	17390	BK	LX51FPD	17409	T	Y409NHK	17428	NS	LX51FKB
17371	BK	Y371NHK	17391	BK	Y391NHK	17410	T	LX51FHV	17429	NS	Y429NHK
17372	BK	Y372NHK	17392	BK	Y392NHK	17411	T	LX51FHW	17430	NS	LX51FKD
17373	BK	Y373NHK	17393	BK	Y393NHK	17412	T	LX51FHY	17431	NS	LX51FKE
17374	BK	Y374NHK	17394	BK	LX51FHN	17413	T	LX51FHZ	17432	NS	LX51FKF
17375	BK	Y511NHK	17395	SD	Y395NHK	17414	T	LX51FJA	17433	NS	LX51FKG
17376	BK	Y376NHK	17396	SD	LX51FHO	17415	T	LX51FJC	17434	NS	Y434NHK
17377	BK	Y377NHK	17397	SD	Y367NHK	17416	T	LX51FJD	17435	NS	LX51FKJ
17378	BK	Y378NHK									

17436-17534 Dennis Trident 9.9m Alexander ALX400 N43/19D 2001

17436	NS	Y436NHK	17461	NS	LX51FKW	17486	BW	LX51FME	17511	SD	LX51FNO
17437	NS	Y437NHK	17462	NS	Y462NHK	17487	BW	LX51FMF	17512	SD	LX51FNP
17438	NS	Y438NHK	17463	NS	LX51FKZ	17488	BW	LX51FMG	17513	SD	LX51FNR
17439	NS	LX51FKL	17464	NS	Y464NHK	17489	BW	LX51FMJ	17514	SD	LX51FNS
17440	NS	Y522NHK	17465	NS	LX51FLB	17490	BW	LX51FMK	17515	SD	LX51FNT
17441	NS	Y441NHK	17466	BW	LX51FLC	17491	BW	LX51FML	17516	SD	LX51FNU
17442	NS	Y442NHK	17467	TL	LX51FLD	17492	BW	LX51FMM	17517	SD	LX51FNV
17443	NS	Y443NHK	17468	TL	LX51FLE	17493	BW	LX51FMO	17518	SD	LX51FNW
17444	NS	LX51FKO	17469	TL	LX51FLF	17494	BW	LX51FMP	17519	SD	LX51FNY
17445	NS	Y445NHK	17470	TL	Y531NHK	17495	BW	LX51FMU	17520	SD	LX51FNZ
17446	NS	Y446NHK	17471	TL	LX51FLG	17496	BW	LX51FMV	17521	SD	LX51FOA
17447	NS	Y447NHK	17472	TL	LX51FLH	17497	BW	LX51FMY	17522	SD	LX51FOC
17448	NS	Y448NHK	17473	TL	LX51FLJ	17498	BW	LX51FMZ	17523	TL	LX51FOD
17449	NS	Y449NHK	17474	TL	LX51FLK	17499	BW	LX51FNA	17524	TL	LX51FOF
17450	NS	Y524NHK	17475	TL	LX51FLL	17500	BW	LX51FNC	17525	TL	LX51FOH
17451	NS	LX51FKR	17476	TL	LX51FLM	17501	BW	LX51FND	17526	TL	LX51FOJ
17452	NS	Y452NHK	17477	TL	LX51FLN	17502	SD	LX51FNE	17527	TL	LX51FOK
17453	NS	Y453NHK	17478	TL	LX51FLP	17503	SD	LX51FNF	17528	TL	LX51FOM
17454	NS	Y454NHK	17479	TL	LX51FLR	17504	SD	LX51FNG	17529	TL	LX51FON
17455	NS	Y526NHK	17480	TL	LX51FLV	17505	SD	LX51FNH	17530	TL	LX51FOP
17456	NS	Y527NHK	17481	TL	LX51FLW	17506	SD	LX51FNJ	17531	TL	LX51FOT
17457	NS	LX51FKT	17482	TL	LX51FLZ	17507	SD	LX51FNK	17532	TL	LX51FOU
17458	NS	Y458NHK	17483	TL	LX51FMA	17508	SD	LX51FNL	17533	TL	LX51FOV
17459	NS	LX51FKU	17484	TL	LX51FMC	17509	SD	LX51FNM	17534	TL	LX51FPA
17460	NS	Y529NHK	17485	TL	LX51FMD	17510	SD	LX51FNN			

17535-17591 Dennis Trident 9.9m Alexander ALX400 N43/21D 2002

17535	BW	LY02OAA	17550	SD	LY02OBB	17564	SD	LV52HDX	17578	TL	LV52HFL
17536	BW	LY02OAB	17551	SD	LY02OBC	17565	SD	LV52HDY	17579	TL	LV52HFM
17537	SD	LY02OAC	17552	SD	LY02OBD	17566	SD	LV52HDZ	17580	TL	LV52HFN
17538	SD	LY02OAD	17553	SD	LY02OBE	17567	TL	LV52HEJ	17581	TL	LV52HFO
17539	SD	LY02OAE	17554	SD	LY02OBF	17568	TL	LV52HFU	17582	TL	LV52HFP
17540	SD	LY02OAG	17555	SD	LY02OBG	17569	TL	LV52HFA	17583	TL	LV52HFR
17541	SD	LY02OAN	17556	SD	LY02OBH	17570	TL	LV52HFB	17584	TL	LV52HFS
17542	SD	LY02OAO	17557	SD	LY02OBJ	17571	TL	LV52HFC	17585	TL	LV52HFT
17543	SD	LY02OAP	17558	SD	LY02OBK	17572	TL	LV52HFD	17586	TL	LV52HFU
17544	SD	LY02OAS	17559	SD	LY02OBL	17573	TL	LV52HFE	17587	TL	LV52HFW
17545	SD	LY02OAU	17560	SD	LY02OBM	17574	TL	LV52HFF	17588	TL	LV52HFX
17546	SD	LY02OAV	17561	SD	LV52USV	17575	TL	LV52HFH	17589	TL	LV52HFY
17547	SD	LY02OAW	17562	SD	LV52HDO	17576	TL	LV52HFJ	17590	TL	LV52HFZ
17548	SD	LY02OAX	17563	SD	LV52HDU	17577	TL	LV52HFK	17591	TL	LV52HGA
17549	SD	LY02OAZ									

Latterly TAS571, LV52HFC is now numbered 17571, and seen on route 194 in East Croydon before anyone had the chance to apply advertisment vinyls. This batch are to the shorter 9.9metre length and currently being delivered are twenty-eight of standard length. The last three of which continue numbers from 17731. Interestingly, the vehicle intended to be TA402 was built to single-door and diverted to Canterbury. Now it has resumed its correct place in the national series. *Richard Godfrey*

17592-17611   Dennis Trident 10.5m   Alexander ALX400 4.4m   N51/23D   2002

17592	LV52HHA	17597	LV52HHF	17602	LV52HHM	17607	LV52HHS
17593	LV52HHB	17598	LV52HHG	17603	LV52HHN	17608	LV52HHT
17594	LV52HHC	17599	LV52HHJ	17604	LV52HHO	17609	LV52HHU
17595	LV52HHD	17600	LV52HHK	17605	LV52HHP	17610	LV52HHW
17596	LV52HHE	17601	LV52HHL	17606	LV52HHR	17611	LV52HHX

17612-17624   Dennis Trident 10.5M   Alexander ALX400 4.4m   N51/28F   1999

17612	HE	T612MNF	17616	ST	V616DJA	17619	ST	V619DJA	17622	ST	V622DJA
17613	HE	T613MNF	17617	PS	V617DJA	17620	ST	V620DJA	17623	ST	V623DJA
17614	ST	V614DJA	17618	PS	V618DJA	17621	ST	V621DJA	17624	ST	V624DJA
17615	ST	V615DJA									

17626-17647   Dennis Trident 10.5M   Alexander ALX400 4.4m   N51/28F   2000

17626	HE	W626RND	17632	HE	W632RND	17637	ST	W637RND	17643	HE	W643RND
17627	HE	W627RND	17633	HE	W633RND	17638	ST	W638RND	17644	HE	W644RND
17628	HE	W628RND	17634	ST	W634RND	17639	ST	W639RND	17645	HE	W645RND
17629	ST	W629RND	17635	ST	W635RND	17641	HE	W641RND	17646	HE	W646RND
17631	HE	W631RND	17636	ST	W636RND	17642	HE	W642RND	17647	HE	W647RND

17651-17672   Dennis Trident 10.5m   Alexander ALX400 4.4m   N51/29F   1999

17651	PS	V151DFT	17657	PS	V157DFT	17663	PS	V163DFT	17668	PS	V168DFT
17652	PS	V152DFT	17658	PS	V158DFT	17664	PS	V164DFT	17669	PS	V169DFT
17653	PS	V153DFT	17659	PS	V159DFT	17665	PS	V165DFT	17670	PS	V170DFT
17654	PS	V154DFT	17660	PS	V160DFT	17666	PS	V166DFT	17671	PS	V171DFT
17655	PS	V155DFT	17661	PS	V161DFT	17667	PS	V167DFT	17672	PS	V172DFT
17656	PS	V156DFT	17662	PS	V162DFT						

The provincial fleet in Manchester received thirty low-height Tridents in 2002 for their contribution to the Commonwealth Games transport shuttles. These carried lettering for the duties as shown by 17714, ML02RWN, and have since have displaced Dominators at Princess Road. Three were transferred to Cheltenham for use on a new service in that town. *Bob Downham*

17673-17688 — Dennis Trident 10.5m — Alexander ALX400 — N51/28F — 1999

17673	GY	T373FUG	17677	GY	T377FUG	17681	GY	V381EWE	17685	GY	V385EWE
17674	GY	T374FUG	17678	GY	V378EWE	17682	GY	V382EWE	17686	GY	T370FUG
17675	GY	T375FUG	17679	GY	V379EWE	17683	GY	V383EWE	17687	GY	T371FUG
17676	GY	T376FUG	17680	GY	V380EWE	17684	GY	V384EWE	17688	GY	T372FUG

17689	CA	X601VDY	Dennis Trident 10.5m	Alexander ALX400	N47/27F	2000
17690	CA	X602VDY	Dennis Trident 10.5m	Alexander ALX400	N47/27F	2000

17691-17697 — Dennis Trident 10.5m — Plaxton President 4.1m — N49/29F — 2000

17691	CB	X701JVV	17693	CB	X703JVV	17695	CB	X705JVV	17697	CB	X707JVV
17692	CB	X702JVV	17694	CB	X704JVV	17696	CB	X706JVV			

17701-17730 — Dennis Trident 10.5m — Alexander ALX400 4.2m — N51/28F — 2002

17701	PS	ML02RWO	17709	PS	ML02KCV	17717	PS	MK02EFW	17724	HE	MK02EGF
17702	PS	ML02RWU	17710	PS	MK02EHC	17718	PS	MK02EFX	17725	HE	MK02EGJ
17703	PS	ML02KCO	17711	PS	MK02EHD	17719	PS	MK02EFY	17726	HE	MK02EGU
17704	PS	ML02KNO	17712	PS	ML02RWJ	17720	PS	MK02EFZ	17727	HE	MK02EGV
17705	PS	ML02RWV	17713	PS	ML02RWK	17721	PS	MK02EGC	17728	CT	MK02EGX
17706	PS	ML02KCU	17714	PS	ML02RWN	17722	CT	MK02EGD	17729	CT	MK02EGY
17707	PS	ML02RWW	17715	PS	MK02EFU	17723	HE	MK02EGE	17730	PS	MK02EGZ
17708	PS	ML02RWX	17716	PS	MK02EFV						

17731		LV52HHY	Dennis Trident 10.5m	Alexander ALX400	N51/27D	2002
17732		LV52HHZ	Dennis Trident 10.5m	Alexander ALX400	N51/27D	2002
17733		LV52HJA	Dennis Trident 10.5m	Alexander ALX400	N51/27D	2002
17734	EX	SK52USN	Dennis Trident 10.5m	Alexander ALX400	N47/27F	2002
17735	EX	SK52USO	Dennis Trident 10.5m	Alexander ALX400	N47/27F	2002
17736	EX	SK52USP	Dennis Trident 10.5m	Alexander ALX400	N47/27F	2002
17737	MD	YM52UOU	Dennis Trident 10.5m	Alexander ALX400	N47/27F	2002
17738	MD	YM52UOV	Dennis Trident 10.5m	Alexander ALX400	N47/27F	2002
17739	MD	YM52UOW	Dennis Trident 10.5m	Alexander ALX400	N47/27F	2002

17740-17854 — Dennis Trident 10.5m — Alexander ALX400 — N51/28F — 2003 and on order

17740	L	17769	L	17798	L	17827	L
17741	L	17770	L	17799	L	17828	L
17742	L	17771	L	17800	L	17829	L
17743	L	17772	L	17801	L	17830	L
17744	L	17773	L	17802	L	17831	L
17745	L	17774	L	17803	L	17832	L
17746	L	17775	L	17804	L	17833	L
17747	L	17776	L	17805	L	17834	L
17748	L	17777	L	17806	L	17835	L
17749	L	17778	L	17807	L	17836	L
17750	L	17779	L	17808	L	17837	L
17751	L	17780	L	17809	L	17838	L
17752	L	17781	L	17810	L	17839	L
17753	L	17782	L	17811	L	17840	L
17754	L	17783	L	17812	L	17841	L
17755	L	17784	L	17813	L	17842	L
17756	L	17785	L	17814	L	17843	L
17757	L	17786	L	17815	L	17844	L
17758	L	17787	L	17816	L	17845	L
17759	L	17788	L	17817	L	17846	L
17760	L	17789	L	17818	L	17847	L
17761	L	17790	L	17819	L	17848	L
17762	L	17791	L	17820	L	17849	L
17763	L	17792	L	17821	L	17850	L
17764	L	17793	L	17822	L	17851	L
17765	L	17794	L	17823	L	17852	L
17766	L	17795	L	17824	L	17853	L
17767	L	17796	L	17825	L	17854	L
17768	L	17797	L	17826	L		

Special event vehicles - (initial owners shown and traditional vintage body codes used)

19909	HS	409DCD	Leyland Titan PD3/4	Northern Counties	FCO39/30F	1964	Southdown
19912	SU	LCU112	Daimler CCG6 DD	Roe	H35/28R	1964	South Shields
19913	WG	UF4813	Leyland Titan TD1	Brush	O27/24R	1929	Southdown
19917	ST	PRX189B	Leyland Titan PD3/4	Northern Counties	FO39/30F	1964	Southdown
19935	ES	HGM335E	Bristol FLF6G	Eastern Coach Works	H44/34F	1967	Central SMT
19945	PM	CD7045	Leyland N Special	Short (1928)	O27/24RO	1922	Southdown
19946	AD	MFN946F	AEC Regent V 3D3RA	Park Royal	H40/32F	1967	East Kent
19952	CB	JAH552D	Bristol FLF6G	Eastern Coach Works	O38/32F	1966	Eastern Counties
19953	CB	JAH553D	Bristol FLF6G	Eastern Coach Works	L38/32F	1966	Eastern Counties
19959	WS	UCS659	Albion Lowlander LR7	Alexander	H40/31F	1963	Western SMT
19982	WS	RCS382	Leyland Titan PD3A/3	Alexander	L35/32RD	1961	Western SMT
19992	EX	LRV992	Leyland Titan PD2/12	Metro-Cammell	O33/26R	1956	Portsmouth

Allocated to Cambridge are the only low-height Presidents so far built. These measure 4.2metres. Shown here is 17697, X705JVV.
Richard Godfrey

The Alexander-bodied PS was the mainstay of the single-deck fleet from the initial large batch for Cumberland in 1992 until the decision to use low floor MAN buses in 1998. Including those bodied by Plaxton (1); Duple (2); East Lancashire (5) and the Paladins (118) the current number in use is 748 which can be found from Inverness to the south coast. Pictured heading north from Inverness is 20109, N209LTN. *Murdoch Currie*

| 20001 | BR | A14RBL | Volvo B10M-50 | | | East Lancashire (1995) | | BC53F | | 1984 | | |

20004-20012
Volvo B10M-55 — Plaxton Paladin — B48F — 1998

20004	OX	R904XFC	20007	OX	R907XFC	20009	OX	R909XFC	20011	OX	R811XFC
20005	OX	R905XFC	20008	OX	R908XFC	20010	OX	R910XFC	20012	OX	R912XFC
20006	OX	R906XFC									

20101-20117
Volvo B10M-55 — Alexander PS — B49F — 1995

20101	SU	N201LTN	20106	SU	N206LTN	20110	AY	N210LTN	20114	AY	N214LTN
20102	SU	N202LTN	20107	BQ	N207LTN	20111	PH	N211LTN	20115	SU	N215LTN
20103	SU	N203LTN	20108	AN	N208LTN	20112	IS	N212LTN	20116	SU	N216LTN
20104	SU	N204LTN	20109	AN	N209LTN	20113	PH	N213LTN	20117	SU	N217LTN
20105	SU	N205LTN									

20118-20135
Volvo B10M-55 — Alexander PS — B49F — 1996

20118	IS	P118XCN	20123	BY	P123XCN	20128	PR	P128XCN	20132	CY	P132XCN
20119	IS	P119XCN	20124	BY	P124XCN	20129	CY	P129XCN	20133	PR	P133XCN
20120	BY	P120XCN	20125	BY	P125XCN	20130	CY	P130XCN	20134	PR	P134XCN
20121	BY	P121XCN	20126	BY	P126XCN	20131	CY	P131XCN	20135	BY	P135XCN
20122	BY	P122XCN	20127	PR	P127XCN						

20141-20154
Volvo B10M-55 — Alexander PS — B49F — 1997-98

20141	AN	R641LSO	20145	AN	R645LSO	20149	BQ	R649LSO	20152	AN	R652VSE
20142	AN	R642LSO	20146	IS	R646LSO	20150	IS	R650LSO	20153	AN	R653VSE
20143	AN	R643LSO	20147	GS	R647LSO	20151	AN	R651VSE	20154	IS	R654VSE
20144	AN	R644LSO	20148	GS	R648LSO						

Rugby supply the buses in Coventry where 20221, R221CRW is seen before heading back home. Alexander supplied two interior layouts for the model, most common is the forty-nine seat bus version, while the forty-eight seat version with high-back seating was supplied for the more rural areas. *Mark Doggett*

20171-20178

| Volvo B10M-55 | | Alexander PS | | B49F | 1993 |

20171	PH	K571LTS	**20173**	PH	K573LTS	**20175**	PH	K575LTS	**20177** PH K577LTS
20172	PH	K572LTS	**20174**	PH	K574LTS	**20176**	PH	K576LTS	**20178** PH K578LTS

20189-20198

| Volvo B10M-55 | | Alexander PS | | BC48F | 1994 |

20189	WI	M589OSO	**20192**	AN	M592OSO	**20195**	AN	M595OSO	**20197** AN M597OSO
20190	HS	M590OSO	**20193**	AN	M593OSO	**20196**	CJ	M596OSO	**20198** WI M598OSO
20191	AN	M591OSO	**20194**	AN	M594OSO				

20201-20220

| Volvo B10M-55 | | Alexander PS | | BC48F* | 1995 | *20206-8 are B49F |

20201	LE	M201LHP	**20206**	NU	N206TDU	**20211**	NU	N211TDU	**20216** NU N216TDU
20202	LE	M202LHP	**20207**	NU	N207TDU	**20212**	NU	N212TDU	**20217** LE P217HBD
20203	OX	M203LHP	**20208**	NU	N208TDU	**20213**	NU	N213TDU	**20218** LE P218HBD
20204	OX	M204LHP	**20209**	NU	M209LHP	**20214**	NU	N214TDU	**20219** LE P219HBD
20205	NU	M205LHP	**20210**	NU	M210LHP	**20215**	NU	N215TDU	**20220** LE P220HBD

20221-20228

| Volvo B10M-55 | | Alexander PS | | B49F | 1997-98 |

20221	RU	R221CRW	**20224**	RU	R224CRW	**20226**	NU	R226CRW	**20228** OX R228CRW
20223	RU	R223CRW	**20225**	RU	R225CRW	**20227**	NU	R227CRW	

20243-20252

| Volvo B10M-55 | | Northern Counties Paladin | B48F | 1995 |

20243	SC	M543SPY	**20246**	SC	M546SPY	**20249**	SC	M549SPY	**20251** SC M551SPY
20244	SC	M544SPY	**20247**	SC	M547SPY	**20250**	SC	M550SPY	**20252** SC M552SPY
20245	SC	M545SPY	**20248**	SC	M548SPY				

20253	SC	R653RPY	Volvo B10M-55	Northern Counties Paladin	B48F	1998
20254	SC	R654RPY	Volvo B10M-55	Northern Counties Paladin	B48F	1998
20255	SC	R655RPY	Volvo B10M-55	Northern Counties Paladin	B48F	1998
20256	HP	R556RPY	Volvo B10M-55	Plaxton Paladin	B48F	1998
20257	HP	R557RPY	Volvo B10M-55	Plaxton Paladin	B48F	1998
20258	HP	R558RPY	Volvo B10M-55	Plaxton Paladin	B48F	1998
20261	DA	N551VDC	Volvo B10M-55	Alexander PS	BC48F	1995
20262	DA	N552VDC	Volvo B10M-55	Alexander PS	BC48F	1995
20263	HP	N553VDC	Volvo B10M-55	Alexander PS	BC48F	1995
20264	HP	R554RPY	Volvo B10M-55	Plaxton Paladin	B48F	1998
20265	HP	R755RPY	Volvo B10M-55	Plaxton Paladin	B48F	1998

20267-20278
Volvo B10M-55 — Northern Counties Paladin — B48F — 1995

20267	HP	M707KRH	20270	HP	M710KRH	20273	DA	M713KRH	20276	HL	M716KRH
20268	HP	M708KRH	20271	HP	M711KRH	20274	HL	M714KRH	20277	HL	M717KRH
20269	HP	M709KRH	20272	SC	M712KRH	20275	HL	M715KRH	20278	HL	M718KRH

20279-20286
Volvo B10M-55 — Northern Counties Paladin — B48F — 1998

20279	HL	R719RPY	20281	HL	R721RPY	20283	HL	R723RPY	20285	HL	R725RPY
20280	HL	R720RPY	20282	HL	R722RPY	20284	HL	R724RPY	20286	HL	R726RPY

20291-20300
Volvo B10M-55 — Northern Counties Paladin — B48F — 1995

20291	HP	M401SPY	20294	HP	M404SPY	20297	HP	M407SPY	20299	HP	M409SPY
20292	HP	M402SPY	20295	HP	M405SPY	20298	HP	M408SPY	20300	HP	M410SPY
20293	HP	M403SPY	20296	HP	M406SPY						

20301-20310
Volvo B10M-55 — Alexander PS — B49F — 1994

20301	CJ	L301PSC	20304	SA	L304PSC	20307	AL	L307PSC	20309	SA	L309PSC
20302	SA	L302PSC	20305	SA	L305PSC	20308	GS	L308PSC	20310	SA	L310PSC
20303	SA	L303PSC	20306	SA	L306PSC						

20311	TH	M311YSC	Volvo B10M-55	Alexander PS	BC48F	1995
20312	CA	M312YSC	Volvo B10M-55	Alexander PS	BC48F	1995
20313	AR	M313YSC	Volvo B10M-55	Alexander PS	BC48F	1995

20314-20329
Volvo B10M-55 — Alexander PS — B49F* — 1995-96 — *20314/5 are BC48F

20314	AL	M314PKS	20318	KY	N318VMS	20322	SA	N322VMS	20326	DE	N326VMS
20315	SA	M315PKS	20319	KY	N319VMS	20323	DE	N323VMS	20327	GS	N327VMS
20316	DE	N316VMS	20320	KY	N320VMS	20324	GS	N324VMS	20328	AL	N328VMS
20317	KY	N317VMS	20321	SA	N321VMS	20325	DE	N325VMS	20329	SA	N329VMS

20330-20342
Volvo B10M-55 — Alexander PS — B49F — 1998

20330	AL	R330HFS	20334	KY	R334HFS	20337	DE	R337HFS	20340	SA	R340HFS
20331	AL	R331HFS	20335	KY	R335HFS	20338	DE	R338HFS	20341	KY	R341HFS
20332	KY	R332HFS	20336	KY	R336HFS	20339	DE	R339HFS	20342	KY	R342HFS

20347	EH	R807JDV	Volvo B10M-55	Alexander PS	B49F	1998

20350-20370
Volvo B10M-55 — Alexander PS — BC48F — 1995

20350	MR	M750LAX	20356	MR	M756LAX	20361	MR	M761LAX	20366	MR	M766RAX
20351	MR	M751LAX	20357	MR	M757LAX	20362	MR	M762LAX	20367	MR	M767RAX
20352	AE	M752LAX	20358	MR	M758LAX	20363	MR	M763LAX	20368	CN	M768RAX
20353	AE	M753LAX	20359	MR	M759LAX	20364	MR	M764LAX	20369	CN	M769RAX
20354	MR	M754LAX	20360	MR	M760LAX	20365	MR	M765RAX	20370	CN	M770RAX
20355	MR	M755LAX									

20385-20392
Volvo B10M-55 — Alexander PS — BC48F — 1997-98

20385	BR	R785DHB	20388	BR	R788DHB	20390	CN	R790DHB	20392	CN	R792DHB
20387	BR	R787DHB	20389	CN	R789DHB	20391	CN	R791DHB			

20401-20406
Volvo B10M-55 — Alexander P — BC53F — 1988

20401	LE	E61JFV	20403	CW	E63JFV	20405	CW	E65JFV	20406	BR	E66JFV
20402	LE	E62JFV	20404	CN	E64JFV						

The 2003 Stagecoach Bus Handbook

Northern Counties was also an approved coachbuilder for Stagecoach and supplied 118 Paladins, the last batch of which were assembled at Scarborough and carry Plaxton body plates. Showing the Paladin styling is 20282, R722RPY, currently allocated to Hull. All the type based with the former Transit operation were fitted with bus seating. *Tony Wilson*

| 20407 | CN | G67PFR | Volvo B10M-55 | | | East Lancashire EL2000 | | B51F | 1990 | | |
| 20408 | CN | G68PFR | Volvo B10M-55 | | | East Lancashire EL2000 | | B51F | 1990 | | |

20411-20414 — Volvo B10M-55 — Alexander PS — BC48F — 1994

| 20411 | WP | M411RRN | 20412 | WP | M412RRN | 20413 | WP | M413RRN | 20414 | WP | M414RRN |

20417-20423 — Volvo B10M-55 — Alexander PS — B51F — 1991

| 20417 | ME | H617ACK | 20419 | ME | H619ACK | 20421 | BR | H621ACK | 20423 | ME | H623ACK |
| 20418 | ME | H618ACK | 20420 | BR | H620ACK | 20422 | ME | H622ACK | | | |

20424	PR	J24MCW	Volvo B10M-50			East Lancashire EL2000		B45F	1992		
20425	PR	J25MCW	Volvo B10M-50			East Lancashire EL2000		B45F	1992		
20430	PR	M230TBV	Volvo B10M-55			Alexander PS		BC48F	1995		
20435	PR	M235TBV	Volvo B10M-55			Alexander PS		BC48F	1995		
20436	CY	M236TBV	Volvo B10M-55			Alexander PS		BC48F	1995		

20438-20447 — Volvo B10M-55 — Alexander PS — BC48F — 1994

20438	AR	L338KCK	20441	CH	L341KCK	20444	CH	L344KCK	20446	AT	L346KCK
20439	CH	L339KCK	20442	CH	L342KCK	20445	AR	L345KCK	20447	AT	L347KCK
20440	CH	L340KCK	20443	CH	L343KCK						

20451-20463 — Volvo B10M-55 — Alexander PS — B48F — 1995

20451	CY	M451VCW	20455	PR	M455VCW	20458	LL	M458VCW	20461	AT	M461VCW
20452	CY	M452VCW	20456	LL	M456VCW	20459	LL	M459VCW	20462	AT	M462VCW
20454	CY	M454VCW	20457	LL	M457VCW	20460	WI	M460VCW	20463	ME	M463VCW

20473-20482 — Volvo B10M-55 — Alexander PS — B49F — 1997

20473	CE	R473MCW	20476	PR	R476MCW	20479	EX	R479MCW	20481	EX	R481MCW
20474	PR	R474MCW	20477	BA	R477MCW	20480	EX	R480MCW	20482	EX	R482MCW
20475	PR	R475MCW	20478	BA	R478MCW						

One consequence of the Stagecoach renumbering has been the placing together of the earlier fragmented batches. Currently at Oxford, 20812, N812DNE was new to the Manchester fleet being displaced there by the arrival of the low-floor MAN buses. *Dave Heath*

20491-20499

		Volvo B10M-55			Alexander PS			BC48F	1995		
20491	CH	M601VHE	20494	WP	M604VHE	20496	MD	M606VHE	20498	CH	M608WET
20492	WP	M602VHE	20495	WP	M605VHE	20497	MD	M607VHE	20499	CH	M609WET
20493	WP	M603VHE									

20502	AY	R502KSA	Volvo B10M-55	Alexander PS	B49F	1997
20503	KK	R503KSA	Volvo B10M-55	Alexander PS	B49F	1997
20504	AY	R504KSA	Volvo B10M-55	Alexander PS	B49F	1997

20505-20512

		Volvo B10M-55			Alexander PS			BC48F	1995		
20505	AY	M488ASW	20507	KK	M871ASW	20509	KK	M469ASW	20511	AS	M483ASW
20506	KK	M869ASW	20508	KK	M485ASW	20510	AS	M481ASW	20512	DS	M468ASW

20513	AY	R513KSA	Volvo B10M-55	Alexander PS	B49F	1997
20514	AY	R514KSA	Volvo B10M-55	Alexander PS	B49F	1997
20515	RO	R515KSA	Volvo B10M-55	Alexander PS	B49F	1997

20516-20526

		Volvo B10M-55			Alexander PS			B49F	1998		
20516	AY	R516VSE	20518	AY	R518VSE	20521	SR	R521VSE	20524	AA	R524VSE
20517	AY	R517VSE	20519	AY	R519VSE	20522	SR	R522VSE	20526	AA	R526VSE

20530-20560

		Volvo B10M-55			Alexander PS			B49F	1997		
20530	CC	P530ESA	20538	AA	P538ESA	20546	ME	P546ESA	20553	SS	P553ESA
20531	CC	P531ESA	20539	AA	P539ESA	20547	ME	P547ESA	20554	SC	P554ESA
20532	AS	P532ESA	20540	ME	P540ESA	20548	AS	P548ESA	20556	AS	P556ESA
20533	CC	P533ESA	20541	ME	P541ESA	20549	AY	P549ESA	20557	LE	P557ESA
20534	CC	P534ESA	20542	ME	P542ESA	20550	BY	P550ESA	20558	LE	P558ESA
20535	CC	P535ESA	20543	ME	P543ESA	20551	SS	P551ESA	20559	LE	P559ESA
20536	AS	P536ESA	20544	ME	P544ESA	20552	SS	P552ESA	20560	LE	P560ESA
20537	AA	P537ESA	20545	ME	P545ESA						

The initial batch of over a hundred buses made a major impact on the Cumberland fleet, especially the Carlisle city services where they displaced Routemaster. Still giving service in the city and now repainted into the new scheme is 20721, K721DAO. *Richard Godfrey*

20565-20594

		Volvo B10M-55			Alexander PS			BC48F	1995	
20565	AY	M480ASW	20573	CC	M473ASW	20581	AY	M484ASW	20588	KK	M788PRS
20566	AY	M486ASW	20574	CC	M474ASW	20582	AY	M872ASW	20589	KK	M789PRS
20567	AY	M487ASW	20575	CC	M475ASW	20583	DS	M466ASW	20590	KK	M790PRS
20568	AS	M489ASW	20576	CC	M476ASW	20584	AY	M784PRS	20591	KK	M791PRS
20569	AS	M482ASW	20577	CC	M477ASW	20585	SR	M785PRS	20592	KK	M792PRS
20570	CC	M470ASW	20578	CC	M478ASW	20586	AY	M786PRS	20593	KK	M793PRS
20571	CC	M471ASW	20579	CC	M479ASW	20587	AY	M787PRS	20594	DS	M467ASW
20572	CC	M472ASW	20580	AY	M870ASW						

20595	AA	R595LSO	Volvo B10M-55		Alexander PS	B49F	1997	
20596	AA	R596LSO	Volvo B10M-55		Alexander PS	B49F	1997	
20597	DS	WLT774	Volvo B10M-56		Duple 300	B53F	1988	A1 Service, 1995
20598	DU	WLT538	Volvo B10M-56		Duple 300	B53F	1988	A1 Service, 1995
20599	DS	WLT439	Volvo B10M-55		Plaxton Derwent II	B55F	1990	A1 Service, 1995

20601-20605

		Volvo B10M-55			Northern Counties Paladin			BC49F	1994	
20601	CR	L601VCD	20603	SB	L603VCD	20604	SB	L424TJK	20605	SB	L425TJK
20602	SB	L602VCD									

20606-20645

		Volvo B10M-55			Alexander PS			BC48F	1994-95	
20606	AT	L426TJK	20616	AT	L616TDY	20626	CR	L626TDY	20636	DO	M636BCD
20607	AR	L427TJK	20617	AR	L617TDY	20627	BE	L627TDY	20637	DO	M637BCD
20608	HS	L608TDY	20618	AT	WVT618	20628	CR	L628TDY	20638	DO	M638BCD
20609	HS	L609TDY	20619	CA	L619TDY	20629	CR	L629TDY	20639	DO	M639BCD
20610	PM	M610APN	20620	HS	L620TDY	20630	PM	L630TDY	20640	DO	N640LPN
20611	PM	M611APN	20621	CR	L621TDY	20631	AR	L631TDY	20641	HS	N641LPN
20612	HS	M612APN	20622	FO	L622TDY	20632	WI	L632TDY	20642	TH	N642LPN
20613	FO	M613APN	20623	CR	L623TDY	20633	DO	L633TDY	20643	BE	N643LPN
20614	HS	M614APN	20624	FO	L624TDY	20634	WI	L634TDY	20644	FO	N644LPN
20615	AN	M615APN	20625	FO	L625TDY	20635	AT	L635TDY	20645	AS	N645LPN

Pictured leaving Basingstoke bus station is 20669, M669ECD which is one of the Paladin buses fitted with high-back seating. The South East fleet was the first to renumber when Winchester depot undertook the task in December 2002. *Richard Godfrey*

20646	HS	R646HCD	Volvo B10M-55	Plaxton Paladin	B48F	1998
20647	HS	R647HCD	Volvo B10M-55	Plaxton Paladin	B48F	1998
20648	BE	R648HCD	Volvo B10M-55	Plaxton Paladin	B48F	1998
20649	BE	R649HCD	Volvo B10M-55	Plaxton Paladin	B48F	1998
20650	HS	M650BCD	Volvo B10M-55	Alexander PS	BC48F	1995
20651	BE	M651BCD	Volvo B10M-55	Alexander PS	BC48F	1995
20652	BE	M652BCD	Volvo B10M-55	Alexander PS	BC48F	1995
20653	HE	R653HCD	Volvo B10M-55	Plaxton Paladin	B48F	1998
20654	HS	R654HCD	Volvo B10M-55	Plaxton Paladin	B48F	1998
20659	AD	K789DAO	Volvo B10M-55	Alexander PS	BC48F	1993
20660	HS	K790DAO	Volvo B10M-55	Alexander PS	BC48F	1993
20661	DO	K791DAO	Volvo B10M-55	Alexander PS	BC48F	1993

20662-20670   Volvo B10M-55   Northern Counties Paladin   BC47F   1995

| 20662 | BE | M662ECD | 20664 | LS | M664ECD | 20667 | BE | M667ECD | 20669 | BE | M669ECD |
| 20663 | BE | M663ECD | 20665 | BE | M665ECD | 20668 | BE | M668ECD | 20670 | BE | M670ECD |

20674-20680   Volvo B10M-55   Plaxton Paladin   B48F   1998

| 20674 | HE | R674HCD | 20676 | DO | R676HCD | 20678 | HS | R678HCD | 20680 | HS | R680HCD |
| 20675 | HS | R675HCD | 20677 | HE | R677HCD | 20679 | HS | R679HCD |

20681-20689   Volvo B10M-55   Alexander PS   BC48F   1995

20681	OX	N401LDF	20684	SN	N404LDF	20686	SN	N406LDF	20688	SN	N408LDF
20682	SN	N402LDF	20685	SN	N405LDF	20687	SN	N407LDF	20689	SN	N409LDF
20683	SN	N403LDF

20694-20698 — Volvo B10M-55 — Alexander PS — BC48F — 1995

20694	OX	P319EFL	20696	BY	P316EFL	20697	MR	P317EFL	20698	MR	P318EFL
20695	SU	P315EFL									

20699-20788 — Volvo B10M-55 — Alexander PS — B49F* — 1992-93 — *20772-788 are BC48F

20699	BA	K699ERM	20721	CE	K721DAO	20744	ME	K744DAO	20767	LL	K767DAO
20700	ME	K700DAO	20722	CE	K722DAO	20745	CE	K745DAO	20768	LL	K768DAO
20701	ME	K701DAO	20723	CE	K723DAO	20746	CE	K746DAO	20769	LL	K769DAO
20702	BA	K702DAO	20724	CE	K724DAO	20748	ME	K748DAO	20770	LL	K770DAO
20703	ME	K703DAO	20725	CE	K725DAO	20749	ME	K749DAO	20771	LL	K771DAO
20704	ME	K704ERM	20726	CE	K726DAO	20750	ME	K750DAO	20772	CE	K772DAO
20705	KL	K705DAO	20727	CE	K727DAO	20751	ME	K751DAO	20773	CE	K773DAO
20706	ME	K706DAO	20728	CE	K728DAO	20752	ME	K752DAO	20774	KL	K774DAO
20707	ME	K707DAO	20729	CE	K729DAO	20753	LL	K753DAO	20775	KL	K775DAO
20708	LL	K708DAO	20730	CE	K730DAO	20754	BA	K754DAO	20776	KL	K776DAO
20709	LL	K709DAO	20731	CE	K731DAO	20755	BA	K755DAO	20777	LL	K777DAO
20710	LL	K710DAO	20732	CE	K732DAO	20756	BA	K756DAO	20778	BA	K778DAO
20711	LL	K711DAO	20733	CE	K733DAO	20757	BA	K757DAO	20779	LL	K779DAO
20712	LL	K712DAO	20734	CE	K734DAO	20758	BA	K758DAO	20780	BA	K780DAO
20713	LL	K713DAO	20735	CE	K735DAO	20759	BA	K759DAO	20781	CE	K781DAO
20714	LL	K714DAO	20736	CE	K736DAO	20760	BA	K760DAO	20783	CE	K783DAO
20715	CE	K715DAO	20737	CE	K737DAO	20761	BA	K761DAO	20784	CE	K784DAO
20716	CE	K716DAO	20738	CE	K738DAO	20762	BA	K762DAO	20785	CE	K785DAO
20717	CE	K717DAO	20739	CE	K739DAO	20763	LL	K763DAO	20786	BA	K786DAO
20718	CE	K718DAO	20741	CE	K741DAO	20764	LL	K764DAO	20787	BA	K787DAO
20719	CE	K719DAO	20742	CE	K742DAO	20765	LL	K765DAO	20788	CE	K788DAO
20720	CE	K720DAO	20743	CE	K743DAO	20766	CE	K766DAO			

20789	CE	N789VRM	Volvo B10M-55	Alexander PS	BC48F	1995
20790	CE	N790VRM	Volvo B10M-55	Alexander PS	BC48F	1995
20793	ME	R793URM	Volvo B10M-55	Alexander PS	B51F	1998
20794	ME	R794URM	Volvo B10M-55	Alexander PS	B51F	1998
20795	ME	R795URM	Volvo B10M-55	Alexander PS	B51F	1998

20801-20868 — Volvo B10M-55 — Alexander PS — B49F — 1996

20801	EX	N801DNE	20818	GR	N818DNE	20835	WG	P835FVU	20852	ST	P852GND
20802	EX	N802DNE	20819	GR	P819GNC	20836	WG	P836GND	20853	ST	P853GND
20803	LE	N803DNE	20820	SMu	P820GNC	20837	SU	P837GND	20854	ST	P854GND
20804	LE	N804DNE	20821	RU	P821FVU	20838	SU	P838GND	20855	ST	P855GND
20805	OX	N805DNE	20822	SMu	P822FVU	20839	BY	P839GND	20856	ST	P856GND
20806	MR	N806DNE	20823	RU	P823FVU	20840	BY	P840GND	20857	PS	P857GND
20807	MR	N807DNE	20824	SZ	P824FVU	20841	BY	P841GND	20858	PS	P858GND
20808	LE	N808DNE	20825	SZ	P825FVU	20842	BY	P842GND	20859	PS	P859GND
20809	NU	N809DNE	20826	SZ	P826FVU	20843	BY	P843GND	20860	PS	P860GND
20810	MR	N810DNE	20827	SZ	P827FVU	20844	SU	P844GND	20861	PS	P861GND
20811	MR	N811DNE	20828	SZ	P828FVU	20845	ST	P845GND	20862	PS	P862GND
20812	OX	N812DNE	20829	CR	P829FVU	20846	ST	P846GND	20863	PS	P863GND
20813	RU	N813DNE	20830	CR	P830FVU	20847	ST	P847GND	20864	PS	P864GND
20814	NU	N814DNE	20831	WG	P831FVU	20848	ST	P848GND	20865	PS	P865GND
20815	MU	N815DNE	20832	WG	XSU682	20849	ST	P849GND	20866	PS	P866GND
20816	LE	N816DNE	20833	WG	P833FVU	20850	ST	P850GND	20867	PS	P867GND
20817	GR	N817DNE	20834	WG	P834FVU	20851	ST	P851GND	20868	PS	P868GND

20869-20894 — Volvo B10M-55 — Northern Counties Paladin — B48F* — 1997 *20869-74/83-5/90/1 are BC47F

20869	CW	P869MNE	20876	ST	P876MNE	20882	ST	P882MNE	20889	CW	P889MNE
20870	CW	P870MNE	20877	ST	P877MNE	20883	PT	P883MNE	20890	PT	P890MNE
20871	PT	P871MNE	20878	ST	P878MNE	20884	PT	P884MNE	20891	PT	P891MNE
20872	PT	P872MNE	20879	ST	P879MNE	20885	PT	P885MNE	20892	CW	P892MNE
20873	BR	P873MNE	20880	ST	P880MNE	20886	CN	P886MNE	20893	ST	P893MNE
20874	PT	P874MNE	20881	ST	P881MNE	20887	CW	P887MNE	20894	ST	P894MNE
20875	ST	P875MNE									

The number of single-deck Volvo B10M buses currently in use numbers 748 in addition to which are the many Interurbans and coaches used on the longer services. Introduced in large numbers to the Manchester fleet, bodywork was supplied by both Alexander to the PS design and Northern Counties with their Paladin model. Illustrating the latter at rest in Stockport bus station is 20995, R995XVM. *Mark Doggett*

20895-20984   Volvo B10M-55   Alexander PS   B49F   1997-98

20895	HE	R895XVM	20919	HE	R919XVM	20941	HE	R941XVM	20963	GP	R963XVM
20896	HE	R896XVM	20920	HE	R920XVM	20942	HE	R942XVM	20964	GP	R964XVM
20897	HE	R897XVM	20921	HE	R921XVM	20943	HE	R943XVM	20965	HE	R965XVM
20898	PS	R898XVM	20922	HE	R922XVM	20944	PS	R944XVM	20966	HE	R966XVM
20899	PS	R899XVM	20923	HE	R923XVM	20945	PS	R945XVM	20967	HE	R967XVM
20901	HE	R901XVM	20924	HE	R924XVM	20946	PS	R946XVM	20968	HE	R968XVM
20902	HE	R902XVM	20925	HE	R925XVM	20947	PS	R947XVM	20969	HE	R969XVM
20903	HE	R903XVM	20926	HE	R926XVM	20948	PS	R948XVM	20970	HE	R970XVM
20904	GP	R904XVM	20927	HE	R927XVM	20949	HE	R949XVM	20971	HE	R971XVM
20905	GP	R905XVM	20928	HE	R928XVM	20950	HE	R950XVM	20972	HE	R972XVM
20906	GP	R906XVM	20929	HE	R929XVM	20951	HE	R951XVM	20973	HE	R973XVM
20907	GP	R907XVM	20930	HE	R930XVM	20952	HE	R952XVM	20974	HE	R974XVM
20908	GP	R908XVM	20931	HE	R932XVM	20953	HE	R953XVM	20975	HE	R975XVM
20909	GP	R909XVM	20932	HE	R933XVM	20954	HE	R954XVM	20976	HE	R976XVM
20910	GP	R910XVM	20933	HE	R934XVM	20955	HE	R955XVM	20977	HE	R977XVM
20912	HE	R912XVM	20934	HE	R935XVM	20956	HE	R956XVM	20978	HE	R978XVM
20913	HE	R913XVM	20935	HE	R936XVM	20957	HE	R957XVM	20979	HE	R979XVM
20914	HE	R914XVM	20936	HE	R936XVM	20958	PS	R958XVM	20980	PS	R980XVM
20915	HE	R915XVM	20937	HE	R937XVM	20959	PS	R959XVM	20981	PS	R981XVM
20916	HE	R916XVM	20938	HE	R938XVM	20960	PS	R960XVM	20982	PS	R982XVM
20917	HE	R917XVM	20939	HE	R939XVM	20961	GP	R961XVM	20983	HE	R983XVM
20918	GP	R918XVM	20940	HE	R940XVM	20962	GP	R962XVM	20984	HE	R984XVM

20985-20996   Volvo B10M-55   Plaxton Paladin   B48F   1998

20985	HE	R985XVM	20988	HE	R988XVM	20991	ST	R991XVM	20994	ST	R994XVM
20986	HE	R986XVM	20989	HE	R989XVM	20992	ST	R992XVM	20995	ST	R995XVM
20987	HE	R987XVM	20990	HE	R990XVM	20993	ST	R993XVM	20996	ST	R996XVM

21001	BY	M901DRG	Volvo B10B	Alexander Strider	B51F	1994
21002	BY	M902DRG	Volvo B10B	Alexander Strider	B51F	1994

21031-21042   Volvo B10B   Plaxton Verde   B52F   1994

21031	SC	L31HHN	21034	SC	L34HHN	21037	SC	L37HHN	21040	SC	M40PVN
21032	SC	L32HHN	21035	SC	L35HHN	21038	SC	M38PVN	21041	SC	M41PVN
21033	SC	L33HHN	21036	SC	L36HHN	21039	SC	M39PVN	21042	SC	M42PVN

21051	AS	M151FGD	Volvo B10B			Wright Endurance		B51F	1994	A1 Service, 1995

21101-21105   Volvo B10BLE   Northern Counties Prestige   N43F   1997

21101	BY	P601JBU	21103	BY	P603JBU	21104	BY	P604JBU	21105	BY	P605JBU
21102	BY	P602JBU									

21136-21158   Volvo B10BLE   Alexander ALX300   N44F   1997-98

21136	BY	R236KRG	21142	BY	R242KRG	21148	BY	R248KRG	21154	BY	R254KRG
21137	BY	R237KRG	21143	BY	R243KRG	21149	BY	R249KRG	21155	BY	R255KRG
21138	BY	R238KRG	21144	BY	R244KRG	21150	BY	R250KRG	21156	BY	R256KRG
21139	BY	R239KRG	21145	BY	R245KRG	21151	BY	R251KRG	21157	BY	R257KRG
21140	BY	R240KRG	21146	BY	R246KRG	21152	BY	R252KRG	21158	BY	R258KRG
21141	BY	R241KRG	21147	BY	R247KRG	21153	BY	R253KRG			

22004-22009   MAN 18.220 HOCL - NR   Alexander ALX300   N42F   2000-01

22004	CA	X604VDY	22006	CA	X606VDY	22008	CA	X948VAP	22009	CA	GX51PUJ
22005	CA	X605VDY	22007	CA	X607VDY						

22011-22060   MAN 18.220 HOCL - NR   Alexander ALX300   N42F   On order

22011	22024	22037	22049
22012	22025	22038	22050
22013	22026	22039	22051
22014	22027	22040	22052
22015	22028	22041	22053
22016	22029	22042	22054
22017	22030	22043	22055
22018	22031	22044	22056
22019	22032	22045	22057
22020	22033	22046	22058
22021	22034	22047	22059
22022	22035	22048	22060
22023	22036		

The first low-floor standard buses for Stagecoach were a batch of Northern Counties-bodied Volvo B10BLEs. Initially allocated to Hyde Road, Manchester they have since seen service on Park & Ride duties in Cambridge and are now at Newcastle's Byker depot. Pictured in its third colour scheme is 21104, P604JBU.
D Kelsey

22101-22159   MAN 18.220 HOCL - NR   Alexander ALX300   N42F   1998

22101	ST	S101TRJ	22116	ST	S116TRJ	22131	ST	S131TRJ	22145	ST	S145TRJ
22102	ST	S102TRJ	22117	ST	S117TRJ	22132	ST	S132TRJ	22146	HE	S146TRJ
22103	ST	S103TRJ	22118	ST	S118TRJ	22133	ST	S133TRJ	22147	ST	S147TRJ
22104	ST	S104TRJ	22119	ST	S119TRJ	22134	ST	S134TRJ	22148	HE	S148TRJ
22105	ST	S105TRJ	22120	ST	S120TRJ	22135	HE	S135TRJ	22149	HE	S149TRJ
22106	ST	S106TRJ	22121	ST	S121TRJ	22136	HE	S136TRJ	22150	ST	S150TRJ
22107	HE	S107TRJ	22122	ST	S122TRJ	22137	HE	S137TRJ	22151	ST	S151TRJ
22108	HE	S108TRJ	22124	ST	S124TRJ	22138	HE	S138TRJ	22152	ST	S152TRJ
22109	AN	S109TRJ	22125	ST	S125TRJ	22139	HE	S139TRJ	22153	HE	S153TRJ
22110	AN	S110TRJ	22126	ST	S126TRJ	22140	HE	S140TRJ	22154	HE	S154TRJ
22112	AN	S112TRJ	22127	ST	S127TRJ	22141	ST	S141TRJ	22156	PS	S156TRJ
22113	ST	S113TRJ	22128	ST	S128TRJ	22142	ST	S142TRJ	22157	PS	S157TRJ
22114	ST	S114TRJ	22129	ST	S129TRJ	22143	ST	S143TRJ	22158	PS	S158TRJ
22115	ST	S115TRJ	22130	ST	S130TRJ	22144	ST	S144TRJ	22159	PS	S159TRJ

22160-22215   MAN 18.220 HOCL - NR   Alexander ALX300   N42F   1999

22160	PS	T160MVM	22178	PS	T178MVM	22191	AS	NDZ3021	22204	BY	T204TND
22161	PS	T161MVM	22179	PS	T179MVM	22192	AS	NDZ3022	22205	BY	T205TND
22162	PS	T162MVM	22180	ST	T180MVM	22193	SY	T193MVM	22206	BY	T206TND
22163	PS	T163MVM	22181	ST	T181MVM	22194	AS	NDZ3023	22207	BY	T207TND
22164	PS	T164MVM	22182	ST	T182MVM	22195	SY	T195MVM	22208	BY	T208TND
22165	PS	T165MVM	22183	ST	T183MVM	22196	SY	T196MVM	22209	BY	T209TND
22166	HE	T166MVM	22184	ST	T184MVM	22197	SY	T197MVM	22210	BY	T210TND
22167	HE	T167MVM	22185	HE	T185MVM	22198	SY	T198TND	22211	BY	T211TND
22168	HE	T168MVM	22186	HE	T186MVM	22199	SY	T199TND	22212	PS	T212TND
22169	GP	T169MVM	22187	HE	T187MVM	22201	SY	T201TND	22213	PS	T213TND
22172	BY	T172MVM	22188	ST	T188MVM	22202	BY	T202TND	22214	SY	T214TND
22173	PS	T173MVM	22189	ST	T189MVM	22203	BY	T203TND	22215	SY	T215TND
22174	BY	T174MVM	22190	SY	T190MVM						

22216-22246   MAN 18.220 HOCL - NR   Alexander ALX300   N42F   2000

22216	ST	X216BNE	22226	ST	X226BNE	22233	ST	X233BNE	22239	ST	X239BNE
22217	ST	X217BNE	22227	ST	X227BNE	22234	ST	X234BNE	22241	ST	X241ATD
22218	ST	X218BNE	22228	ST	X228BNE	22235	PS	X235BNE	22242	ST	X242ATD
22219	ST	X219BNE	22229	ST	X229BNE	22236	PS	X236BNE	22243	ST	X243ATD
22221	ST	X221BNE	22231	ST	X231BNE	22237	PS	X237BNE	22244	ST	X244ATD
22223	ST	X223BNE	22232	ST	X232BNE	22238	PS	X238BNE	22246	ST	X246ATD
22224	ST	X224BNE									

22252-22268   MAN 18.220 HOCL - NR   Alexander ALX300   N47F   1999

22252	CJ	V252ESX	22257	CJ	V257ESX	22261	CJ	V261ESX	22265	CJ	V265ESX
22253	CJ	V253ESX	22258	CJ	V258ESX	22262	CJ	V262ESX	22266	GS	V266ESX
22254	CJ	V254ESX	22259	CJ	V259ESX	22263	CJ	V263ESX	22267	GS	V267ESX
22255	CJ	V255ESX	22260	CJ	V260ESX	22264	CJ	V264ESX	22268	GS	V268ESX
22256	CJ	V256ESX									

22269-22279   MAN 18.220 HOCL - NR   Alexander ALX300   N47F   2000-01

22269	CJ	X269MTS	22273	CJ	X273MTS	22276	CJ	X276MTS	22278	CB	SP51AMK
22271	CJ	X271MTS	22274	CJ	X274MTS	22277	CJ	X277MTS	22279	OX	SP51AMO
22272	CJ	X272MTS									

22301-22340   MAN 18.220 HOCL - NR   Alexander ALX300   N42F   2001

22301	CB	AE51RXW	22311	CB	AE51RYH	22321	CB	AE51RYX	22331	CB	AE51RZK
22302	CB	AE51RXX	22312	CB	AE51RYK	22322	CB	AE51RYY	22332	CB	AE51RZL
22303	CB	AE51RXY	22313	CB	AE51RYN	22323	CB	AE51RYZ	22333	CB	AE51RZM
22304	CB	AE51RXZ	22314	CB	AE51RYO	22324	CB	AE51RZA	22334	CB	AE51RZN
22305	CB	AE51RYA	22315	CB	AE51RYP	22325	CB	AE51RZB	22335	CB	AE51RZO
22306	CB	AE51RYB	22316	CB	AE51RYR	22326	CB	AE51RZC	22336	CB	AE51RZP
22307	CB	AE51RYC	22317	CB	AE51RYT	22327	CB	AE51RZF	22337	CB	AE51RZR
22308	CB	AE51RYD	22318	CB	AE51RYU	22328	CB	AE51RZG	22338	CB	AE51RZS
22309	CB	AE51RYF	22319	CB	AE51RYV	22329	CB	AE51RZH	22339	CB	AE51RZT
22310	CB	AE51RYG	22320	CB	AE51RYW	22330	CB	AE51RZJ	22340	CB	AE51RZU

The MAN with Alexander ALX300 bodywork was chosen as the provincial low-floor vehicle in 1997 and the initial supply went into service in Oxford the following year. Three hundred and sixty-five have now entered service with a further fifty due in 2003. The largest concentration is in the Manchester area, where 22187, T187MVM is seen heading for Reddish. *Cliff Beeton*

22451-22495

MAN 18.220 HOCL - NR Alexander ALX300 N45F 1999

22451	SY	S451OFT	22463	SY	T463BNL	22474	SY	T474BNL	22485	SY	T485BNL
22452	SY	S452OFT	22464	SY	T464BNL	22475	SY	T475BNL	22486	SU	T486BNL
22453	SY	S453OFT	22465	SY	T465BNL	22476	SY	T476BNL	22487	SU	T487BNL
22454	SY	S454OFT	22466	SY	T466BNL	22477	SY	T477BNL	22488	SU	T488BNL
22455	SY	S455OFT	22467	SY	T467BNL	22478	SY	T478BNL	22489	SU	T489BNL
22456	SY	S456OFT	22468	SY	T468BNL	22479	SY	T479BNL	22490	SU	T490BNL
22457	CB	S457OFT	22469	SY	T469BNL	22480	SY	T480BNL	22491	SU	T491BNL
22458	CB	S458OFT	22470	SY	T470BNL	22481	SY	T481BNL	22492	SY	T492BNL
22459	CB	S459OFT	22471	SY	T471BNL	22482	SY	T482BNL	22493	SY	T493BNL
22460	CB	S460OFT	22472	SY	T472BNL	22483	SY	T483BNL	22494	SU	T494BNL
22461	CB	T461BNL	22473	SY	T473BNL	22484	SY	T484BNL	22495	SU	T495BNL
22462	SY	T462BNL									

22601-22606

MAN 18.220 HOC L - NR Alexander ALX300 N42F 1999

22601	KK	V601GCS	22603	KK	V603GCS	22605	KK	V605GCS	22606	KK	V606GCS
22602	KK	V602GCS	22604	KK	V604GCS						

22656-22665

MAN 18.220 HOCL - NR Alexander ALX300 N42F 1999

22656	SC	T656OEF	22659	SC	T659OEF	22662	SC	T662OEF	22664	SC	T664OEF
22657	SC	T657OEF	22660	SC	T660OEF	22663	SC	T663OEF	22665	SC	T665OEF
22658	SC	T658OEF	22661	SC	T661OEF						

22666-22675

MAN 18.220 HOCL - NR Alexander ALX300 N42F 1999

22666	SC	V166DEF	22669	SC	V669DDC	22672	SC	V672DDC	22674	SC	V674DDC
22667	SC	V667DDC	22670	SC	V670DDC	22673	SC	V673DDC	22675	SC	V675DDC
22668	SC	V668DDC	22671	SC	V671DDC						

Most of the 2001 intake of MAN buses entered service in Cambridge, supported by others exchanged for B10Bs with the North East fleet. In the city they carry large reflective city logos, illustrated by 22319, AE51RYV. *Richard Godfrey*

22701-22713   MAN 18.220 HOCL - NR   Alexander ALX300   N42F   1999

22701	AN	V701DSA	22705	AN	V705DSA	22708	AN	V708DSA	22711	AN	V711DSA
22702	AN	V702DSA	22706	AN	V706DSA	22709	AN	V709DSA	22712	PH	V712DSA
22703	AN	V703DSA	22707	AN	V707DSA	22710	AN	V710DSA	22713	PH	V713DSA
22704	AN	V704DSA									

22714-22725   MAN 18.220 HOCL - NR   Alexander ALX300   N42F   2000

22714	PH	X714NSE	22716	PH	X716NSE	22718	PH	X718NSE	22721	ME	X721NSO
22715	PH	X715NSE	22717	PH	X717NSE	22719	PH	X719NSE	22722	PH	X722NSO

22727-22736   MAN 18.220 HOCL - NR   Alexander ALX300   N42F   1999

22727	SU	T727OEF	22730	SU	T730OEF	22733	SU	T733OEF	22735	SU	T735OEF
22728	SU	T728OEF	22731	SU	T731OEF	22734	SU	T734OEF	22736	SU	T736OEF
22729	SU	T729OEF	22732	SU	T732OEF						

22801-22812   MAN 18.220 HOCL - NR   Alexander ALX300   N42F   1999-2000

22801	CE	V801DFV	22804	CE	V804DFV	22807	CE	V807DFV	22811	CE	V811DFV
22802	CE	V802DFV	22805	CE	X805SRM	22808	CE	V808DFV	22812	CE	V812DFV
22803	CE	V803DFV	22806	CE	V806DFV	22809	CE	V809DFV			

22813-22827   MAN 18.220 HOCL - NR   Alexander ALX300   N42F   1999-2000

22813	CE	X813SRM	22817	ME	X817SRM	22822	ME	X822SRM	22825	ME	X825SRM
22814	CE	X814SRM	22818	ME	X818SRM	22823	ME	X823SRM	22826	ME	X826SRM
22815	ME	X815SRM	22819	ME	X819SRM	22824	ME	X824SRM	22827	ME	X827SRM
22816	ME	X816SRM	22821	ME	X821SRM						

Ashford Town Centre Shuttle employs two MAN buses remain painted in a dedicated livery based on yellow. Transferred from the Manchester fleet in 2000 they were given cherished index marks by South. Pictured in the town is 22194, NDZ3023. *Richard Godfrey*

22913-22941

		MAN 18.220 HOCL - NR		Alexander ALX300		N42F		1998	

22913	OX	S913CFC	22921	OX	S921CFC	22928	OX	S928CFC	22935	OX	S935CFC
22914	OX	S914CFC	22922	OX	S922CFC	22929	OX	S929CFC	22936	OX	S936CFC
22915	OX	S915CFC	22923	OX	S923CFC	22930	OX	S930CFC	22937	OX	S937CFC
22916	OX	S916CFC	22924	OX	S924CFC	22931	OX	S931CFC	22938	OX	S938CFC
22917	OX	S917CFC	22925	OX	S925CFC	22932	OX	S932CFC	22940	OX	S940CFC
22918	OX	S918CFC	22926	OX	S926CFC	22933	OX	S933CFC	22941	OX	S941CFC
22919	OX	S919CFC	22927	OX	S927CFC	22934	OX	S934CFC			
22920	OX	S920CFC									

22942-22948

		MAN 18.220 HOCL - NR		Alexander ALX300		N42F		2001

22942	OX	OU51WLK	22944	OX	OU51WLN	22946	OX	OU51KAG	22948	OX	OU51KAO
22943	OX	OU51WLL	22945	OX	OU51KAE	22947	OX	OU51KAK			

23001-23035

		Mercedes-Benz Citaro O536		Mercedes-Benz		AN--F		2003

23001	PD	LV52VFW	23010		LV52VGG	23019		LV52VGT	23028		LV52VHE
23002	PD	LV52VFX	23011		LV52VGJ	23020		LV52VGU	23029		LV52VHF
23003	PD	LV52VFY	23012		LV52VGK	23021		LV52VGX	23030		LV52VHG
23004	PD	LV52VFZ	23013		LV52VGL	23022		LV52VGY	23031		LV52VHH
23005		LV52VGA	23014		LV52VGM	23023		LV52VGZ	23032		LV52VHJ
23006		LV52VGC	23015		LV52VGN	23024		LV52VHA	23033		LV52VHK
23007		LV52VGD	23016		LV52VGO	23025		LV52VHB	23034		LV52VHL
23008		LV52VGE	23017		LV52VGP	23026		LV52VHC	23035		LV52VHM
23009		LV52VGF	23018		LV52VGR	23027		LV52VHD			

23950	PT	N550MTG	Mercedes-Benz O405		Optare Prisma	B49F	1995	Rhondda, 1997
23951	PT	N551MTG	Mercedes-Benz O405		Optare Prisma	B49F	1995	Rhondda, 1997

The numbers of Nationals, Leopards and Tigers in normal service continues to decline as new buses enter service. Many of the type are now restricted to ancillary roles, particularly training duties. Chesterfield currently use six Tigers with Alexander P-type bodywork, represented by 25826, B626DWF, seen at Sheffield Interchange. *Mark Doggett*

25402	NU	NOE602R	Leyland National 11351A/1R (DAF)		B49F	1977	
25405	RU	NOE605R	Leyland National 11351A/1R (DAF)		B49F	1977	
25410	RU	TOF710S	Leyland National 11351A/1R (DAF)		B49F	1978	
25421	OXt	PUK621R	Leyland National 11351A/1R (DAF)		TV	1977	
25453	OXt	XOV753T	Leyland National 11351A/1R (DAF)		TV	1978	
25472	RYw	BVP772V	Leyland National 11351A/1R (DAF)		B49F	1980	
25475	KK	OIW7025	Leyland National 11351A/3R		B48F	1979	British Airways, 1993
25476	DU	UIB3076	Leyland National 11351A/3R		B48F	1979	British Airways, 1993
25493	EXw	XIA857	Leyland National 11351/1R		B48F	1976	

25704	MEt	SHH124M	Leyland Leopard PSU3/3R	Alexander AY	TV	1974	
25724	EMu	DWF24V	Leyland Leopard PSU3E/4R	Alexander P (1985)	B52F	1979	
25728	WSu	WLT546	Leyland Leopard PSU3F/4R	Plaxton Supreme IV Exp	B53F	1981	
25738	HEt	WFS138W	Leyland Leopard PSU3F/4R	Alexander AYS	TV	1980	
25739	ESt	GSU839T	Leyland Leopard PSU3E/2R	Alexander AYS	TV	1979	Graham, Perth, 1997
25753	LLt	EGB53T	Leyland Leopard PSU3E/3R	Alexander AY	TV	1978	
25759	MEt	GSU859T	Leyland Leopard PSU3E/2R	Alexander AYS	TV	1979	Graham, Perth, 1997
25761	SR	GCS61V	Leyland Leopard PSU3E/4R	Alexander AY	B53F	1980	
25769	AY	GCS69V	Leyland Leopard PSU3E/4R	Alexander AY	B53F	1980	
25771	SR	TSJ71S	Leyland Leopard PSU3E/4R	Alexander AY	B53F	1977	
25775	EMw	EFU935Y	Leyland Leopard PSU5C/4R	Duple Dominant I	C53F	1983	
25785	HEt	TSJ85S	Leyland Leopard PSU3E/4R	Alexander AY	TV	1977	
25797	SR	BSJ917T	Leyland Leopard PSU3E/4R	Alexander AY	B53F	1979	

25800	KL	B900WRN	Leyland Tiger TRCTL11/1R	Duple Dominant	B49F	1984	
25821	CH	E927PBE	Leyland Tiger TRBLXCT/2RH	Alexander P	B51F	1987	
25822	CH	E928PBE	Leyland Tiger TRBLXCT/2RH	Alexander P	BC51F	1987	
25823	CH	E929PBE	Leyland Tiger TRBLXCT/2RH	Alexander P	BC51F	1987	
25824	CH	E930PBE	Leyland Tiger TRBLXCT/2RH	Alexander P	BC51F	1987	

25825-25833

		Leyland Tiger TRCTL11/2RH	Alexander P	B52F	1985

25825	CH	B625DWF	25828	CHu	B628DWF	25830	EMu	B630DWF	25832	HLt	B632DWF
25826	EMw	B626DWF	25829	HL	B629DWF	25831	EMu	B631DWF	25833	EMt	B633DWF
25827	CH	B627DWF								

While all Optare Deltas are used in the London fleet as training buses the Dennis single-decks are more commonly found in service. Transferred to Ribble from Hampshire Bus in 1991, the trio of Javelin buses operated by Stagecoach are now to be found on Lancaster duties, and allocated to Morecambe. Illustrating the Duple 300 body is 27036, F136SPX, a type not found elsewhere in the Group. *Bod Downham*

26001	NSt	J401LKO	DAF SB220LC550	Optare Delta	TV	1991
26002	Ut	J402LKO	DAF SB220LC550	Optare Delta	TV	1991
26003	TBt	J403LKO	DAF SB220LC550	Optare Delta	TV	1991
26010	BKt	G684KNW	DAF SB220LC550	Optare Delta	TV	1989

26011-26035   DAF SB220LC550   Optare Delta   TV   1992-93

26011	TBt	J711CYG	26018	Ut	J718CYG	26024	TBt	J724CYG	26030	Ut	K630HWX
26012	BKt	J712CYG	26019	BKt	J719CYG	26025	Tt	J725CYG	26031	BKt	K631HWX
26013	PDt	J713DAP	26020	Ut	J720CYG	26026	PDt	J726CYG	26032	Tt	K632HWX
26014	TLt	J714CYG	26021	Tt	J721CYG	26027	BKt	J727CYG	26033	BKt	K633HWX
26015	PDt	J715DAP	26022	Ut	J722CYG	26028	TBt	J728CYG	26034	PDt	K634HWX
26016	TLt	J716CYG	26023	Tt	J723CYG	26029	Ut	J729CYG	26035	PDt	K635HWX
26017	TLt	J717CYG								

27035	ME	F135SPX	Dennis Javelin 11SDL1914	Duple 300	B63F	1989
27036	ME	F136SPX	Dennis Javelin 11SDL1914	Duple 300	B63F	1989
27037	ME	F137SPX	Dennis Javelin 11SDL1914	Duple 300	B63F	1989

27201-27212   Dennis Lance 11SDA3108   Plaxton Verde   B46F   1994

27201	CE	L201YAG	27204	CE	L204YAG	27207	CE	L207YAG	27210	CE	L210YAG
27202	CE	L202YAG	27205	CE	L205YAG	27208	CE	L208YAG	27211	CE	L211YAG
27203	CE	L203YAG	27206	CE	L206YAG	27209	CE	L209YAG	27212	CE	L942RJN

27301	GY	M201DRG	Dennis Lance 11SDA3113	Plaxton Verde	B49F	1994
27302	GY	M202DRG	Dennis Lance 11SDA3113	Plaxton Verde	B49F	1994
27303	GY	M203DRG	Dennis Lance 11SDA3113	Plaxton Verde	B49F	1994
27304	GY	M204DRG	Dennis Lance 11SDA3113	Optare Sigma	B47F	1994

27404-27408   Dennis Lance SLF   Berkhof 2000   N40F   1994

27404	WG	414DCD	27406	WG	416DCD	27407	WG	417DCD	27408	WG	418DCD
27405	WG	415DCD								

All of the East Lancashire-bodied Scania N112s at Hull have been transferred to Devon, where many Scania double-decks are located. Pictured in Exeter bus station, 28702, F702BAT displays the former Stagecoach scheme still found on many vehicles. *Martin Smith*

27701-27709

| | | | Dennis Lance 11SDA3106* | | | East Lancashire EL2000 | | B45F | 1993 | *27705-9 are type 11SDA3111 |

27701	GY	K701NDO	27704	GY	K704NDO	27706	GY	L706HFU	27708	GY	L708HFU
27702	GY	K702NDO	27705	GY	L705HFU	27707	GY	L707HFU	27709	GY	L709HFU
27703	GY	K703NDO									

27832	SNt	EJV32Y	Dennis Falcon H SDA411	Wadham Stringer Vanguard	B42F	1983
27834	GRt	EJV34Y	Dennis Falcon H SDA411	Wadham Stringer Vanguard	B42F	1983
27901	OX	N901PFC	Dennis Lance 11SDA3113	Plaxton Verde	B49F	1996
27902	OX	N902PFC	Dennis Lance 11SDA3113	Plaxton Verde	B49F	1996
27903	OX	N903PFC	Dennis Lance 11SDA3113	Plaxton Verde	B49F	1996

28615-28630

| | | | Scania N113CRL | | | Wright Pathfinder 320 | | N37D | 1994 |

28615	U	RDZ6115	28619	U	RDZ6119	28623	U	RDZ6123	28627	U	RDZ6127
28616	U	RDZ6116	28620	U	RDZ6120	28624	U	RDZ6124	28628	U	RDZ6128
28617	U	RDZ6117	28621	U	RDZ6121	28625	U	RDZ6125	28629	U	RDZ6129
28618	U	RDZ6118	28622	U	RDZ6122	28626	U	RDZ6126	28630	U	RDZ6130

28701-28706

| | | | Scania N112CRB | | | East Lancashire European | | B50F | 1988 |

28701	EX	F701BAT	28703	EXu	F703BAT	28705	EX	F705BAT	28706	EX	F706CAG
28702	EX	F702BAT	28704	EX	F704BAT						

28901-28920

| | | | Scania N113CRB | | | Alexander PS | | B51F* | 1989 | *28901-5 are B48F; |
| | | | | | | | | | | *28906 is B49F |

28901	SY	F901JRG	28906	SY	F906JRG	28911	SY	F911JRG	28916	SY	F916JRG
28902	SY	F902JRG	28907	SY	F907JRG	28912	SY	F912JRG	28917	SY	F917JRG
28903	SY	F903JRG	28908	SY	F908JRG	28913	SY	F913JRG	28918	SY	F918JRG
28904	SY	F904JRG	28909	SY	F909JRG	28914	SY	F914JRG	28919	SY	F919JRG
28905	SY	F905JRG	28910	SY	F910JRG	28915	SY	F915JRG	28920	SY	F920JRG

Before becoming part of the Stagecoach Group, Busways took delivery of a number of buses from a variety of manufacturers as part of an evaluation. The Scania L113s are now at Slatyford depot from where 28951, M951DRG, is seen operating. Of the four Scania buses used in the trial, two carry Northern Counties bodywork and two feature the Alexander Strider model. *Richard Godfrey*

28921-28926

| | | | | | | | | | | Scania N113CRB | Alexander PS | B51F* | 1989-90 | *28926 is B49F |

| 28921 | SY | G921TCU | 28923 | SY | G923TCU | 28925 | SY | G925TCU | 28926 | SY | G926TCU |
| 28922 | SY | G922TCU | 28924 | SY | G924TCU | | | | | | |

| 28927 | SY | G113SKX | | Scania N113CRB | | Alexander PS | | B49F | 1989 |

28928-28937

Scania N113CRB — Alexander PS — B51F — 1991

28928	SY	H428EFT	28931	SY	H431EFT	28934	SY	H434EFT	28936	SY	H436EFT
28929	SY	H429EFT	28932	SY	H432EFT	28935	SY	H435EFT	28937	SY	H437EFT
28930	SY	H430EFT	28933	SY	H433EFT						

28938	SY	G108CEH	Scania N113CRB	Alexander PS	B49F	1990	
28951	SY	M951DRG	Scania L113CRL	Northern Counties Paladin	N49F	1994	
28952	SY	M952DRG	Scania L113CRL	Northern Counties Paladin	NC49F	1994	
28953	SY	M953DRG	Scania L113CRL	Alexander Strider	N51F	1994	
28954	SY	M954DRG	Scania L113CRL	Alexander Strider	N51F	1994	
28955	DS	M100AAB	Scania L113CRL	Alexander Strider	N51F	1994	AA Buses, Ayr, 1997

29101-29125

Leyland Lynx LX112L10ZR1S — Leyland Lynx — B49F — 1988-89

29101	SS	F101HVK	29108	SS	F108HVK	29114	NEw	F114HVK	29120	SS	F120HVK
29102	SS	F102HVK	29109	SS	F109HVK	29115	HP	F115HVK	29121	NEu	F121HVK
29103	SS	F103HVK	29110	NEu	F110HVK	29116	SS	F116HVK	29122	SC	F122HVK
29104	SS	F104HVK	29111	SS	F111HVK	29117	SSu	F117HVK	29123	SS	F123HVK
29105	SS	F105HVK	29112	HP	F112HVK	29118	NEu	F118HVK	29124	SS	F124HVK
29106	SS	F106HVK	29113	SUu	F113HVK	29119	SS	F119HVK	29125	HP	F125HVK
29107	SC	F107HVK									

29126	SSu	H126ACU	Leyland Lynx LX2R11C15Z4S	Leyland Lynx	BC47F	1990	
29127	SS	H127ACU	Leyland Lynx LX2R11C15Z4S	Leyland Lynx	BC47F	1990	
29541	HP	F251JRM	Leyland Lynx LX112L10ZR1	Leyland Lynx	B51F	1989	
29542	HP	F252JRM	Leyland Lynx LX112L10ZR1	Leyland Lynx	B51F	1989	
29544	HP	C544RAO	Leyland Lynx LX1126LXCTFR1 (Cummins)	Leyland Lynx	B51F	1986	
29545	HP	E709MFV	Leyland Lynx LX112L10ZR1	Leyland Lynx	B51F	1988	

29601-29610 — Leyland Lynx LX112L10ZR1R — Leyland Lynx — B49F — 1989

29601	HP	F601UVN	29604	HP	F604UVN	29607	SC	F607UVN	29609	SC	F609UVN
29602	HP	F602UVN	29605	HP	F605UVN	29608	SC	F608UVN	29610	SC	F610UVN
29603	HP	F603UVN	29606	HP	F606UVN						

29611-29620 — Leyland Lynx LX2R11C15Z4R — Leyland Lynx — B49F — 1989

29611	SC	G611CEF	29614	SC	G614CEF	29617	SC	G617CEF	29619	SC	G610CEF
29612	SC	G612CEF	29615	SC	G615CEF	29618	SC	G618CEF	29620	SC	G620CEF
29613	SC	G613CEF	29616	SC	G616CEF						

29621	SC	J901UKV	Leyland Lynx LX2R11V18Z4S	Leyland Lynx 2	B49F	1991

29622-29630 — Leyland Lynx LX2R11V18Z4S — Leyland Lynx 2 — B49F — 1992

29622	SC	K622YVN	29625	SC	K625YVN	29627	SC	K627YVN	29629	SC	K629YVN
29623	SC	K623YVN	29626	SC	K626YVN	29628	SC	K628YVN	29630	SC	K630YVN
29624	SC	K624YVN									

30101-30108 — Volvo B6-9.9M — Plaxton Pointer — B41F — 1993-94

30101	DA	L101GHN	30103	DA	L103GHN	30105	DA	M105PVN	30107	DA	M107PVN
30102	DA	L102GHN	30104	DA	M104PVN	30106	DA	M106PVN	30108	DA	M108PVN

30141	WI	N421PWV	Volvo B6-9.9m	Plaxton Pointer	BC35F	1997	Citybus, Hong Kong, 2000
30142	WI	N422PWV	Volvo B6-9.9m	Plaxton Pointer	BC35F	1997	Citybus, Hong Kong, 2000

30237-30269 — Volvo B6-9.9M — Alexander Dash — BC40F — 1993

30237	CE	L237CCW	30243	DA	L243CCK	30249	DA	L249CCK	30255	PR	L255CCK
30238	DA	L238CCW	30244	DA	L244CCK	30250	DA	L250CCK	30256	PR	L256CCK
30239	HL	L239CCW	30245	DA	L245CCK	30251	CW	L251CCK	30267	FH	L267CCK
30240	CW	L240CCW	30246	DA	L246CCK	30252	PR	L252CCK	30268	FH	L268CCK
30241	CY	L241CCK	30247	DA	L247CCK	30253	AE	L253CCK	30269	SA	L269CCK
30242	DA	L242CCK	30248	RY	L248CCK	30254	DA	L254CCK			

30270-30274 — Volvo B6-9.9M — Alexander Dash — B40F — 1993

30270	KL	L270LHH	30272	PR	L272LHH	30273	PR	L273LHH	30274	PR	L274LHH
30271	PR	L271LHH									

30275-30283 — Volvo B6-9.9M — Alexander Dash — B40F — 1994

30275	KL	L275JAO	30277	ME	L277JAO	30279	HL	L279JAO	30282	KL	L282JAO
30276	KL	L276JAO	30278	PR	L278JAO	30281	PR	L281JAO	30283	PR	L283JAO

30301-30310 — Volvo B6-9.9M — Alexander Dash — B40F — 1994

30301	PR	M741PRS	30304	PR	M744PRS	30307	CY	M847PRS	30309	CE	M749PRS
30302	PR	M742PRS	30305	PR	M745PRS	30308	PR	M748PRS	30310	BA	M750PRS
30303	CY	M743PRS	30306	CY	M746PRS						

30312-30341 — Volvo B6-9.9M — Alexander Dash — BC40F — 1994

30312	KK	M772BCS	30322	KK	M722BCS	30332	AS	M732BSJ	30337	KK	M737BSJ
30313	KK	M773BCS	30323	KK	M723BCS	30333	CE	M733BSJ	30338	KK	M738BSJ
30318	KK	M718BCS	30324	KK	M724BCS	30334	CE	M734BSJ	30339	KK	M739BSJ
30319	KK	M719BCS	30325	AS	M725BCS	30335	KK	M735BSJ	30340	KK	M740BSJ
30320	KK	M720BCS	30326	AS	M726BCS	30336	AY	M736BSJ	30341	KK	M741BSJ
30321	KK	M721BCS	30327	KK	M727BCS						

30401-30422 — Volvo B6-9.9M — Alexander Dash — B40F — 1993

30401	BD	L401JBD	30407	BD	L407JBD	30413	BD	L413JBD	30418	BD	L418JBD
30402	BD	L402JBD	30408	BD	L408JBD	30414	BD	L414JBD	30419	BD	L419JBD
30403	BD	L403JBD	30409	BD	L409JBD	30415	BD	L415JBD	30420	BD	L420JBD
30404	BD	L404JBD	30410	BD	L410JBD	30416	BD	L416JBD	30421	BD	L421JBD
30405	BD	L405JBD	30411	BD	L411JBD	30417	BD	L417JBD	30422	BD	L422MVV
30406	BD	L406JBD	30412	BD	L412JBD						

In the early 1990s, the low floor midibus chosen for the group was the Volvo B6 with Alexander Dash bodywork. There are almost 200 of the combination in service, illustrated here by 30241, L241CCK, seen in Chorley. *Bob Downham*

30423	BD	L423XVV				Volvo B6-9.9M		Alexander Dash	BC40F	1994
30424	BD	L424XVV				Volvo B6-9.9M		Alexander Dash	BC40F	1994
30425	BD	L425XVV				Volvo B6-9.9M		Alexander Dash	BC40F	1994

30426-30431
Volvo B6-9.9M — Alexander Dash — B40F — 1993

| 30426 | KY | L426MVV | 30428 | KY | L428MVV | 30430 | KY | L424MVV | 30431 | KY | L425MVV |
| 30427 | KY | L427MVV | 30429 | KY | L423MVV | | | | | | |

30435-30453
Volvo B6-9.9M — Alexander Dash — B40F — 1993

30435	MD	L435LWA	30440	MD	L440LWA	30446	MD	L446LWA	30450	MD	L450LWA
30436	MD	L436LWA	30441	MD	L441LWA	30447	MD	L447LWA	30451	MD	L451LWA
30437	MD	L437LWA	30442	MD	L442LWA	30448	MD	L448LWA	30452	MD	L452LWA
30438	MD	L438LWA	30443	MD	L443LWA	30449	MD	L449LWA	30453	MD	L453LHL
30439	MD	L439LWA	30445	MD	L445LWA						

30454-30462
Volvo B6-9.9M — Alexander Dash — B40F — 1994

30454	CE	M454VHE	30457	ME	M457VHE	30459	PR	M459VHE	30461	BA	M461VHE
30455	CE	M455VHE	30458	CE	M458VHE	30460	CE	M460VHE	30462	PR	M462VHE
30456	CE	M456VHE									

30551-30556
Volvo B6-9.9M — Alexander Dash — BC40F — 1994

| 30551 | BD | L451YAC | 30553 | BD | L453YAC | 30555 | CB | L455YAC | 30556 | CB | L456YAC |
| 30552 | BD | L452YAC | 30554 | BD | L454YAC | | | | | | |

30651-30660
Volvo B6-9.9M — Alexander Dash — B40F — 1993-94

30651	DE	L651HKS	30654	DE	L654HKS	30657	DE	L657HKS	30659	DE	L659HKS
30652	KY	L652HKS	30655	DE	L655HKS	30658	DE	L658HKS	30660	CT	L660HKS
30653	DE	L653HKS	30656	DE	L656HKS						

Lakeland services requiring single-decks led to the Lakeland colours being applied to 30282, L282JAO, seen here on local route 44 to Hallgarth. The Lakes network has proved popular with passengers, with car trafic discouraged from the area. *Bob Downham*

30661-30669   Volvo B6-9.9M   Alexander Dash   BC40F   1993

| 30661 | CT | L661MSF | 30663 | CTu | L663MSF | 30665 | PR | L665MSF | 30668 | PR | L668MSF |
| 30662 | PR | L662MSF | 30664 | AE | L664MSF | 30667 | CT | L667MSF | 30669 | AE | L669MSF |

30670-30681   Volvo B6-9.9M   Alexander Dash   B40F   1993

30670	DE	M670SSX	30673	KY	M673SSX	30676	AY	M676SSX	30679	FH	M679SSX
30671	DE	M671SSX	30674	KK	M674SSX	30677	AY	M677SSX	30680	FH	M680SSX
30672	DE	M672SSX	30675	AY	M675SSX	30678	AY	M678SSX	30681	FH	M681SSX

| 30700 | EX | M343NOD | Volvo B6B | | Alexander Dash | | B34F | 1995 | Citybus, Hong Kong, 2001 |

30701-30708   Volvo B6-9.9M   Alexander Dash   B40F   1994

30701	AE	L701FWO	30704	BR	L704FWO	30707	AEu	L707FWO	30710	CN	L710FWO
30702	AE	L702FWO	30705	BR	L705FWO	30708	AE	L708FWO	30711	GR	L711FWO
30703	AE	L703FWO		AEu	L706FWO	30709	RY	L709FWO	30712	GR	L712FWO

30721	AEu	M71HHB	Volvo B6-9m	Plaxton Pointer	B35F	1994
30723	GR	M73HHB	Volvo B6-9m	Plaxton Pointer	B35F	1994
30724	CY	M74HHB	Volvo B6-9m	Plaxton Pointer	B35F	1994
30725	BR	M75HHB	Volvo B6-9m	Plaxton Pointer	B35F	1994
30726	CY	M76HHB	Volvo B6-9m	Plaxton Pointer	B35F	1994
30728	CN	M78HHB	Volvo B6-9m	Plaxton Pointer	B35F	1994
30729	AE	L79CWO	Volvo B6-9.9M	Plaxton Pointer	B40F	1994
30732	AE	L82CWO	Volvo B6-9.9M	Plaxton Pointer	B40F	1994
30800	WI	M510FWV	Volvo B6-9.9M	Alexander Dash	BC35F	1994
30801	WI	M511FWV	Volvo B6-9.9M	Alexander Dash	BC35F	1994
30802	WI	M512FWV	Volvo B6-9.9M	Alexander Dash	BC35F	1994
30803	WI	YLJ332	Volvo B6-9.9M	Alexander Dash	BC31F	1994

30831-30845   Volvo B6-9.9M   Alexander Dash   B40F   1994

30831	CW	L831CDG	30835	CNt	L835CDG	30839	GR	L839CDG	30843	GR	M843EMW
30832	CW	L832CDG	30836	CN	L836CDG	30840	GR	L840CDG	30844	CT	M844EMW
30833	CN	L833CDG	30837	CB	L837CDG	30841	GR	L841CDG	30845	GR	M845EMW
30834	BR	L834CDG	30838	CB	L838CDG	30842	GR	L842CDG			

| 30846 | BA | M753PRS | Volvo B6-9.9M | Alexander Dash | B40F | 1994 |
| 30847 | CT | M847HDF | Volvo B6-9.9M | Alexander Dash | B40F | 1994 |

The low-floor Volvo B6BLE appears in the Stagecoach fleet only with Alexander ALX200 bodywork. These have been numbered in the 31000 series. Initially delivered to Manchester the entire batch were exchanged with Oxford's double-decks. Now numbered 31332, P332JND is seen on Oxford Express duties. *Dave Heath*

31043-31052

| | | | | | | | | | | | Volvo B6BLE | Alexander ALX200 | N34F | 1997 | Citybus, Hong Kong, 2000-01 |

31043	PM	R133NPN	31046	PM	R196NPN	31049	PM	R119NPN	31051	PM	R71NPN
31044	PM	R144NPN	31047	PM	R177NPN	31050	PM	R270NPN	31052	PM	R132NPN
31045	PM	R95NPN	31048	PM	R178NPN						

31319	BB	P321EFL	Volvo B6BLE			Alexander ALX200		N35F	1997
31320	BB	P320EFL	Volvo B6BLE			Alexander ALX200		N35F	1997

31321-31357

Volvo B6BLE   Alexander ALX200   N36F   1997

31321	RU	P321JND	31327	NU	P327JND	31333	OX	P677NOJ	31353	NU	P353JND
31322	RU	P322JND	31328	NU	P328JND	31334	NU	P344JND	31354	NU	P354JND
31323	RU	P323JND	31329	NU	P329JND	31350	NU	P350JND	31355	NU	P355JND
31324	RU	P324JND	31330	OX	P330JND	31351	NU	P351JND	31356	NU	P356JND
31325	RU	P325JND	31331	OX	P331JND	31352	NU	P352JND	31357	NU	P357JND
31326	RU	P326JND	31332	NU	P332JND						

31361-31386

Volvo B6BLE   Alexander ALX200   NC36F   1997

31361	BB	P361DSA	31368	KK	P368DSA	31375	KK	P375DSA	31381	AY	P381DSA
31362	BB	P362DSA	31369	KK	P369DSA	31376	KK	P376DSA	31382	AY	P382DSA
31363	NU	P363DSA	31370	KK	P370DSA	31377	KK	P377DSA	31383	AY	P383DSA
31364	NU	P364DSA	31371	KK	P371DSA	31378	AY	P378DSA	31384	AY	P384DSA
31365	BB	P365DSA	31372	KK	P372DSA	31379	AY	P379DSA	31385	AY	P385DSA
31366	AY	P366DSA	31373	KK	P373DSA	31380	AY	P380DSA	31386	AY	P386DSA
31367	AY	P367DSA	31374	KK	P374DSA						

31491-31499

Volvo B6BLE   Alexander ALX200   N36F   1996

31491	IS	P491BRS	31494	PH	P494BRS	31496	PH	P496BRS	31498	PH	P498BRS
31492	AN	P492BRS	31495	PH	P495BRS	31497	PH	P497BRS	31499	PH	P499BRS
31493	AN	P493BRS									

31701-31714 — Volvo B6BLE — Alexander ALX200 — N35F — 1997

31701	EX	P701BTA	31705	EX	P706BTA	31709	EX	P709BTA	31712	EX	P712BTA
31702	EX	P702BTA	31706	EX	P707BTA	31710	EX	P710BTA	31713	EX	P713BTA
31703	EX	P703BTA	31707	EX	P708BTA	31711	EX	P711BIA	31714	EX	P714BTA
31704	EX	P704BTA	31708	EX	P708BTA						

31852	BB	P852SMR	Volvo B6BLE	Alexander ALX200	N35F	1997
31853	BB	P853SMR	Volvo B6BLE	Alexander ALX200	N35F	1997
31854	BB	P854SMR	Volvo B6BLE	Alexander ALX200	N35F	1997

32001-32008 — Dennis Dart 9.8m — Alexander Dash — BC40F — 1996

32001	NU	P101HNH	32003	RU	P103HNH	32005	NU	P105HNH	32007	NU	P451KRP
32002	NU	P102HNH	32004	NU	P104HNH	32006	NU	P450KRP	32008	NU	P452KRP

32009-32022 — Dennis Dart 9.8SDL3035 — Plaxton Pointer — B33D — 1994

32009	BE	L709JUD	32013	BE	L713JUD	32017	TQ	L717JUD	32020	TQ	L720JUD
32010	BE	L710JUD	32014	TQ	L714JUD	32018	TQ	L718JUD	32021	TQ	L721JUD
32011	BE	L711JUD	32015	TQ	L715JUD	32019	TQ	L719JUD	32022	TQ	L722JUD
32012	BE	L712JUD	32016	TQ	L716JUD						

32041	PM	M61VJO	Dennis Dart 9.8SDL3054	Plaxton Pointer	B40F	1995
32047	WI	N47EJO	Dennis Dart 9.8SDL3054	Plaxton Pointer	B40F	1995
32048	CS	N48EJO	Dennis Dart 9.8SDL3054	Plaxton Pointer	B40F	1995

32051-32064 — Dennis Dart 9.8SDL3054 — Plaxton Pointer — B40F — 1996

32051	OX	N51KBW	32054	OX	N54KBW	32058	OX	N58KBW	32062	OX	N62KBW
32052	OX	N52KBW	32056	OX	N56KBW	32059	OX	N59KBW	32063	OX	N63KBW
32053	OX	N53KBW	32057	OX	N57KBW	32061	OX	N61KBW	32064	OX	N64KBW

32065-32099 — Dennis Dart 9.8SDL3054 — Plaxton Pointer — B37D — 1995

32065	LS	M65VJO	32075	ATw	M75VJO	32084	SWu	M84WBW	32092	LS	M92WBW
32066	HL	M59VJO	32076	WI	M76VJO	32085	SN	M85WBW	32093	LS	M93WBW
32067	HL	M67VJO	32077	WG	M63VJO	32086	SN	M86WBW	32094	LS	M94WBW
32068	HL	M68VJO	32078	AE	M78VJO	32087	HL	M87WBW	32095	LS	M95WBW
32069	HL	M69VJO	32079	SWu	M79VJO	32088	LS	M101WBW	32096	WG	M96WBW
32070	BE	M62VJO	32080	HL	M64VJO	32089	HL	M89WBW	32097	LS	M97WBW
32071	HL	M71VJO	32081	HL	M81WBW	32090	LS	M102WBW	32098	LS	M98WBW
32073	HL	M73VJO	32082	HL	M82WBW	32091	LS	M91WBW	32099	EX	M103WBW
32074	PM	M74VJO	32083	HL	M83WBW						

32101-32110 — Dennis Dart 9.8SDL3017 — Alexander Dash — B40F — 1993

32101	AN	K101XHG	32104	FH	K104XHG	32107	AT	K107XHG	32109	PM	K109XHG
32102	FH	K102XHG	32105	IS	K105XHG	32108	PM	K108XHG	32110	AN	K110XHG
32103	AN	K103XHG	32106	FH	K106XHG						

32111-32148 — Dennis Dart 9SDL3024 — Plaxton Pointer — B34F — 1993

32111	CH	K211SRH	32120	DS	K120SRH	32128	SU	K128SRH	32139	EX	L139VRH
32112	SU	K112SRH	32121	SU	K121SRH	32129	SU	K129SRH	32140	EX	L140VRH
32113	CH	K113SRH	32122	GS	K122SRH	32130	SN	K130SRH	32141	EX	L141VRH
32114	CH	K114SRH	32123	HL	K123SRH	32132	SN	K132SRH	32145	AY	L145VRH
32115	CH	K115SRH	32124	HP	K124SRH	32133	SU	K133SRH	32146	RO	L146VRH
32116	HL	K116SRH	32125	SU	K125SRH	32134	SU	K134SRH	32147	CH	K109SRH
32117	SU	K117SRH	32126	SN	K126SRH	32137	AY	L137VRH	32148	CH	K110SRH
32118	HL	K118SRH	32127	SU	K127SRH	32138	AS	L138VRH			

32163	OX	R63UFC	Dennis Dart 10m	Plaxton Pointer	B40F	1997
32164	OX	R64UFC	Dennis Dart 10m	Plaxton Pointer	B40F	1997
32165	OX	R65UFC	Dennis Dart 10m	Plaxton Pointer	B40F	1997

32201-32205   Dennis Dart 9.8SDL3017   Alexander Dash   B40F   1992

32201	ESu	K601ESH	32203	KY	K603ESH	32204	KY	K604ESH	32205	KY	K605ESH
32202	KY	K602ESH									

32206-32213   Dennis Dart 9.8m   Alexander Dash   B40F   1996

32206	DE	P606CMS	32208	CJ	P608CMS	32210	AL	P610CMS	32212	KY	P612CMS
32207	CJ	P607CMS	32209	CJ	P609CMS	32211	GS	P611CMS	32213	KY	P613CMS

32215-32226   Dennis Dart 9SDL3016   Wright Handy-bus   B35F   1993

32215	AL	NDZ3015	32221	TH	K921OWV	32223	TH	K923OWV	32225	TH	NDZ3025
32216	AL	NDZ3016	32222	TH	K922OWV	32224	TH	NDZ3024	32226	TH	NDZ3026

32233-32259   Dennis Dart 8.5SDL3015   Wright Handy-bus   B29F   1993

32233	MR	NDZ3133	32240	CL	NDZ3140	32247	CL	NDZ3147	32254	CL	NDZ3154
32234	SN	NDZ3134	32241	CL	NDZ3141	32248	CL	NDZ3148	32255	CL	NDZ3155
32235	CLu	NDZ3135	32242	CL	NDZ3142	32249	CL	NDZ3149	32256	CL	NDZ3156
32236	SN	NDZ3136	32243	CL	NDZ3143	32250	CL	NDZ3150	32257	PTu	NDZ3157
32237	CL	NDZ3137	32244	CL	NDZ3144	32251	EHu	NDZ3151	32258	MR	NDZ3158
32238	CL	NDZ3138	32245	CL	NDZ3145	32252	EH	NDZ3152	32259	CL	NDZ3159
32239	CL	NDZ3139	32246	AL	NDZ3146	32253	EH	NDZ3153			

32260-32271   Dennis Dart 8.5SDL3003   Wright Handy-bus   B28F   1991

32260	EH	JDZ2360	32261	SWw	JDZ2361	32269	CL	JDZ2359	32271	SWw	JDZ2371

32301-32327   Dennis Dart 9.8SDL3054   Alexander Dash   B36F   1995

32301	HP	N301AMC	32308	DE	N308AMC	32315	BE	N315AMC	32322	BE	N322AMC
32302	HP	N302AMC	32309	WI	N309AMC	32316	AT	N316AMC	32323	WI	N323AMC
32303	HP	N303AMC	32310	WI	N310AMC	32317	SN	N317AMC	32324	WI	N324AMC
32304	DE	N304AMC	32311	HS	N311AMC	32318	SNt	N318AMC	32325	WI	N325AMC
32305	HP	N305AMC	32312	AT	N312AMC	32319	SN	N319AMC	32326	WI	N326AMC
32306	DE	N306AMC	32313	SN	N313AMC	32320	SN	N320AMC	32327	HS	N327AMC
32307	DE	N307AMC	32314	WI	N314AMC	32321	BE	N321AMC			

32328-32341   Dennis Dart 8.5SDL3003   Carlyle Dartline   B28F   1990

32328	EX	G28TGW	32332	EX	G32TGW	32333	EX	G33TGW	32335	EX	G35TGW
32330	EX	G30TGW									

32341	AL	H151MOB	Dennis Dart 8.5SDL3003	Carlyle Dartline	B28F	1990	Allisons, Dunfermline, 2000
32342	GS	H162NON	Dennis Dart 8.5SDL3003	Carlyle Dartline	B28F	1991	Allisons, Dunfermline, 2000
32343	AL	H153MOB	Dennis Dart 8.5SDL3003	Carlyle Dartline	B28F	1990	Allisons, Dunfermline, 2000
32344	DE	H154MOB	Dennis Dart 8.5SDL3003	Carlyle Dartline	B28F	1990	Allisons, Dunfermline, 2000
32346	AL	H146MOB	Dennis Dart 8.5SDL3003	Carlyle Dartline	B28F	1990	Allisons, Dunfermline, 2000
32347	ESu	H71MOB	Dennis Dart 8.5SDL3003	Carlyle Dartline	B28F	1990	Allisons, Dunfermline, 2000
32348	ESu	H79MOB	Dennis Dart 8.5SDL3003	Carlyle Dartline	B28F	1990	Allisons, Dunfermline, 2000
32349	ESu	G49GTW	Dennis Dart 8.5SDL3003	Carlyle Dartline	B28F	1990	

32351-32368   Dennis Dart 9.8m   Plaxton Pointer   B37D   1997

32351	CS	R701YWC	32356	CS	R706YWC	32361	CS	R711YWC	32365	CS	R715YWC
32352	CS	R702YWC	32357	CS	R707YWC	32362	CS	R712YWC	32366	CS	R716YWC
32353	CS	R703YWC	32358	CS	R708YWC	32363	CS	R713YWC	32367	CS	R717YWC
32354	CS	R704YWC	32359	CS	R709YWC	32364	CS	R714YWC	32368	CS	R718YWC
32355	CS	R705YWC	32360	CS	R710YWC						

32380	RO	M949EGE	Dennis Dart 9.8SDL3054	Plaxton Pointer	B40F	1994	AA Buses, Ayr, 1997
32381	DU	M950EGE	Dennis Dart 9.8SDL3054	Plaxton Pointer	B40F	1994	AA Buses, Ayr, 1997
32382	WSu	L208PSB	Dennis Dart 9SDL3031	Marshall C36	B39F	1994	Arran Coaches, 1994

32390-32398   Dennis Dart 9.8m   Alexander Dash   B40F*   1996-97   *32395-8 are BC40F

32390	DS	P390LPS	32393	DS	P393LPS	32395	DS	P395BRS	32397	AY	P397BRS
32391	DS	P391LPS	32394	DS	P394LPS	32396	AY	P396BRS	32398	DS	P398BRS
32392	DS	P392LPS									

32400-32409

Dennis Dart 9.8SDL3017 — Alexander Dash — B40F — 1992

32400	DU	J310BRM	32403	RO	J303BRM	32406	RO	J306BRM	32408	RO	J308BRM
32401	DU	J301BRM	32404	RO	J304BRM	32407	RO	J307BRM	32409	SR	J309BRM
32402	DU	J302BRM	32405	DU	J305BRM						

32410-32427

Dennis Dart 9.8SDL3054 — Plaxton Pointer — B40F — 1996

32410	EX	N410MBW	32415	CH	N415MBW	32420	GY	N420MBW	32424	MD	N424MBW
32411	EX	N411MBW	32416	MD	N416MBW	32421	CH	N421MBW	32425	CH	N425MBW
32412	ATu	N412MBW	32417	WP	N417MBW	32422	CH	N422MBW	32426	WP	N426MBW
32413	ATu	N413MBW	32418	CH	N418MBW	32423	CH	N423MBW	32427	CH	N427MBW
32414	ATu	N414MBW	32419	GY	N419MBW						

32429-32450

Dennis Dart 9.8SDL3060 — Plaxton Pointer — BC39F — 1995 — Citybus, Hong Kong, 1999

32429	PM	403DCD	32435	EX	N735XDV	32440	EX	N740XDV	32446	PM	406DCD
32430	PM	404DCD	32436	EX	N736XDV	32441	EX	N731XDV	32447	PM	407DCD
32432	EXu	N732XDV	32437	EX	N737XDV	32442	EX	N742XDV	32448	PM	400DCD
32433	EX	N733XDV	32438	EX	N738XDV	32443	EX	N743XDV	32449	PM	401DCD
32434	EX	N734XDV	32439	EX	N739XDV	32444	EX	N744XDV	32450	PM	402DCD

32451-32467

Dennis Dart 9.8m — Alexander Dash — B40F* — 1996 — *32451-5 are BC40F

32451	PM	N451PAP	32456	LS	N456PAP	32460	BE	N460PAP	32464	HS	N464PAP
32452	PM	N452PAP	32457	HS	N457PAP	32461	BE	N461PAP	32465	CA	N465PAP
32453	PM	N453PAP	32458	CA	N458PAP	32462	BE	N462PAP	32466	HS	N466PAP
32454	PM	N454PAP	32459	BE	N459PAP	32463	BE	N463PAP	32467	FO	N467PAP
32455	PM	N455PAP									

32501-32552

Dennis Dart 9.8SDL3017 — Alexander Dash — B40F* — 1992 — *32501-34 are B41F

32501	HS	J501GCD	32514	HS	J514GCD	32528	AR	J528GCD	32541	WG	J541GCD
32502	HS	J502GCD	32515	HS	J515GCD	32529	AT	J529GCD	32542	WI	J542GCD
32503	HS	J503GCD	32516	HS	J516GCD	32530	AR	J530GCD	32543	SB	J543GCD
32504	SEu	J504GCD	32517	SEu	J517GCD	32531	BE	J531GCD	32544	AR	J544GCD
32505	HS	J505GCD	32518	SEu	J518GCD	32532	SB	J532GCD	32545	AR	J545GCD
32506	HS	J506GCD	32519	HS	J519GCD	32533	BE	J533GCD	32546	CR	J546GCD
32507	HSt	J507GCD	32520	CHu	J520GCD	32534	AT	J534GCD	32547	BE	J547GCD
32508	HS	J508GCD	32521	AR	J521GCD	32535	BE	J535GCD	32548	WIu	J548GCD
32509	HS	J509GCD	32522	AT	J522GCD	32536	WI	J536GCD	32549	BE	J549GCD
32510	HS	J510GCD	32523	AT	J523GCD	32537	SB	J537GCD	32550	WI	J550GCD
32511	SEu	J511GCD	32524	SB	J524GCD	32538	WI	J538GCD	32551	AN	J551GCD
32512	HS	J512GCD	32526	BE	J526GCD	32539	WI	J539GCD	32552	CR	J552GCD
32513	HS	J513GCD	32527	WG	J527GCD						

32553-32580

Dennis Dart 9.8SDL3017 — Alexander Dash — B40F — 1992

32553	CR	K553NHC	32560	WG	K660NHC	32567	AR	K567NHC	32574	BE	K574NHC
32554	CR	K554NHC	32561	WG	K561NHC	32568	WG	K568NHC	32575	AT	K575NHC
32555	CR	K655NHC	32562	WG	K562NHC	32569	WI	K569NHC	32576	WG	K576NHC
32556	CR	K556NHC	32563	WG	K563NHC	32570	WG	K570NHC	32577	WG	K577NHC
32557	CR	K557NHC	32564	WG	K564NHC	32571	PM	K571NHC	32578	BE	K578NHC
32558	WG	K558NHC	32565	WI	K565NHC	32572	AT	K572NHC	32579	WG	K579NHC
32559	WG	K559NHC	32566	WG	K566NHC	32573	BE	K573NHC	32580	CR	K580NHC

32581	BE	J701YRM	Dennis Dart 9.8SDL3017	Alexander Dash	B41F	1991
32582	BE	J702YRM	Dennis Dart 9.8SDL3017	Alexander Dash	B41F	1992
32583	HSu	J703YRM	Dennis Dart 9.8SDL3017	Alexander Dash	B41F	1992

32584-32588

Dennis Dart 9.8DL3017 — Alexander Dash — B40F — 1992

32584	WIu	K584ODY	32586	WIu	K586ODY	32587	AT	K587ODY	32588	AT	K588ODY
32585	AT	K585ODY									

32599	EX	N599DWY	Dennis Dart 9.8SDL3054	Plaxton Pointer	B40F	1995	East Devon, Aylesbeare, 1997

Allocated to Witney, Oxfordshire, are six of the Alexander Dash-bodied Darts ordered for London in 1995. The batch carry the later styling of the Dash which eliminated the 'v'-shape windscreen. *Richard Godfrey*

32601-32640

Dennis Dart 9.8SDL3054 — Alexander Dash — B40F — 1995-96

32601	HS	N601KGF	32611	OX	N611LGC	32621	SU	P621PGP	32631	SU	P631PGP
32602	HS	N602KGF	32612	OX	N612LGC	32622	SU	P622PGP	32632	SU	P632PGP
32603	HS	N603KGF	32613	OX	N613LGC	32623	SU	P623PGP	32633	SU	P633PGP
32604	TH	N604KGF	32614	OX	N614LGC	32624	SU	P624PGP	32634	SU	P634PGP
32605	TH	N605KGF	32615	HP	P615PGP	32625	WY	P625PGP	32636	TQ	P636PGP
32606	AD	N606KGF	32616	HP	P616PGP	32626	WY	P626PGP	32637	SU	P637PGP
32607	AD	N607KGF	32617	HP	P617PGP	32627	WY	P627PGP	32638	SU	P638PGP
32608	FO	N608KGF	32618	EX	P618PGP	32628	WY	P628PGP	32639	EX	P639PGP
32609	OX	N609KGF	32619	TQ	P619PGP	32629	WY	P629PGP	32640	EX	P640PGP
32610	OX	N610KGF	32620	SU	P620PGP	32630	WY	P630PGP			

32650	PE	N350YFL	Dennis Dart 9.8m	Alexander Dash	B40F	1996
32651	PE	N351YFL	Dennis Dart 9.8m	Alexander Dash	B40F	1996
32652	PEw	N352YFL	Dennis Dart 9.8m	Alexander Dash	B40F	1996

32655-32661

Dennis Dart 9.8m — Alexander Dash — B40F — 1996

32655	DA	P455EEF	32657	DA	P457EEF	32659	DA	P459EEF	32661	DA	P461EEF
32656	DA	P456EEF	32658	DA	P458EEF	32660	DA	P460EEF			

32701	BY	J701KCU	Dennis Dart 9.8SDL3017	Plaxton Pointer	B40F	1992
32702	SU	J702KCU	Dennis Dart 9.8SDL3017	Plaxton Pointer	B40F	1992

32703-32743

Dennis Dart 9.8SDL3017* — Alexander Dash — B40F — 1992-93 — *32723-28 are 9.8SDL3025; *32729-43 are 9.8SDL3035

32703	SS	K703PCN	32714	BY	K714PCN	32724	SY	K724PNL	32734	SU	L734VNL
32704	BB	K704PCN	32715	SS	K715PCN	32725	SY	K725PNL	32735	SU	L735VNL
32705	BB	K705PCN	32716	PM	NFX667	32726	SY	K726PNL	32736	SU	L736VNL
32706	BB	K706PCN	32717	DA	K717PCN	32727	SY	K727PNL	32737	SU	L737VNL
32707	PE	K707PCN	32718	SU	K718PCN	32728	SY	K728PNL	32738	SU	L738VNL
32708	PE	K708PCN	32719	PM	XYK976	32729	SY	L729VNL	32739	SU	L739VNL
32709	SS	K709PCN	32720	BY	K720PCN	32730	SU	L730VNL	32740	SS	L740VNL
32710	SS	K710PCN	32721	SY	K721PCN	32731	SU	L731VNL	32741	SS	L741VNL
32711	SS	K711PCN	32722	SU	K722PCN	32732	SU	L732VNL	32742	SS	L742VNL
32712	SS	K712PCN	32723	SY	K723PNL	32733	SU	L733VNL	32743	SS	L743VNL
32713	HL	K713PCN									

Seen in Cambridge is Alexander-bodied Dart 32776, N776RVK, one of 315 of this combination in the current fleet. Since this picture was taken in April 2002, the vehicle has been transferred to Peterborough.
Richard Godfrey

32744-32759

Dennis Dart 9.8SDL3035   Plaxton Pointer   B40F   1993

32744	BY	L744VNL	32749	SS	L749VNL	32753	BY	L753VNL	32757	CB	L757VNL
32745	BY	L745VNL	32750	SU	L750VNL	32754	PE	L754VNL	32758	CB	L758VNL
32746	SC	L746VNL	32751	SU	L751VNL	32755	PE	L755VNL	32759	SS	L759VNL
32748	SU	L748VNL	32752	BY	L752VNL	32756	CB	L756VNL			

321760-32765

Dennis Dart 9.8SDL3040   Alexander Dash   B40F   1994

32760	SU	L760ARG	32762	SU	L762ARG	32764	SU	L764ARG	32765	SU	L765ARG
32761	SU	L761ARG	32763	SU	L763ARG						

32766-32771

Dennis Dart 9.8SDL3040   Plaxton Pointer   B40F   1994

32766	SS	M766DRG	32768	SS	M768DRG	32770	SU	M770DRG	32771	PE	M771DRG
32767	SS	M767DRG	32769	SS	M769DRG						

32772-32785

Dennis Dart 9.8m   Alexander Dash   B40F   1996

32772	PE	N772RVK	32776	PE	N776RVK	32780	SU	P780WCN	32783	SS	P783WCN
32773	SU	N773RVK	32777	PE	N778RVK	32781	SU	P781WCN	32784	SS	P784WCN
32774	PE	N774RVK	32778	SU	N779RVK	32782	SU	P782WCN	32785	SS	P785WCN
32775	PE	N775RVK	32779	SU	N780RVK						

32786-32793

Dennis Dart 9.8m   Alexander Dash   B40F   1996-97

32786	SU	P786WVK	32788	SU	P788WVK	32790	SU	P790WVK	32792	SS	P792WVK
32787	SU	P787WVK	32789	SU	P789WVK	32791	SS	P791WVK	32793	SS	P793WVK

32794	SU	M387KVR	Dennis Dart 9.8SDL3054	Northern Counties Paladin	B40F	1995	Redby, Sunderland, 2001
32797	SU	M597SSB	Dennis Dart 9.8SDL3031	Plaxton Pointer	B31F	1995	Redby, Sunderland, 2002

Wright Handy-bus bodywork is carried by Dennis Dart 32995, K95AAX, seen at Bridgend. The bus entered Stagecoach ownership with the purchase of Rhondda in 1997. Vehicle operation in the valleys is hampered by the steep and twisting roads which cause considerable flexing of the chassis and body. The bus is seen in a promotional livery for Honda. *Richard Godfrey*

32801-32812

			Dennis Dart 9.8SDL3017	Alexander Dash	B41F	1992	

32801	AN	J501FPS	32804	AN	J504FPS	32807	IS	J507FPS	32810	IS	J510FPS
32802	AN	J502FPS	32805	AN	J505FPS	32808	IS	J508FPS	32811	AN	J511FPS
32803	AN	J503FPS	32806	IS	J506FPS	32809	IS	J509FPS	32812	IS	J512FPS

32818	CH	P418KWF	Dennis Dart 9.8m	Alexander Dash	B41F	1996	
32819	WP	P419KWF	Dennis Dart 9.8m	Alexander Dash	B41F	1996	
32820	CH	P420KWF	Dennis Dart 9.8m	Alexander Dash	B41F	1996	
32901	SZ	P901SMR	Dennis Dart 9.8m	Alexander Dash	B40F	1997	
32902	SZ	P902SMR	Dennis Dart 9.8m	Alexander Dash	B40F	1997	
32903	SZ	P903SMR	Dennis Dart 9.8m	Alexander Dash	B40F	1997	
32936	SZ	M85DEW	Dennis Dart 9.8SDL3054	Marshall C37	B40F	1994	Glossopdale, Dukinfield, 1999
32937	SZ	M86DEW	Dennis Dart 9.8SDL3054	Marshall C37	B40F	1994	Glossopdale, Dukinfield, 1999
32960	AE	L414SFL	Dennis Dart 9.8SDL3054	Marshall C37	BC37F	1994	
32962	SN	N62MTG	Dennis Dart 9.8SDL3054	Plaxton Pointer	B40F	1995	
32963	SN	N63MTG	Dennis Dart 9.8SDL3054	Plaxton Pointer	B40F	1995	
32964	MR	M64HHB	Dennis Dart 9.8SDL3054	Wright Handy-bus	B39F	1995	
32965	PT	M65HHB	Dennis Dart 9.8SDL3054	Wright Handy-bus	B39F	1995	
32966	MR	M562JTG	Dennis Dart 9.8SDL3040	Plaxton Pointer	B43F	1994	
32967	CL	M67HHB	Dennis Dart 9.8SDL3054	Wright Handy-bus	B39F	1995	
32968	PT	M68HHB	Dennis Dart 9SDL3031	Marshall C36	B34F	1994	
32969	PT	M69HHB	Dennis Dart 9SDL3031	Marshall C36	B34F	1994	
32970	MR	M625KKG	Dennis Dart 9.8SDL3040	Plaxton Pointer	B43F	1994	
32983	PT	L83CWO	Dennis Dart 9SDL3034	Plaxton Pointer	B35F	1993	
32984	PT	L84CWO	Dennis Dart 9SDL3034	Plaxton Pointer	B35F	1993	
32985	PT	L85CWO	Dennis Dart 9SDL3034	Plaxton Pointer	B35F	1993	
32986	CL	L86CWO	Dennis Dart 9SDL3024	Wright Handy-bus	B35F	1993	
32987	CL	L87CWO	Dennis Dart 9SDL3024	Wright Handy-bus	B35F	1993	
32988	PT	L270EHB	Dennis Dart 9.8SDL3035	Plaxton Pointer	B43F	1994	
32989	PT	L89CWO	Dennis Dart 9SDL3024	Wright Handy-bus	B35F	1993	
32990	MR	K402EDT	Dennis Dart 9SDL3016	Northern Counties Paladin	B35F	1992	
32991	PT	K91BNY	Dennis Dart 9SDL3011	Plaxton Pointer	B35F	1993	
32992	PT	K92BNY	Dennis Dart 9SDL3011	Plaxton Pointer	B35F	1993	
32993	PT	K93BNY	Dennis Dart 9SDL3011	Plaxton Pointer	B35F	1993	

32994	PT	K94AAX	Dennis Dart 9SDL3011	Wright Handy-bus	B35F	1993
32995	PT	K95AAX	Dennis Dart 9SDL3011	Wright Handy-bus	B35F	1993
32996	PT	K96AAX	Dennis Dart 9SDL3016	Plaxton Pointer	B35F	1992
32997	MR	K97XNY	Dennis Dart 9SDL3011	Plaxton Pointer(1995)	B35F	1992
32998	P I	K98XNY	Dennis Dart 9.8SDL3017	Wright Handy-bus	B39F	1992
32999	PT	J454JRH	Dennis Dart 9.8SDL3017	Plaxton Pointer	B40F	1991

33001-33019 Dennis Dart SLF 322 Alexander ALX200 N37F 1997-98

33001	HL	R701DNJ	**33006**	WG	R706DNJ	**33011**	WG	R711DNJ	**33016**	WI	R816HCD
33002	WG	R702DNJ	**33007**	WG	R707DNJ	**33012**	WG	XSU612	**33017**	AT	R817HCD
33003	WG	R703DNJ	**33008**	WG	R708DNJ	**33013**	WG	R813HCD	**33018**	AD	R818HCD
33004	WG	R704DNJ	**33009**	WG	R709DNJ	**33014**	WI	R814HCD	**33019**	AD	R819HCD
33005	WG	405DCD	**33010**	WG	R710DNJ	**33015**	WI	R815HCD			

33020	AT	T593CGT	Dennis Dart SLF 10.7m	Plaxton Pointer 2	N39F	1999
33021	AD	R821HCD	Dennis Dart SLF 322	Alexander ALX200	N37F	1998
33022	AD	R822HCD	Dennis Dart SLF 322	Alexander ALX200	N37F	1998
33023	AD	R823HCD	Dennis Dart SLF 322	Alexander ALX200	N37F	1998
33024	AD	R824HCD	Dennis Dart SLF 322	Alexander ALX200	N37F	1998
33025	WI	NDZ3019	Dennis Dart SLF 10.7m	Plaxton Pointer 2	N37F	2000
33026	WI	424DCD	Dennis Dart SLF 10.7m	Plaxton Pointer 2	N37F	2000
33027	WI	NDZ3017	Dennis Dart SLF 10.7m	Plaxton Pointer 2	N37F	2000
33028	WI	NDZ3018	Dennis Dart SLF 10.7m	Plaxton Pointer 2	N37F	2000

33029-33040 Dennis Dart SLF 10.7m Plaxton Pointer 2 N37F 1997 Citybus, Hong Kong, 2000

33029	AT	P299AYJ	**33032**	AT	P302AYJ	**33035**	BE	P435AYJ	**33038**	BE	P458AYJ
33030	BE	P330AYJ	**33033**	AT	P343AYJ	**33036**	BE	P426AYJ	**33039**	BE	P479AYJ
33031	AT	P301AYJ	**33034**	BE	P434AYJ	**33037**	BE	P457AYJ	**33040**	BE	P466AYJ

33053-33072 Dennis Dart SLF 11.3m Plaxton Pointer SPD N41F 2000

33053	PM	X953VAP	**33059**	PM	X959VAP	**33064**	PM	X964VAP	**33068**	PM	X968VAP
33054	PM	X954VAP	**33061**	PM	X961VAP	**33065**	PM	X965VAP	**33069**	PM	X969VAP
33056	PM	X956VAP	**33062**	PM	X962VAP	**33066**	PM	X966VAP	**33071**	PM	X971VAP
33057	PM	X957VAP	**33063**	PM	X963VAP	**33067**	PM	X967VAP	**33072**	PM	X972VAP
33058	PM	X958VAP									

33088	DS	T35VCS	Dennis Dart SLF 8.5m	Plaxton Pointer MPD	N29F	1999
33089	DS	T36VCS	Dennis Dart SLF 8.5m	Plaxton Pointer MPD	N29F	1999

33101-33128 Dennis Dart SLF 322 Alexander ALX200 N37F 1997-98

33101	SS	R101KRG	**33109**	HL	R109KRG	**33117**	HL	R117KRG	**33123**	SU	R123KRG
33102	SS	R102KRG	**33110**	HL	R110KRG	**33118**	SU	R118KRG	**33124**	SU	R124KRG
33103	HL	R103KRG	**33112**	HL	R112KRG	**33119**	WG	R119KRG	**33125**	SU	R125KRG
33104	HL	R104KRG	**33113**	HL	R113KRG	**33120**	SU	R120KRG	**33126**	SU	R126KRG
33105	HL	R105KRG	**33114**	HL	R114KRG	**33121**	SU	R121KRG	**33127**	SU	R127KRG
33107	HL	R107KRG	**33115**	HL	R115KRG	**33122**	SU	R122KRG	**33128**	SU	R128KRG
33108	HL	R108KRG	**33116**	HL	R116KRG						

33158	EX	P758FOD	Dennis Dart SLF 10.7m	Plaxton Pointer	N37F	1997	Citybus, Hong Kong, 2000
33159	EX	P762FOD	Dennis Dart SLF 10.7m	Plaxton Pointer	N37F	1997	Citybus, Hong Kong, 2000
33160	EX	P760FOD	Dennis Dart SLF 10.7m	Plaxton Pointer	N37F	1997	Citybus, Hong Kong, 2000
33200	EX	W102PMS	Dennis Dart SLF 322	Alexander ALX200	N28F	1999	
33201	EX	WA51OSE	Dennis Dart SLF 322	Alexander ALX200	N28F	2001	
33202	EX	WA51OSF	Dennis Dart SLF 322	Alexander ALX200	N28F	2001	
33322	PE	P322EFL	Dennis Dart SLF 10.7m	Plaxton Pointer	N39F	1997	
33323	PE	P323EFL	Dennis Dart SLF 10.7m	Plaxton Pointer	N39F	1997	
33324	PE	P324EFL	Dennis Dart SLF 10.7m	Plaxton Pointer	N39F	1997	

33351-33361 Dennis Dart SLF 10m Alexander ALX200 N29D 1997-99

33351	SD	P801NJN	**33354**	SD	P804NJN	**33357**	SD	P807NJN	**33360**	SD	S410TNO
33352	SD	P802NJN	**33355**	SD	P805NJN	**33358**	SD	P208XNO	**33361**	SD	S411TNO
33353	SD	P803NJN	**33356**	SD	P806NJN	**33359**	SD	P209XNO			

Stagecoach currently operate four hundred and eighty-five low-floor Darts with Alexander ALX200 bodywork. As the model has ceased to be offered by Mayflower, the owners of the Falkirk assembly plant, future needs on the Dart will be met by the Pointer. Perth town services were converted from Routemaster to low-floor buses in 2001 and 33432, X432NSE, is seen in South Street while heading for Scone. *Murdoch Currie*

33393	PE	R353LER	Dennis Dart SLF 322	Alexander ALX200	N39F	1997	
33394	PE	R354LER	Dennis Dart SLF 322	Alexander ALX200	N39F	1997	
33395	PE	R355LER	Dennis Dart SLF 322	Alexander ALX200	N39F	1997	
33396	NN	R356LER	Dennis Dart SLF 322	Alexander ALX200	N39F	1997	
33397	PE	P564APM	Dennis Dart SLF 322	Plaxton Pointer	N39F	1996	Plaxton demonstrator, 1997
33398	PE	R365JVA	Dennis Dart SLF 322	Alexander ALX200	N39F	1997	
33399	NN	R366JVA	Dennis Dart SLF 322	Alexander ALX200	N39F	1997	
33401	CH	T801OHL	Dennis Dart SLF	Plaxton Pointer 2	NC38F	1999	
33402	CH	T802OHL	Dennis Dart SLF	Plaxton Pointer 2	NC38F	1999	
33403	CH	T803OHL	Dennis Dart SLF	Plaxton Pointer 2	NC38F	1999	
33404	GY	S401SDT	Dennis Dart SLF	Alexander ALX200	N37F	1998	
33405	GY	S402SDT	Dennis Dart SLF	Alexander ALX200	N37F	1998	
33406	GY	S403SDT	Dennis Dart SLF	Alexander ALX200	N37F	1998	
33407	ZZ	T905XCD	Dennis Dart SLF	Plaxton Pointer SPD	N36F	1999	On loan to Solent Blue Line

33414-33419

Dennis Dart SLF 322 Alexander ALX200 N37F 1997-98

33414	DE	R614GFS	33416	DE	S616CSC	33418	DE	S618CSC	33419	DE	S619CSC
33415	DE	S615CSC	33417	DE	S617CSC					

33428-33439

Dennis Dart SLF 322 Alexander ALX200 N37F 2001

33428	PH	X428NSE	33431	PH	X431NSE	33434	PH	X434NSE	33437	IS	X437NSE
33429	PH	X429NSE	33432	PH	X432NSE	33435	PH	X435NSE	33438	IS	X438NSE
33430	PH	X441NSE	33433	PH	X433NSE	33436	PH	X436NSE	33439	IS	X439NSE

33443-33447

Dennis Dart SLF 322 Alexander ALX200 N38F 2001

33443	AY	X613JCS	33445	AY	X615JCS	33446	AY	X616JCS	33447	AY	X617JCS
33444	AY	X614JCS								

33453-33464

Dennis Dart SLF 322 Alexander ALX200 N37F 1998-9

33453	NN	S453CVV	33456	NN	S456CVV	33459	NN	S459CVV	33462	NN	V462TVV
33454	NN	S454CVV	33457	NN	S457CVV	33460	NN	S460CVV	33463	NN	V463TVV
33455	NN	S455CVV	33458	NN	S458CVV	33461	NN	S461CVV	33464	NN	V464TVV

33469-33479 — Dennis Dart SLF 322 — Alexander ALX200 — N37F — 1998

33469	BQ	T469GPS	33472	IS	S472JSE	33475	IS	S475JSE	33478	FH	S478JSE
33470	BQ	T470GPS	33473	IS	S473JSE	33476	IS	S476JSE	33479	IS	S479JSE
33471	BQ	T471GPS	33474	IS	S474JSE	33477	FH	S477JSE			

33482-33492 — Dennis Dart SLF 322 — Alexander ALX200 — N37F — 1997

33482	HP	R462SEF	33485	HP	R465SEF	33488	HP	R468SEF	33491	SC	R471MVN
33483	HP	R463SEF	33486	HP	R466SEF	33489	SC	R469MVN	33492	SC	R472MVN
33484	HP	R464SEF	33487	HP	R467SEF	33490	SC	R470MVN			

33501-33513 — Dennis Dart SLF 11.3m — Plaxton Pointer SPD — N41F — 2000

33501	CT	W501VDD	33505	CT	W805VDD	33508	CT	W508VDD	33511	CT	X511ADF
33502	CT	X502ADF	33506	CT	X506ADF	33509	CT	W509VDD	33512	CT	X512ADF
33503	CT	X503ADF	33507	CT	X507ADF	33510	CT	X510ADF	33513	CT	X513ADF
33504	CT	W504VDD									

33554	BR	P54XBO	Dennis Dart SLF 322	Wright Crusader	N43F	1997
33556	BR	P56XBO	Dennis Dart SLF 322	Marshall Capital C39	N43F	1997
33557	BR	P57XBO	Dennis Dart SLF 322	Marshall Capital C39	N43F	1997
33558	BR	P58XBO	Dennis Dart SLF 322	Marshall Capital C39	N43F	1997
33559	PT	P59VTG	Dennis Dart SLF 9.8m	Marshall Capital C37	N40F	1997
33561	MR	P61VIG	Dennis Dart SLF 9.8m	Marshall Capital C37	N40F	1997

33601-33627 — Dennis Dart SLF 322 — Alexander ALX200 — N37F — 1998

33601	GR	R601SWO	33609	CL	R609SWO	33616	CL	R616SWO	33622	PT	S622TDW
33602	GR	R602SWO	33610	CL	R610SWO	33617	CL	R617SWO	33623	PT	S623TDW
33603	GR	R603SWO	33611	CL	R611SWO	33618	CL	R618SWO	33624	PT	S624TDW
33604	PE	R604SWO	33612	CL	R612SWO	33619	CL	R619SWO	33625	PT	S625TDW
33606	PT	R606SWO	33613	CL	R613SWO	33620	CL	R620SWO	33626	PT	S626TDW
33607	PT	R607SWO	33614	CL	R614SWO	33621	PT	R621SWO	33627	PT	S627TDW
33608	PT	R608SWO	33615	CL	R615SWO						

33650-33655 — Dennis Dart SLF 322 — Alexander ALX200 — N37F — 1998

33650	NU	R150CRW	33652	NU	R152CRW	33654	NU	R154CRW	33655	NU	R155CRW
33651	NU	R151CRW	33653	NU	R153CRW						

33751	EX	R751BDV	Dennis Dart SLF 322	Alexander ALX200	N37F	1997

33760-33771 — Dennis Dart SLF — Alexander ALX200 — N37F — 1997

33760	CH	R460LSO	33763	CH	R463LSO	33766	CH	R466LSO	33769	HL	R469LSO
33761	CH	R461LSO	33764	CH	R464LSO	33767	CH	R467LSO	33770	HL	R470LSO
33762	CH	R462LSO	33765	CH	R465LSO	33768	CH	R468LSO	33771	HL	R471LSO

33772	DS	T402UCS	Dennis Dart SLF 322	Alexander ALX200	N37F	1999
33773	DS	T403UCS	Dennis Dart SLF 322	Alexander ALX200	N37F	1999
33774	EX	T404UCS	Dennis Dart SLF 322	Alexander ALX200	N37F	1999

33775-33780 — Dennis Dart SLF 11.3m — Plaxton Pointer SPD — N41F — 2000

33775	AY	X739JCS	33777	AY	X742JCS	33779	AY	X744JCS	33780	AY	X59RCS
33776	AY	X741JCS	33778	AY	X743JCS					

33781	EH	T575KGB	Dennis Dart SLF 322	Marshall Capital	N43F	1999	Dart Buses, 2001
33782	EH	T131MGB	Dennis Dart SLF 322	Marshall Capital	N43F	1999	Dart Buses, 2001
33783	EH	T132MGB	Dennis Dart SLF 322	Marshall Capital	N43F	1999	Dart Buses, 2001

33801-33829 — Dennis Dart SLF 10.1m — Alexander ALX200 — B37F — 1998

33801	EX	R801YUD	33809	SZ	R809YUD	33816	PE	R816YUD	33823	EX	R823YUD
33802	CB	R802YUD	33810	SZ	R810YUD	33817	PE	R817YUD	33824	EX	R824YUD
33803	EX	R803YUD	33811	SZ	R811YUD	33818	PE	R818YUD	33825	SS	R825YUD
33804	EH	R804YUD	33812	SZ	R812YUD	33819	PE	R819YUD	33826	SS	R826YUD
33805	EH	R805YUD	33813	PE	R813YUD	33820	PE	R720YUD	33827	SS	R827YUD
33806	PE	R706YUD	33814	CB	R814YUD	33821	NN	R821YUD	33828	SS	R828YUD
33807	EX	R807YUD	33815	PE	R815YUD	33822	NN	R822YUD	33829	SS	R829YUD
33808	SN	R808YUD									

Stagecoach's solitary Wright-bodied Dart 33554, P54XBO, illustrates the Crusader body style as it heads for Maerdy on route 132, *John Jones*

33831-33837 Dennis Dart SLF 11.3m · Plaxton Pointer SPD · N41F · 2001

33831	MD	X831AKW	33833	MD	X833AKW	33835	MD	X835AKW	33837	MD	X837AKW
33832	MD	X832AKW	33834	MD	X834AKW	33836	MD	X836AKW			

33828-33841 Dennis Dart SLF · Plaxton Pointer 2 · N37F · 2001

33838	CH	X838HHE	33839	CH	X839HHE	33840	CH	X840HHE	33841	CH	X841HHE

33847	MD	X827AKW	Dennis Dart SLF 11.3m	Plaxton Pointer SPD	N41F	2001
33848	MD	X828AKW	Dennis Dart SLF 11.3m	Plaxton Pointer SPD	N41F	2001
33849	MD	X829AKW	Dennis Dart SLF 11.3m	Plaxton Pointer SPD	N41F	2001

33904-33914 Dennis Dart SLF 10m · Alexander ALX200 · N36F · 1996-97

33904	SN	P904SMR	33907	SN	P907SMR	33910	SN	P910SMR	33913	SN	P913SMR
33905	SN	P905SMR	33908	SN	P908SMR	33911	SN	P911SMR	33914	SN	P914SMR
33906	SN	P906SMR	33909	SN	P909SMR	33912	SN	P912SMR			

33915-33918 Dennis Dart SLF 322 · Alexander ALX200 · N37F · 1997

33915	SN	R915GMW	33916	SN	R916GMW	33917	SN	R917GMW	33918	SN	R918GMW

33924-33930 Dennis Dart SLF 322 · Alexander ALX200 · N37F · 1998

33924	SN	S924PDD	33926	CT	S926PDD	33928	CT	S928PDD	33930	CT	S930PDD
33925	SN	S925PDD	33927	CT	S927PDD	33929	CT	S929PDD			

33938-33962 Dennis Dart SLF 322 · Alexander ALX200 · N37F · 1999

33938	CT	V938DFH	33945	GR	V945DFH	33951	GR	V951DDG	33957	CT	V957DDG
33939	CT	V939DFH	33946	GR	V946DFH	33952	GR	V952DDG	33958	CT	V958DDG
33940	CT	V940DFH	33947	GR	V947DFH	33953	CT	V953DDG	33959	CT	V959DDG
33941	CT	V941DFH	33948	GR	V948DDG	33954	CT	V954DDG	33960	GR	V960DDG
33942	SN	V942DFH	33949	GR	V949DDG	33955	CT	V955DDG	33961	CT	V961DFH
33943	SN	V943DFH	33950	GR	V950DDG	33956	CT	V956DDG	33962	CT	V962DFH
33944	GR	V944DFH									

33966-33977 — Dennis Dart SLF — Alexander ALX200 — N37F — 2001

33966	GR	X966AFH	33969	GR	X969AFH	33972	GR	X972AFH	33975	GR	X975AFH
33967	GR	X967AFH	33970	GR	X978AFH	33973	GR	X973AFH	33976	GR	X976AFH
33968	GR	X968AFH	33971	GR	X971AFH	33974	GR	X974AFH	33977	GR	X977AFH

33978	RY	VX51NXR	Dennis Dart SLF	Alexander ALX200	N38F	2001
33979	RY	VX51NXS	Dennis Dart SLF	Alexander ALX200	N38F	2001
33979	RY	VX51NXT	Dennis Dart SLF	Alexander ALX200	N38F	2001

34001-34009 — Dennis Dart SLF 10m — Alexander ALX200 — N36F — 1996

34001	WP	P21HMF	34004	WP	P24HMF	34006	WP	P26HMF	34008	WP	P28HMF
34002	WP	P31HMF	34005	WP	P25HMF	34007	WP	P27HMF	34009	WP	P29HMF
34003	WP	P23HMF									

34010-34020 — Dennis Dart SLF 10m — Alexander ALX200 — N36F — 1997

34010	AT	410DCD	34013	AT	413DCD	34016	AT	422DCD	34019	AT	419DCD
34011	AT	411DCD	34014	ATu	NDZ3020	34017	AT	423DCD	34020	AT	420DCD
34012	AT	412DCD	34015	AT	421DCD	34018	AT	408DCD			

34021-34029 — Dennis Dart SLF 10m — Alexander ALX200 — N33F — 1997

34021	KK	R121VPU	34024	BK	R124VPU	34026	KK	R126VPU	34028	TB	R128VPU
34022	BK	R122VPU	34025	KK	R125VPU	34027	BKu	R127VPU	34029	TB	R129VPU
34023	BK	R123VPU									

34030-34041 — Dennis Dart SLF 10m — Alexander ALX200 — N29F — 1998

34030	SD	R930FOO	34033	SD	R933FOO	34036	BK	R936FOO	34039	BK	R939FOO
34031	SD	R931FOO	34034	SD	R934FOO	34037	CS	R937FOO	34040	BK	R940FOO
34032	SD	R932FOO	34035	NS	R935FOO	34038	CS	R938FOO	34041	CS	R941FOO

34042-34058 — Dennis Dart SLF 9.4m — Alexander ALX200 — N29F — 1998

34042	PD	R942FOO	34047	TL	R947FOO	34051	SD	R451FVX	34055	SD	R455FVX
34043	TL	R943FOO	34048	TL	R948FOO	34052	SD	R452FVX	34056	SD	R456FVX
34044	TL	R944FOO	34049	SD	R949FOO	34053	SD	R453FVX	34057	SD	R457FVX
34045	TL	R945FOO	34050	SD	R950FOO	34054	SD	R454FVX	34058	SD	R458FVX
34046	SD	R946FOO									

34059-34078 — Dennis Dart SLF 10m — Alexander ALX200 — N33F — 1998

34059	TL	S459BWC	34064	PD	S464BWC	34069	TB	S469BWC	34074	TL	S474BWC
34060	NS	S460BWC	34065	PD	S465BWC	34070	TB	S470BWC	34075	PD	S475BWC
34061	TB	S461BWC	34066	PD	S466BWC	34071	TL	S471BWC	34076	BK	S476BWC
34062	BK	S462BWC	34067	TB	S467BWC	34072	PD	S472BWC	34077	PD	S477BWC
34063	KK	S463BWC	34068	TB	S468BWC	34073	PD	S473BWC	34078	PD	S478BWC

34079-34088 — Dennis Dart SLF 9.4m — Alexander ALX200 — N29F — 1999

34079	PD	S479BWC	34082	PD	S482BWC	34085	PD	S485BWC	34087	PD	S487BWC
34080	PD	S480BWC	34083	PD	S483BWC	34086	PD	S486BWC	34088	PD	S488BWC
34081	PD	S481BWC	34084	PD	S484BWC						

34089-34095 — Dennis Dart SLF 10m — Alexander ALX200 — N33F* — 1999 — *34089 is N29F, 34090 is N31F

34089	NS	S489BWC	34091	NS	S491BWC	34093	NS	S493BWC	34095	NS	S495BWC
34090	NS	S490BWC	34092	NS	S492BWC	34094	TL	S494BWC			

34096-34106 — Dennis Dart SLF 9.4m — Alexander ALX200 — N29F* — 1999

34096	TB	S496BWC	34099	SD	S499BWC	34102	SD	S102WHK	34105	SD	S105WHK
34097	SD	S497BWC	34100	SD	WLT898	34103	SD	S103WHK	34106	SD	S106WHK
34098	SD	S498BWC	34101	SD	S101WHK	34104	SD	S104WHK			

34107	NS	V107MVX	Dennis Dart SLF 10.1m	Plaxton Pointer 2	N33F	1999
34108	NS	V108MVX	Dennis Dart SLF 10.1m	Plaxton Pointer 2	N33F	1999
34109	TL	V109MVX	Dennis Dart SLF 10.1m	Plaxton Pointer 2	N33F	1999
34110	NS	V110MVX	Dennis Dart SLF 10.1m	Plaxton Pointer 2	N33F	1999

Stagecoach London's single-deck Darts form the 34000 series although the first have already been transferred to provincial fleets. Pictured in Bromley is Pointer 34204, W204DNO. The Pointer model is currently assembled at Falkirk from kits produced at Larbert under the new arrangements introduced by TransBus, the company formed by Mayflower and Henlys to build buses in the UK. *Richard Godfrey*

34111-34138

			Dennis Dart SLF 10.1m			Plaxton Pointer 2		N31D	1999	
34111	SD	V173MVX	34118	SD	V118MVX	34125	BK	V125MVX	34132	BK	V132MVX
34112	SD	V112MVX	34119	SD	V119MVX	34126	BK	V126MVX	34133	BK	V133MVX
34113	SD	V113MVX	34120	SD	V120MVX	34127	BK	V127MVX	34134	BK	V134MVX
34114	SD	V114MVX	34121	SD	V174MVX	34128	BK	V128MVX	34135	BK	V135MVX
34115	SD	V115MVX	34122	SD	V122MVX	34129	BK	V129MVX	34136	BK	V136MVX
34116	SD	V116MVX	34123	SD	V123MVX	34130	BK	V130MVX	34137	BK	V137MVX
34117	SD	V117MVX	34124	BK	V124MVX	34131	BK	V131MVX	34138	BK	V138MVX

34139-34172

			Dennis Dart SLF 9.3m			Plaxton Pointer 2		N27D	1999-2000	
34139	SD	V139MVX	34148	SD	V148MVX	34157	U	V157MVX	34165	SD	V165MVX
34140	SD	V140MVX	34149	SD	V149MVX	34158	U	V158MVX	34166	SD	V166MVX
34141	SD	V141MVX	34150	SD	V150MVX	34159	U	V159MVX	34167	SD	V167MVX
34142	SD	V142MVX	34151	SD	V151MVX	34160	U	V160MVX	34168	SD	V168MVX
34143	SD	V143MVX	34152	SD	V152MVX	34161	U	V161MVX	34169	SD	V169MVX
34144	SD	V144MVX	34153	SD	V153MVX	34162	U	V162MVX	34170	SD	V170MVX
34145	SD	V145MVX	34154	SD	V154MVX	34163	U	V163MVX	34171	SD	V171MVX
34146	SD	V146MVX	34155	SD	V155MVX	34164	SD	V164MVX	34172	SD	V172MVX
34147	SD	V147MVX	34156	U	V156MVX						

34173-34203

			Dennis Dart SLF 10.1m			Plaxton Pointer 2		N31D	2000	
34173	U	W173DNO	34181	U	W181DNO	34189	U	W189DNO	34197	U	W197DNO
34174	U	W174DNO	34182	U	W182DNO	34190	U	W231DNO	34198	BK	W198DNO
34175	U	W224DNO	34183	U	W183DNO	34191	U	W191DNO	34199	BK	W199DNO
34176	U	W176DNO	34184	U	W184DNO	34192	U	W192DNO	34200	TL	W233DNO
34177	U	W177DNO	34185	U	W185DNO	34193	U	W193DNO	34201	TL	W201DNO
34178	U	W178DNO	34186	U	W186DNO	34194	U	W194DNO	34202	BK	W202DNO
34179	U	W226DNO	34187	U	W187DNO	34195	U	W195DNO	34203	TL	W203DNO
34180	U	W227DNO	34188	U	W188DNO	34196	U	W196DNO			

34204-34211

			Dennis Dart SLF 9.3m			Plaxton Pointer 2		N27D	2000	
34204	TB	W204DNO	34206	TL	W229DNO	34208	TL	W208DNO	34210	TL	W232DNO
34205	TL	W228DNO	34207	TL	W207DNO	34209	TL	W209DNO	34211	TL	W211DNO

The 2003 Stagecoach Bus Handbook

34204-34223 — Dennis Dart SLF 9.3m — Plaxton Pointer 2 — N30F — 2000

34212	PD	W212DNO	34215	PD	W215DNO	34218	TB	W218DNO	34221	TB	W221DNO
34213	PD	W213DNO	34216	PD	W216DNO	34219	TB	W219DNO	34222	TB	W236DNO
34214	PD	W214DNO	34217	TB	W234DNO	34220	TB	W235DNO	34223	TB	W223DNO

34224-34236 — Dennis Dart SLF 11.3m — Plaxton Pointer SPD — N37D — 2001

34224	TB	X224WNO	34228	TB	X228WNO	34231	TB	X231WNO	34234	TB	X234WNO
34225	TB	X237WNO	34229	TB	X229WNO	34232	TB	X232WNO	34235	TB	X235WNO
34226	TB	X226WNO	34230	TB	X238WNO	34233	TB	X233WNO	34236	TB	X236WNO
34227	TB	X227WNO									

34237-34253 — Dennis Dart SLF 9m — Alexander ALX200 — N28F — 2001

34237	TL	Y237FJN	34242	TL	Y242FJN	34246	TL	Y246FJN	34250	TL	Y349FJN
34238	TL	Y238FJN	34243	TL	Y243FJN	34247	TL	Y247FJN	34251	TL	Y251FJN
34239	TL	Y239FJN	34244	TL	Y244FJN	34248	TB	Y248FJN	34252	TL	Y252FJN
34240	TB	Y347FJN	34245	TB	Y348FJN	34249	TL	Y249FJN	34253	TL	Y253FJN
34241	TL	Y241FJN									

34254-34272 — Dennis Dart SLF 10m — Alexander ALX200 — N30D — 2001

34254	BK	Y254FJN	34259	BK	Y259FJN	34264	BK	Y264FJN	34269	BK	Y269FJN
34255	BK	Y351FJN	34260	BK	Y352FJN	34265	BK	Y265FJN	34270	BK	Y353FJN
34256	BK	Y256FJN	34261	BK	Y261FJN	34266	BK	Y266FJN	34271	BK	Y271FJN
34257	BK	Y257FJN	34262	BK	Y262FJN	34267	BK	Y267FJN	34272	BK	Y272FJN
34258	BK	Y258FJN	34263	BK	Y263FJN	34268	BK	Y268FJN			

34273-34327 — Dennis Dart SLF 10m — Alexander ALX200 — N30D — 2001

34273	BK	Y273FJN	34287	BK	Y287FJN	34301	T	Y301FJN	34315	PD	LX51FGU
34274	BK	Y274FJN	34288	BK	Y671JSG	34302	T	Y302FJN	34316	PD	LX51FGZ
34275	BK	Y354FJN	34289	T	Y289FJN	34303	TL	LX51FGA	34317	PD	LX51FHG
34276	BK	Y276FJN	34290	T	LX51FFW	34304	TL	LX51FGF	34318	PD	LX51FHB
34277	BK	Y277FJN	34291	T	Y291FJN	34305	TL	LX51FGE	34319	PD	LX51FHA
34278	BK	LX51FPE	34292	T	Y292FJN	34306	TL	LX51FGD	34320	PD	LX51FHC
34279	BK	Y279FJN	34293	T	Y293FJN	34307	TL	LX51FGG	34321	PD	LX51FHD
34280	BK	Y356FJN	34294	T	Y294FJN	34308	TL	LX51FGM	34322	PD	LX51FHE
34281	BK	Y281FJN	34295	T	Y295FJN	34309	TL	LX51FGK	34323	PD	LX51FHF
34282	BK	Y282FJN	34296	T	Y296FJN	34310	TL	LX51FGV	34324	PD	LX51FHK
34283	BK	Y283FJN	34297	T	Y297FJN	34311	TL	LX51FGJ	34325	PD	LX51FHL
34284	BK	Y284FJN	34298	T	Y298FJN	34312	TL	LX51FGN	34326	PD	LX51FHH
34285	BK	Y285FJN	34299	T	Y299FJN	34313	PD	LX51FGO	34327	PD	LX51FHJ
34286	BK	Y286FJN	34300	T	LX51FPJ	34314	PD	LX51FGP			

To meet tender requirements a variety of styles of Pointer-Darts have been taken into stock. These attracted class identities of DL, DM, DS and DSS dependent on length. Seen at Lewisham is 34310, LX51FGV which is a member of the DM class, this now being displayed on the side of the bus.
Richard Godfrey

34328-34346
Dennis Dart SLF 10.8m — Alexander ALX200 — N33D — 2001

34328	BK	Y371FJN	34333	BK	Y373FJN	34338	BK	Y338FJN	34343	BK	Y343FJN
34329	BK	Y329FJN	34334	BK	Y334FJN	34339	BK	Y339FJN	34344	BK	Y344FJN
34330	BK	Y372FJN	34335	BK	Y335FJN	34340	BK	Y374FJN	34345	BK	Y376FJN
34331	BK	Y331FJN	34336	BK	Y336FJN	34341	BK	LX51FFO	34346	BK	Y346FJN
34332	BK	Y332FJN	34337	BK	Y337FJN	34342	BK	Y342FJN			

34347-34365
Dennis Dart SLF 10.8m — Transbus Pointer — N30D — 2002

34347	BK	LV52HJY	34352	BK	LV52HKD	34357		LV52HKJ	34362	LV52HKO
34348	BK	LV52HJZ	34353	BK	LV52HKE	34358		LV52HKK	34363	LV52HKP
34349		LV52HKA	34354		LV52HKF	34359		LV52HKL	34364	LV52HKT
34350		LV52HKB	34355		LV52HKG	34360		LV52HKM	34365	LV52HKU
34351		LV52HKC	34356		LV52HKH	34361		LV52HKN		

34366-34376
Dennis Dart SLF 8.8m — Transbus Pointer — N28F — 2003

34366	LV52HGC	34369	LV52HGF	34372	LV52HGK	34375	LV52HGN
34367	LV52HGD	34370	LV52HGG	34373	LV52HGL	34376	
34368	LV52HGE	34371	LV52HGJ	34374	LV52HGM		

34377-34386
Dennis Dart SLF 9.3m — Transbus Pointer — N30F — Due 2003

34377	L	34380	L	34383	L	34385	L
34378	L	34381	L	34384	L	34386	L
34379	L	34382	L				

34387-34397
Dennis Dart SLF10.2m — Transbus Pointer — N30D — Due 2003

34387	L	34390	L	34393	L	34396	L
34388	L	34391	L	34394	L	34397	L
34389	L	34392	L	34395	L		

35000-35515
Optare Excel L1150 — Optare — N40F — 2001-02

35000	CH	YN51VHH	35004	CH	YN51VHM	35008	WP	YN51VHT	35012	WP	YN51VHX
35001	CH	YN51VHJ	35005	CH	YN51VHN	35009	WP	YN51VHU	35013	WP	YN51VHY
35002	CH	YN51VHK	35006	CH	YN51VHP	35010	WP	YN51VHV	35014	WP	YN51VHZ
35003	CH	YN51VHL	35007	WP	YN51VHR	35011	WP	YN51VHW	35015	WP	YN51VJA

Special event vehicle - - (initial owners shown and traditional vintage body codes used)

39925	ES	DGS625	Leyland Tiger PS1/1	McLennan	C39F	1951	McLennan, Spittalfield
39957	NWu	VY957	Leyland Lion PLSC3	Ribble 1984 replica	B32R	1929	Ribble
39995	NWu	CK3825	Leyland Lion PLSC1	Ribble 1982 replica	B31F	1927	Ribble

Twelve Optare Excel buses were taken into the fleet for 2002 and these have all be placed with East Midlands. Pictured at Chesterfield is 35002, YN51VHK.
Tony Wilson

Many of the early Mercedes-Benz 709Ds have now been displaced, though almost 800 Alexander-bodied examples have been included in the renumbering plan. The type is being replaced by the short Dart model. Two versions of destination roof boxes can be found, the shallower one, as seen here on Lakeland liveried 40040, K877GHH, and the deeper version as shown on page 89. *Bob Downham*

40001-40015

		Mercedes-Benz 709D		Alexander Sprint		B23F	1995

40001	KL	N201UHH	40005	BA	N205UHH	40009	KL	N209UHH	40013	KL	N213UHH
40002	KL	N202UHH	40006	LL	N206UHH	40010	KL	N210UHH	40014	LL	N214UHH
40003	KL	N203UHH	40007	KL	N207UHH	40011	KL	N211UHH	40015	LL	N215UHH
40004	BA	N204UHH	40008	KL	N208UHH	40012	KL	N212UHH			

40016-40033

		Mercedes-Benz 709D		Alexander Sprint		B23F	1996

40016	BA	N116YHH	40021	BA	N121YHH	40026	BA	N126YRM	40030	LL	N130YRM
40017	BA	N117YHH	40022	BA	N122YHH	40027	LL	N127YRM	40031	LL	N131YRM
40018	BA	N118YHH	40023	BA	N123YHH	40028	LL	N128YRM			
40019	BA	N119YHH	40024	LL	N124YHH	40029	LL	N129YRM	40033	LL	N133YRM
40020	BA	N120YHH	40025	LL	N125YHH						

40034-40040

		Mercedes-Benz 709D		Alexander Sprint		B25F	1993

40034	BA	K871GHH	40036	LL	K873GHH	40038	LL	K875GHH	40040	CE	K877GHH
40035	BA	K872GHH	40037	LL	K874GHH	40039	CE	K876GHH			

40041-40052

		Mercedes-Benz 709D		Alexander Sprint		B25F	1996

40041	BQ	P341ASO	40044	FH	P344ASO	40047	PH	P347ASO	40050	AN	P350ASO
40042	BQ	P342ASO	40045	PH	P345ASO	40048	BQ	P348ASO	40051	IS	P351ASO
40043	BQ	P343ASO	40046	PH	P346ASO	40049	BQ	P349ASO	40052	IS	P352ASO

40053-40069

		Mercedes-Benz 709D		Alexander Sprint		B25F	1995

40053	DS	M653FYS	40058	KK	M658FYS	40062	DS	M662FYS	40066	DS	M651FYS
40054	AA	M654FYS	40059	AA	M659FYS	40063	DS	M663FYS	40067	KK	M667FYS
40055	AA	M655FYS	40060	AS	M660FYS	40064	CC	M664FYS	40068	AS	M668FYS
40056	CC	M656FYS	40061	AS	M661FYS	40065	CC	M665FYS	40069	DS	M652FYS
40057	CC	M657FYS									

The 2003 Stagecoach Bus Handbook

40070-40080 — Mercedes-Benz 709D — Alexander Sprint — B25F — 1994

40070	DE	M770TFS	40073	AL	M773TFS	40076	SA	M776TFS	40079	BQ	M779TFS
40071	DE	M771TFS	40074	AL	M774TFS	40078	BQ	M778TFS	40080	GS	M780TFS
40072	AL	M772TFS	40075	SA	M775TFS						

40081	CE	K878GHH	Mercedes-Benz 709D	Alexander Sprint	B25F	1993
40082	WSu	L882LFS	Mercedes-Benz 709D	Alexander Sprint	B25F	1994

40085-40094 — Mercedes-Benz 709D — Alexander Sprint — B25F — 1993

40085	SY	K485FFS	40088	IS	K488FFS	40091	ESu	K491FFS	40093	BY	K493FFS
40086	ISu	K486FFS	40089	GS	K489FFS	40092	BY	K492FFS	40094	SS	K494FFS
40087	ISu	K487FFS	40090	ESu	K490FFS						

40095	GS	N95ALS	Mercedes-Benz 709D	Alexander Sprint	B25F	1996
40096	GS	N96ALS	Mercedes-Benz 709D	Alexander Sprint	B25F	1996
40097	GS	N97ALS	Mercedes-Benz 709D	Alexander Sprint	B25F	1996
40098	AS	M648FYS	Mercedes-Benz 709D	Alexander Sprint	B25F	1995
40099	DS	M649FYS	Mercedes-Benz 709D	Alexander Sprint	B25F	1995
40100	DS	M650FYS	Mercedes-Benz 709D	Alexander Sprint	B25F	1995
40101	DU	L301JSA	Mercedes-Benz 709D	Alexander Sprint	BC25F	1993
40102	BQ	L302JSA	Mercedes-Benz 709D	Alexander Sprint	BC25F	1993
40103	AL	L303JSA	Mercedes-Benz 709D	Alexander Sprint	BC25F	1993
40106	OXu	K306ARW	Mercedes-Benz 709D	Wright Nimbus	B25F	1992
40107	OXu	L307SKV	Mercedes-Benz 709D	Wright Nimbus	B25F	1993

40108-40130 — Mercedes-Benz 709D — Alexander Sprint — B23F — 1994

40108	OXu	L308YDU	40115	AT	L315YDU	40121	PMu	L321YDU	40126	OX	L326YKV
40109	OX	L309YDU	40116	AR	L316YDU	40122	AR	L322YDU	40127	OXu	L327YKV
40110	OXu	L310YDU	40117	AR	L317YDU	40123	AT	L323YDU	40128	OXu	L328YKV
40112	AT	L312YDU	40118	AT	L318YDU	40124	AR	L324YDU	40129	AT	L329YKV
40113	AT	L313YDU	40119	AT	L319YDU	40125	AT	L325YDU	40130	AT	L330YKV
40114	AT	L314YDU	40120	AT	L320YDU						

40131-40146 — Mercedes-Benz 709D — Alexander Sprint — B23F — 1995

40131	AR	M331LHP	40136	LE	M336LHP	40140	LE	M340LHP	40144	CN	M344LHP
40132	AT	M332LHP	40137	LE	M337LHP	40141	LE	M341LHP	40145	CN	M345LHP
40134	LE	M334LHP	40138	LE	M338LHP	40142	NU	M342LHP	40146	NU	M346KWK
40135	LE	M335LHP	40139	LE	M339LHP	40143	NU	M343LHP			

40147-40172 — Mercedes-Benz 709D — Alexander Sprint — B25F — 1996

40147	NU	N347AVV	40154	RU	N354AVV	40161	NU	N361AVV	40167	NU	N367AVV
40148	NU	N348AVV	40155	RU	N355AVV	40162	BB	N362AVV	40168	NU	N368AVV
40149	NU	N349AVV	40156	RU	N356AVV	40163	BB	N363AVV	40169	NU	N369AVV
40150	NU	N350AVV	40157	RU	N357AVV	40164	SB	N364AVV	40170	NU	N370AVV
40151	NU	N351AVV	40158	RU	N358AVV	40165	NU	N365AVV	40171	NU	N371AVV
40152	NU	N352AVV	40159	RU	N359AVV	40166	NU	N366AVV	40172	NU	N372AVV
40153	RU	N353AVV	40160	RU	N360AVV						

40192-40203 — Mercedes-Benz 709D — Alexander Sprint — BC25F — 1990

40192	MEu	G192PAO	40195	BJ	G195PAO	40198	BJ	G198PAO	40203	BJ	G203PAO
40194	BJ	G194PAO	40197	IS	G197PAO						

40204	HPw	E306BWL	Mercedes-Benz 709D	Reeve Burgess Beaver	BC25F	1988
40205	CNu	F392DHL	Mercedes-Benz 709D	Reeve Burgess Beaver	Publicity	1989
40211	HEt	E510PVV	Mercedes-Benz 709D	Alexander Sprint	TV	1988

40226-40250 — Mercedes-Benz 709D — Marshall C19 — B21D — 1995

40226	EX	M226UTM	40233	EX	M233UTM	40239	EX	M239UTM	40245	EX	M245UTM
40227	EX	M227UTM	40234	EX	M234UTM	40240	EX	M240UTM	40246	EX	M246UTM
40228	EX	M228UTM	40235	EX	M235UTM	40241	EX	M241UTM	40247	EX	M247UTM
40229	EX	M229UTM	40236	EX	M236UTM	40242	EX	M242UTM	40248	EX	M248UTM
40230	EX	M230UTM	40237	EX	M237UTM	40243	EX	M243UTM	40249	EX	M249UTM
40231	EX	M231UTM	40238	EX	M238UTM	40244	EX	M244UTM	40250	EX	M250UTM
40232	EX	M232UTM									

40251-40286

Mercedes-Benz 709D   Alexander Sprint   B25F*   1990   *40277/83/6 are B23F

40251	SY	G251TSL	40267	PR	G267TSL	40270	KY	G270TSL	40283	SY	G283TSL
40254	SYt	G254TSL	40268	LLu	G268TSL	40277	SY	G277TSL	40286	SY	G286TSL
40263	LLu	G263TSL	40269	LLu	G269TSL	40282	SYt	G282TSL			

40301-40329

Mercedes-Benz 709D   Alexander Sprint   B23F   1996

40301	NN	N301XRP	40309	KG	N309XRP	40316	KG	N316XRP	40323	BD	N323XRP
40302	BD	N302XRP	40310	KG	N310XRP	40317	KG	N317XRP	40324	BD	N324XRP
40303	BD	N303XRP	40311	KG	N311XRP	40318	BD	N318XRP	40325	BD	N325XRP
40304	BD	N304XRP	40312	KG	N312XRP	40319	BD	N319XRP	40326	BD	N326XRP
40305	NN	N305XRP	40313	KG	N313XRP	40320	BD	N320XRP	40327	BA	N327XRP
40306	KG	N306XRP	40314	KG	N314XRP	40321	BD	N321XRP	40328	LL	N328XRP
40307	KG	N307XRP	40315	KG	N315XRP	40322	BD	N322XRP	40329	CE	N329XRP
40308	KG	N308XRP									

40332-40349

Mercedes-Benz 709D   Alexander Sprint   B25F   1994

40332	BD	M332DRP	40338	BD	M338DRP	40342	KG	M342DRP	40346	KG	M346DRP
40334	BD	M334DRP	40339	BD	M339DRP	40343	KG	M343DRP	40347	KG	M347DRP
40335	BD	M335DRP	40340	KG	M340DRP	40344	KG	M344DRP	40348	KG	M348DRP
40336	BD	M336DRP	40341	KG	M341DRP	40345	KG	M345DRP	40349	KG	M349DRP
40337	BD	M337DRP									

40350-40383

Mercedes-Benz 709D   Alexander Sprint   B25F*   1992-93   *40351-66 are B21F

40350	BD	K350ANV	40359	CX	K359ANV	40368	BD	L368JBD	40376	NN	L376JBD
40351	BD	K351ANV	40360	CX	L360JBD	40369	BD	L369JBD	40377	NN	L377JBD
40352	CBu	K352ANV	40361	CX	L361JBD	40370	BD	L370JBD	40378	NN	L378JBD
40353	CXu	K353ANV	40362	CX	L362JBD	40371	BD	L371JBD	40379	NN	L379JBD
40354	CX	K354ANV	40363	CX	L363JBD	40372	BD	L372JBD	40380	NN	L380JBD
40355	CXu	K355ANV	40364	CX	L364JBD	40373	NN	L373JBD	40381	NN	L381NBD
40356	CX	K356ANV	40365	CX	L365JBD	40374	NN	L374JBD	40382	CX	L382NBD
40357	CX	K357ANV	40366	CX	L366JBD	40375	NN	L375JBD	40383	KG	L383NBD
40358	CXu	K358ANV	40367	BD	L367JBD						

40394-40402

Mercedes-Benz 709D   Alexander Sprint   B25F   1996

40394	PR	N194LFV	40396	PR	N196LFV	40398	PR	N198LFV	40401	PR	N201LFV
40395	PR	N195LFV	40397	PR	N197LFV	40399	CY	N199LFV	40402	PR	N202LFV

40412-40428

Mercedes-Benz 709D   Alexander Sprint   B25F   1993

40412	ME	K112XHG	40417	ME	K117XHG	40421	LL	K121XHG	40425	CY	L125DRN
40413	LL	K113XHG	40418	CY	K118XHG	40422	ME	L122DRN	40426	CE	L126DRN
40414	LL	K114XHG	40419	PR	L119DRN	40423	LL	L123DRN	40427	ME	L127DRN
40416	ME	K116XHG	40420	ME	K120XHG	40424	ME	K124XHG	40428	PR	L128DRN

40429-40435

Mercedes-Benz 709D   Alexander Sprint   B25F   1996

40429	CS	N879AVV	40431	CS	N881AVV	40433	CS	N883AVV	40435	BA	N885AVV
40430	CS	N880AVV	40432	CS	N882AVV	40434	CS	N884AVV			

40441-40455

Mercedes-Benz 709D   Alexander Sprint   B25F   1996

40441	BA	N461VOD	40443	PR	N463VOD	40446	PR	N456VOD	40452	PR	N452VOD
40442	CY	N462VOD	40445	PR	N465VOD	40447	PR	N457VOD	40455	PR	N455VOD

40461-40500

Mercedes-Benz 709D   Alexander Sprint   B23F   1996

40461	BY	N461RVK	40471	SY	N471RVK	40481	SY	N481RVK	40491	SS	N492RVK
40462	BY	N462RVK	40472	SY	N472RVK	40482	SY	N482RVK	40492	SS	N492RVK
40463	BY	N463RVK	40473	SY	N473RVK	40483	SY	N483RVK	40493	SS	N493RVK
40464	BY	N464RVK	40474	SY	N474RVK	40484	SY	N484RVK	40494	SS	N494RVK
40465	BY	N465RVK	40475	SY	N475RVK	40485	BY	N485RVK	40495	SS	N495RVK
40466	BY	N466RVK	40476	SY	N476RVK	40486	SY	N486RVK	40496	SS	N496RVK
40467	BY	N467RVK	40477	SY	N477RVK	40487	SS	N487RVK	40497	SS	N497RVK
40468	BY	N468RVK	40478	SY	N478RVK	40488	SS	N488RVK	40498	SS	N498RVK
40469	SY	N469RVK	40479	SY	N479RVK	40489	SS	N489RVK	40499	SU	N499RVK
40470	SY	N470RVK	40480	SY	N480RVK	40490	SU	N490RVK	40501	SS	N501RVK

Now numbered 40138, M338LHP illustrates the deeper and more common destination display of the Sprint. It is seen operating with South Midlands at Leamington Spa in July 2002.

40506-40520

		Mercedes-Benz 709D			Alexander Sprint			B23F		1996					
40506	TQ	N506BJA	**40510**	TQ	N510BJA	**40514**	TQ	N514BJA	**40518**	TQ	N518BJA
40507	TQ	N507BJA	**40511**	TQ	N511BJA	**40515**	TQ	N515BJA	**40519**	ME	N519BJA
40508	EX	N508BJA	**40512**	EX	N512BJA	**40516**	TQ	N516BJA	**40520**	ME	N520BJA
40509	TQ	N509BJA	**40513**	TQ	N513BJA	**40517**	TQ	N517BJA			

40525	SY	J217XKY	Mercedes-Benz 709D	Alexander Sprint	B25F	1993
40529	WSu	L577NSB	Mercedes-Benz 709D	Dormobile Routemaker	B21FL	1993	Arran Coaches, 1994
40530	KK	N446TOS	Mercedes-Benz 709D	Alexander Sprint	B29F	1996	Shuttle Buses, Kilwinning,

40534-40560

		Mercedes-Benz 709D			Alexander Sprint			B25F		1994					
40534	IS	L334FWO	**40541**	BR	L341FWO	**40548**	MR	M348JBO	**40555**	CN	M355JBO
40535	IS	L335FWO	**40542**	PHu	L342FWO	**40549**	EH	M349JBO	**40556**	CN	M356JBO
40536	IS	L336FWO	**40543**	CN	L343FWO	**40550**	EH	M350JBO	**40557**	CN	M357JBO
40537	CN	L337FWO	**40544**	CN	M344JBO	**40551**	EH	M351JBO	**40558**	CN	M358JBO
40538	CN	L338FWO	**40545**	TQ	M345JBO	**40552**	EHu	M352JBO	**40559**	CN	M359JBO
40539	CN	L339FWO	**40546**	CW	M346JBO	**40553**	EH	M353JBO	**40560**	TQ	M360JBO
40540	SOu	L340FWO	**40547**	CN	M347JBO	**40554**	EH	M354JBO			

40561-40571

		Mercedes-Benz 709D			Alexander Sprint			B25F		1995					
40561	MR	M361LAX	**40564**	MR	M364LAX	**40567**	BR	M367LAX	**40570**	BR	M370LAX
40562	MR	M362LAX	**40565**	MR	M365LAX	**40568**	BR	M368LAX	**40571**	BR	M371LAX
40563	MR	M363LAX	**40566**	CN	M366LAX	**40569**	CN	M369LAX			

New to Stagecoach South 40878, K878ODY is one the last of the batch remaining following its transfer to Lancashire. This view illustrates the nearside of the Mercedes-Benz 709D. *Bob Downham*

40572-40584

			Mercedes-Benz 709D			Alexander Sprint			B25F	1996		

40572	CN	N372PNY	40576	BR	N376PNY	40579	CN	N379PNY	40582	CN	N382PNY
40573	MR	N373PNY	40577	BR	N377PNY	40580	CN	N380PNY	40583	CN	N383PNY
40574	MR	N374PNY	40578	CN	N378PNY	40581	CN	N381PNY	40584	CN	N384PNY
40575	CN	N375PNY									

40585-40591

			Mercedes-Benz 709D			Alexander Sprint			BC25F	1993-94		

40585	BQ	L315JSA	40587	AL	M317RSO	40589	BQ	M319RSO	40591	AL	M321RSO
40586	AL	L316JSA	40588	CJ	M318RSO	40590	BQ	M320RSO			

40593	BJ	K320YKG	Mercedes-Benz 709D	Wright NimBus	B25F	1992
40594	AEw	K321YKG	Mercedes-Benz 709D	Wright NimBus	B25F	1992

40601-40665

			Mercedes-Benz 709D			Alexander Sprint			B25F	1996		

40601	KK	N601VSS	40618	CN	N618VSS	40634	KK	N634VSS	40650	LL	N650VSS
40602	AY	N602VSS	40619	KL	N619VSS	40635	KK	N635VSS	40651	KL	N651VSS
40603	DU	N603VSS	40620	SY	N620VSS	40636	BQ	N636VSS	40652	BA	N652VSS
40604	AY	N604VSS	40621	KK	N621VSS	40637	BQ	N637VSS	40653	OX	N653VSS
40605	AY	N605VSS	40622	SR	N622VSS	40638	AY	N638VSS	40654	RU	N654VSS
40606	AY	N606VSS	40623	DU	N623VSS	40639	GW	N639VSS	40655	SB	N655VSS
40607	AY	N607VSS	40624	AS	N624VSS	40640	BQ	N640VSS	40656	WY	N656VSS
40608	AY	N608VSS	40625	AS	N625VSS	40641	KL	N641VSS	40657	WY	N657VSS
40609	KK	N609VSS	40626	AS	N626VSS	40642	SS	N642VSS	40658	WY	N658VSS
40610	SR	N610VSS	40627	AS	N627VSS	40643	AE	N643VSS	40659	WY	N659VSS
40611	AS	N611VSS	40628	KK	N628VSS	40644	CTu	N644VSS	40660	HEu	N660VSS
40612	SR	N612VSS	40629	RO	N629VSS	40645	ME	N645VSS	40661	CR	N661VSS
40613	KL	N613VSS	40630	AA	N630VSS	40646	BA	N646VSS	40662	CA	N662VSS
40614	KL	N614VSS	40631	AA	N631VSS	40647	PR	N647VSS	40663	HEu	N663VSS
40615	KL	N615VSS	40632	AS	N632VSS	40648	PR	N648VSS	40664	HEu	N664VSS
40616	KL	N616VSS	40633	AA	N633VSS	40649	LL	N649VSS	40665	HEu	N665VSS
40617	KL	N617VSS									

40666-40678
Mercedes-Benz 709D   Alexander Sprint   BC25F   1990

| 40666 | MEw | G566PRM | 40670 | MEw | G570PRM | 40675 | MEw | G665PHH | 40678 | SLt | G578PRM |
| 40667 | MEw | G567PRM | 40671 | MEw | G571PRM | | | | | | |

40685-40703
Mercedes-Benz 709D   Alexander Sprint   B25F   1994

40685	TQ	L685CDD	40690	CR	L690CDD	40695	TQ	L695CDD	40699	TQ	M699EDD
40686	AT	L686CDD	40691	TQ	L691CDD	40696	TQ	L696CDD	40701	TQ	M701EDD
40687	AT	L687CDD	40692	TQ	L692CDD	40697	TQ	M697EDD	40702	TQ	M702EDD
40688	WG	L688CDD	40693	TQ	L693CDD	40698	TQ	M698EDD	40703	TQ	M703EDD
40689	WG	L689CDD	40694	TQ	L694CDD						

40704-40717
Mercedes-Benz 709D   Alexander Sprint   B25F*   1995   *40704 is BC25F

40704	TQ	M704JDG	40708	CN	M708JDG	40712	BR	M712FMR	40715	BR	M715FMR
40705	TQ	M705JDG	40709	CN	M709JDG	40713	CN	M713FMR	40716	EH	N716KAM
40706	TQ	M706JDG	40710	CN	M710JDG	40714	AE	M714FMR	40717	EH	N717KAM
40707	TQ	M707JDG	40711	EH	M711FMR						

40718-40735
Mercedes-Benz 709D   Alexander Sprint   B25F*   1996   *40731-5 are BC25F

40718	CTu	N718RDD	40723	CTu	N723RDD	40728	CT	N728RDD	40732	CT	N732RDD
40719	CTu	N719RDD	40724	CTu	N724RDD	40729	CT	N729RDD	40733	GRu	N733RDD
40720	SZ	N720RDD	40725	SZu	N725RDD	40730	CT	N730RDD	40734	GRu	N734RDD
40721	SZ	N721RDD	40726	SZ	N726RDD	40731	CT	N731RDD	40735	SZ	N735RDD
40722	SZ	N722RDD	40727	SZ	N727RDD						

40736-40751
Mercedes-Benz 709D   Alexander Sprint   B25F   1993

40736	WP	L736LWA	40740	WP	L740LWA	40744	MD	L744LWA	40749	CH	L749LWA
40737	WP	L737LWA	40741	WP	L741LWA	40745	MD	L745LWA	40750	CH	L750LWA
40738	WP	L738LWA	40742	WP	L742LWA	40746	CH	L746LWA	40751	CH	L751LHL
40739	WP	L739LWA	40743	WP	L743LWA	40748	MD	L748LWA			

40752-40761
Mercedes-Benz 709D   Alexander Sprint   B23F   1995

40752	CH	N752CKU	40755	CH	N755CKU	40758	CH	N758CKU	40760	CH	N760CKU
40753	CH	N753CKU	40756	CH	N756CKU	40759	CH	N759CKU	40761	CH	N761CKU
40754	CH	N754CKU	40757	CH	N757CKU						

40762-40776
Mercedes-Benz 709D   Alexander Sprint   B25F   1996

40762	CH	N762EWG	40767	GY	N767EWG	40771	GY	N771EWG	40774	MD	N774EWG
40763	CH	N763EWG	40768	GY	N768EWG	40772	MD	N772EWG	40775	MD	N775EWG
40764	CH	N764EWG	40769	GY	N769EWG	40773	MD	N773EWG	40776	MD	N776EWG
40765	CH	N765EWG	40770	GY	N770EWG						

40777-40781
Mercedes-Benz 709D   Alexander Sprint   B25F   1993

| 40777 | GY | L731LWA | 40779 | WP | L733LWA | 40780 | WP | L734LWA | 40781 | WP | L735LWA |
| 40778 | GY | L732LWA | | | | | | | | | |

40791-40800
Mercedes-Benz 709D   Alexander Sprint   B23F   1996

40791	DA	N341KKH	40794	SC	N344KKH	40797	CH	N347KKH	40799	CH	N349KKH
40792	SC	N342KKH	40795	BY	N345KKH	40798	HL	N348KKH	40800	WP	N350KKH
40793	SC	N343KKH	40796	DA	N346KKH						

40801-40804
Mercedes-Benz 709D   Alexander Sprint   B23F   1996

| 40801 | GY | P351NKH | 40802 | GY | P352NKH | 40803 | GY | P353NKH | 40804 | WP | P354NKH |

| 40806 | SSw | G976ARV | Mercedes-Benz 709D | Alexander Sprint | B23F | 1990 |

40810-40828
Mercedes-Benz 709D   Alexander Sprint   B25F   1993

40810	LL	K610UFR	40815	ME	K615UFR	40820	ME	K620UFR	40825	ME	K625UFR
40811	LL	K611UFR	40816	ME	K616UFR	40822	CE	K622UFR	40826	CE	K626UFR
40812	LL	K612UFR	40818	BA	K618UFR	40823	CE	K623UFR	40827	SY	K627UFR
40813	BA	K613UFR	40819	CY	K619UFR	40824	PR	K624UFR	40828	SY	K628UFR
40814	BA	K614UFR									

40829-40836   Mercedes-Benz 709D   Alexander Sprint   B25F   1993

40829	CY	L629BFV	40831	PR	L631BFV	40833	CY	L633BFV	40835	PR	L635BFV
40830	PR	L630BFV	40832	LL	L632BFV	40834	BA	L634BFV	40836	CY	L636BFV

40833	HEw	N746YVN	Mercedes-Benz 711D	Marshall C19	B27F	1995	Glossopdale, Dukinfield, 1999
40834	HEw	N748YVR	Mercedes-Benz 711D	Marshall C19	B27F	1995	Glossopdale, Dukinfield, 1999

40875-40878   Mercedes-Benz 709D   Alexander Sprint   B25F   1993

40875	CE	K875ODY	40876	CE	K876ODY	40877	ME	L877SDY	40878	CY	L878SDY

40881-40904   Mercedes-Benz 709D   Alexander Sprint   B23F*   1993-95   *seating varies

40881	LL	L881SDY	40887	LL	L887SDY	40893	SB	N193LPN	40899	WG	N199LPN
40882	BA	L882SDY	40888	LL	L188SDY	40894	WI	N194LPN	40901	AR	N201LPN
40883	BA	L883SDY	40889	LS	M889ECD	40895	CR	N195LPN	40902	AR	N202LPN
40884	CY	L884SDY	40890	WG	M890ECD	40896	WI	N196LPN	40903	CR	N203LPN
40885	BA	L885SDY	40891	SB	N191LPN	40897	CR	N197LPN	40904	CR	N204LPN
40886	BA	L886SDY	40892	ATu	N192LPN	40898	AD	N198LPN			

40905-40982   Mercedes-Benz 709D   Alexander Sprint   B25F*   1996   *40905-23 are B23F

40905	AT	N905NAP	40925	TH	N925NAP	40945	WG	N945NAP	40964	DO	N964NAP
40906	AT	N906NAP	40926	TH	N926NAP	40946	AS	N946NAP	40965	DO	N965NAP
40907	AT	N907NAP	40927	TH	N927NAP	40947	CA	N947NAP	40966	DO	N966NAP
40908	AT	N908NAP	40928	TH	N928NAP	40948	AS	N948NAP	40967	DO	N967NAP
40909	AT	N909NAP	40929	TH	N929NAP	40949	AS	N949NAP	40968	FO	N968NAP
40910	AT	N910NAP	40930	TH	N930NAP	40950	AS	N950NAP	40969	FO	N969NAP
40911	AT	N911NAP	40931	TH	N931NAP	40951	AS	N951NAP	40970	FO	N970NAP
40912	AT	N912NAP	40932	TH	N932NAP	40952	AS	N952NAP	40971	LS	N971NAP
40913	AT	N913NAP	40933	TH	N933NAP	40953	DO	N953NAP	40972	FO	N972NAP
40914	AT	N914NAP	40934	TH	N934NAP	40954	DO	N954NAP	40973	FO	N973NAP
40915	AR	N915NAP	40935	CA	N935NAP	40955	DO	N955NAP	40974	FO	N974NAP
40916	BEu	N916NAP	40936	CA	N936NAP	40956	DO	N956NAP	40975	FO	N975NAP
40917	CR	N917NAP	40937	CA	N937NAP	40957	DO	N957NAP	40976	FO	N976NAP
40918	CR	N918NAP	40938	CA	N938NAP	40958	FO	N958NAP	40977	TH	N977NAP
			40939	CA	N939NAP	40959	DO	N959NAP	40978	TQ	N978NAP
40920	AN	N920NAP	40940	CA	N940NAP	40960	DO	N960NAP	40979	EX	N979NAP
40921	AN	N921NAP	40941	CA	N941NAP	40961	DO	N961NAP	40980	TQ	N980NAP
40922	AN	N922NAP	40942	CA	N942NAP	40962	DO	N962NAP	40981	EX	N981NAP
40923	WG	N923NAP	40943	CA	N943NAP	40963	DO	N963NAP	40982	TQ	N982NAP
40924	AN	N924NAP	40944	LS	N944NAP						

40985	KK	M395KVR	Mercedes-Benz 709D	Alexander Sprint	B27F	1995	AA Buses, Ayr, 1997
40986	KK	M396KVR	Mercedes-Benz 709D	Alexander Sprint	B27F	1995	AA Buses, Ayr, 1997
40987	KK	M397KVR	Mercedes-Benz 709D	Alexander Sprint	B27F	1995	AA Buses, Ayr, 1997
40989	HEt	F409KOD	Mercedes-Benz 709D	Reeve Burgess Beaver	TV	1989	

40990-40998   Mercedes-Benz 709D   Alexander Sprint   B25F   1988

40990	CHw	E90YWB	40994	CHw	E94YWB	40995	CHw	E95YWB	40998	CHw	E98YWB
40991	CHw	E91YWB									

40999	CHw	H257THL	Mercedes-Benz 709D	Reeve Burgess Beaver	B25F	1991	
41150	PTu	M866LNY	Mercedes-Benz 711D	Plaxton Beaver	B27F	1995	
41151	CN	N151MTG	Mercedes-Benz 811D	UVG Wessex	B31F	1995	

41152-41160   Mercedes-Benz 711D   UVG CitiStar   B27F   1995   Rhondda, 1997

41152	GR	N152MTG	41155	PT	N155MTG	41157	PT	N157MTG	41159	GR	N159MTG
41153	GR	N153MTG	41156	PT	N156MTG	41158	GR	N158MTG	41160	PT	N160MTG
41154	PTu	N154MTG									

41161	GR	P161TDW	Mercedes-Benz 709D	Plaxton Beaver	B27F	1996	Rhondda, 1997
41162	PT	P162TDW	Mercedes-Benz 709D	Plaxton Beaver	B27F	1996	Rhondda, 1997

41163-41171 — Mercedes-Benz 711D — Plaxton Beaver — B27F — 1996 — Rhondda, 1997

41163	PT	P163TNY	41166	PT	P166TNY	41168	PT	P168TNY	41170	PT	P170TNY
41164	PT	P164TNY	41167	GR	P167TNY	41169	PT	P169TNY	41171	GR	P171TNY
41165	PT	P165TNY									

41163-41171   Mercedes-Benz 711D   Plaxton Beaver   B27F   1996   Rhondda, 1997

41163 PT P163TNY   41166 PT P166TNY   41168 PT P168TNY   41170 PT P170TNY
41164 PT P164TNY   41167 GR P167TNY   41169 PT P169TNY   41171 GR P171TNY
41165 PT P165TNY

41304-41324   Mercedes-Benz 811D   Wright NimBus   B33F   1992

41304 PH J304UKG   41311 GRu K311YKG   41317 BJ K317YKG   41323 CN K323YKG
41308 SZ K308YKG   41315 CN K315YKG   41322 CN K322YKG   41324 CN K324YKG
41309 CN K309YKG   41316 CN K316YKG

41326-41330   Mercedes-Benz 811D   Marshall C16   B33F   1993

41326 AE L326CHB   41330 SZ L330CHB

41401-41430   Mercedes-Benz 811D   Alexander Sprint   B31F   1995-96

41401 MR N401WVR   41409 MR N409WVR   41417 CN N417WVR   41424 AE N424WVR
41402 MR N402WVR   41410 MR N410WVR   41418 PT N418WVR   41425 CN N425WVR
41403 AE N403WVR   41411 MR N411WVR   41419 CN N419WVR   41426 PT N426WVR
41404 AE N404WVR   41412 CN N412WVR   41420 CN N420WVR   41427 PT N427WVR
41405 CN N405WVR   41413 CN N413WVR   41421 AE N421WVR   41428 PT N428WVR
41406 MR N406WVR   41414 CN N414WVR   41422 CN N422WVR   41429 CN N429WVR
41407 MR N407WVR   41415 CN N415WVR   41423 CN N423WVR   41430 CN N430WVR
41408 CN N408WVR   41416 CN N416WVR

41503-41518   Mercedes-Benz 811D   Wright NimBus   BC31F*   1991   *41503/5/6/13/7/8 are B31F

41503 RY H403MRW   41507 AN J407PRW   41512 BJ J412PRW   41516 RY J416PRW
41504 RU H404MRW   41509 PH J409PRW   41513 PH J413PRW   41517 PH J417PRW
41505 RU H405MRW   41510 OXu J410PRW   41515 WY J415PRW   41518 LE J418PRW
41506 RU H406MRW   41511 AN J411PRW

41520-41525   Mercedes-Benz 811D   Wright   B31F   1993

41520 RUu K420ARW   41522 OXu K422ARW   41523 WY K423ARW   41525 BB K425ARW
41521 LE K421ARW

41634 HEw M634FJF   Mercedes-Benz 811D   Marshall   B31F   1997   Glossopdale, Dukinfield, 1999

41713-41719   Mercedes-Benz 811D   Alexander Sprint   B31F   1992

41713 HL J213AET   41715 CH J215AET   41717 CH J217AET   41719 CH J219AET
41714 HL J214AET   41716 HL J216AET   41718 WP J218AET

41801	BJ	K801OMW	Mercedes-Benz 811D	Wright NimBus	B22FL	1993	
41802	GY	K802OMW	Mercedes-Benz 811D	Wright NimBus	B22FL	1993	
41803	SZ	L803XDG	Mercedes-Benz 811D	Marshall C16	B33F	1993	
41804	SZ	L804XDG	Mercedes-Benz 811D	Marshall C16	B33F	1993	
41805	SZ	L805XDG	Mercedes-Benz 811D	Marshall C16	B33F	1993	
41806	SZ	L806XDG	Mercedes-Benz 811D	Marshall C16	B33F	1993	
41950	PH	L550JFS	Mercedes-Benz 814D	Dormobile Routemaker	B33F	1993	John G Gordon, 1996
41981	CNt	E316HLO	Mercedes-Benz L307D	Pilcher Green	TV	1988	
41983	CXt	H838GLD	Mercedes-Benz 609D	North West Coach Sales	TV	1990	
41984	BDt	H839GLD	Mercedes-Benz 609D	North West Coach Sales	TV	1990	
41998	BDt	D560RCK	Mercedes-Benz L608D	Reeve Burgess	TV	1988	
42000	BA	R36LSO	Mercedes-Benz Vario O810	Plaxton Beaver 2	B27F	1997	

42001-42018   Mercedes-Benz Vario O810   Plaxton Beaver 2   B29F   1997

42001 PD R501YWC   42006 PD R506YWC   42011 PD R511YWC   42015 PD R515YWC
42002 CS R502YWC   42007 PD R507YWC   42012 PD R512YWC   42016 CS R516YWC
42003 CS R503YWC   42008 PD R508YWC   42013 CS R513YWC   42017 CS R517YWC
42004 CS R504YWC   42009 PD R509YWC   42014 CS R514YWC   42018 PD R518YWC
42005 PD R505YWC   42010 PD R510YWC

42090-42096   Mercedes-Benz Vario O814   Alexander ALX100   B29F   1998

42090 BA S190RAO   42092 BA S192RAO   42094 BA S194RAO   42096 BA S196RAO
42091 BA S191RAO   42093 BA S193RAO   42095 BA S195RAO

Turning into the Windermere rail interchange and displaying the nearside of the Alexander ALX100 is 42094, S194RAO. Stagecoach took just forty-one of the Alexander ALX100 bodied Vario minibuses, now to be found at Hull, Devon, Oxford and Barrow. The styling can be compared with the Plaxton product shown on the next page. *Bob Downham*

42101-42118

		Mercedes-Benz Vario O814			Alexander ALX100			B29F	1998	
42101	EX	R101NTA	42105	EX	R105NTA	42110	EX	R110NTA	42115	EX	R115NTA
42102	EX	R102NTA	42107	EX	R107NTA	42112	EX	R112NTA	42116	EX	R116NTA
42103	EX	R103NTA	42108	EX	R108NTA	42113	EX	R113NTA	42117	EX	S117JFJ
42104	EX	R104NTA	42109	EX	R109NTA	42114	EX	R114NTA	42118	EX	S118JFJ

42355-42358

		Mercedes-Benz Vario O814			Alexander ALX100			B29F	1998	
42355	HL	S355KEF	42356	HL	S356KEF	42357	HL	S357KEF	42358	HL	S358KEF

42371-42383

		Mercedes-Benz Vario O814			Alexander ALX100			B29F	1998	
42371	OX	S371DFC	42375	WY	S375DFC	42378	WY	S378DFC	42381	WY	S381DFC
42372	OX	S372DFC	42376	OX	S376DFC	42379	WY	S379DFC	42382	WY	S382DFC
42373	WY	S373DFC	42377	WY	S377DFC	42380	WY	S380DFC	42383	OX	S383DFC
42374	OX	S374DFC									

42530-42566

		Mercedes-Benz Vario O814			Plaxton Beaver 2			B27F	1997	
42530	HE	P530PNE	42539	CS	P539PNE	42548	CS	P548PNE	42557	CS	P557PNE
42531	HE	P531PNE	42540	CS	P540PNE	42549	CS	P549PNE	42558	CS	P558PNE
42532	HE	P532PNE	42541	HE	P541PNE	42550	GP	P550PNE	42559	CS	P559PNE
42533	CS	P533PNE	42542	CS	P542PNE	42551	GP	P551PNE	42562	GP	P562PNE
42534	CS	P534PNE	42543	CS	P543PNE	42552	GP	P552PNE	42563	GP	P563PNE
42535	CS	P535PNE	42544	CS	P544PNE	42553	GP	P553PNE	42564	GP	P564PNE
42536	CS	P536PNE	42545	CS	P545PNE	42554	CS	P554PNE	42565	GP	P565PNE
42537	CS	P537PNE	42546	CS	P546PNE	42556	CS	P556PNE	42566	GP	P566PNE
42538	CS	P538PNE	42547	CS	P547PNE						

42567	CS	R276CBU	Mercedes-Benz Vario O814	Plaxton Beaver 2	B31F	1998	Glossopdale, Dukinfield, 1999
42568	CS	R277CBU	Mercedes-Benz Vario O814	Plaxton Beaver 2	B31F	1998	Glossopdale, Dukinfield, 1999
42569	CS	R446YNF	Mercedes-Benz Vario O814	Plaxton Beaver 2	B31F	1997	Glossopdale, Dukinfield, 1999
42570	CS	R447YNF	Mercedes-Benz Vario O814	Plaxton Beaver 2	B31F	1997	Glossopdale, Dukinfield, 1999
42571	CS	R899AVM	Mercedes-Benz Vario O814	Plaxton Beaver 2	B27F	1997	Glossopdale, Dukinfield, 1999
42572	CS	R898AVM	Mercedes-Benz Vario O814	Plaxton Beaver 2	B27F	1997	Glossopdale, Dukinfield, 1999
42573	CS	R901AVM	Mercedes-Benz Vario O814	Plaxton Beaver 2	B27F	1997	Glossopdale, Dukinfield, 1999

The new numbering system progresses with 41xxx for the 8xx series of Mercedes-Benz mini buses and other sundry types with the Vario O814 in the 42xxx series. Pictured in Stockport is Plaxton Beaver 2 - bodied Vario 42570, R447YNF, which was acquired with the Glossopdale operation based in Dukinfield. Since rationalisation within TransBus, the Vario is now only bodied by Plaxton, the ALX100 being discontinued.
Mark Doggett

42576-42590

Mercedes-Benz Vario O814 — Plaxton Beaver 2 — B31F — 1999 — Phil Anslow, Pontypool, 2000

42576	CH	T56JKG	42582	CH	T582SKG	42585	MD	T585SKG	42588	BB	T588SKG
42577	MD	T57JKG	42583	MD	T583SKG	42586	LE	T586SKG	42589	CH	T589SKG
42578	CH	T58JKG	42584	MD	T584SKG	42587	CH	T587SKG	42590	MD	T590SKG
42579	CH	T38PTG								

42624	SMu	R624LTX	Mercedes-Benz Vario O814	UVG CitiStar	B29F	1997
42670	PR	R670LFV	Mercedes-Benz Vario O814	Plaxton Beaver 2	B27F	1997
42672	PR	R672LFV	Mercedes-Benz Vario O814	Plaxton Beaver 2	B27F	1997

46300-46314

Iveco TurboDaily 59.12 — Mellor Duet — B21D — 1994 — 46313 is a staff shuttle

46300	EX	L929CTT	46304	EX	L933CTT	46308	EX	L937CTT	46312	EX	L941CTT
46301	EX	L930CTT	46305	EX	L934CTT	46309	EX	L938CTT	46313	TQu	L942CTT
46302	EX	L931CTT	46306	EX	L935CTT	46310	EX	L939CTT	46314	EX	L943CTT
46303	EX	L932CTT	46307	EX	L936CTT	46311	EX	L940CTT			

46315-46333

Iveco TurboDaily 59.12 — WS Wessex II — B21D — 1994

46315	EX	M638HDV	46320	EH	M629HDV	46325	EH	M626HDV	46330	EH	M622HDV
46316	EX	M640HDV	46321	EX	M624HDV	46326	EH	M192HTT	46331	EX	M194HTT
46317	EX	M637HDV	46322	EH	M623HDV	46327	EH	M630HDV	46332	EX	M191HTT
46318	EX	M636HDV	46323	EH	M625HDV	46328	EH	M193HTT	46333	EX	M641HDV
46319	EX	M639HDV	46324	EH	M628HDV	46329	EX	M627HDV			

46335-46363

Iveco TurboDaily 59.12 — Mellor Duet — B29F — 1993

46335	TQw	K711UTT	46339	TQw	K719UTT	46344	TQw	K725UTT	46363	TQw	K816WFJ

46365-46377

Iveco TurboDaily 59.12 — Marshall C31 — B29F — 1994

46365	TQ	L193FDV	46369	TQ	L201FDV	46372	TQ	L208FDV	46375	TQ	L211FDV
46366	TQ	L194FDV	46370	TQ	L203FDV	46373	TQ	L209FDV	46376	TQ	L212FDV
46367	TQ	L195FDV	46371	TQ	L204FDV	46374	TQ	L210FDV	46377	TQ	L214FDV
46368	TQ	L197FDV								

No, not a tram, but an Optare Solo seen running along Fleetwood's Lord Street, Now an outstation to Preston, Fleetwood had a peak vehicle requirement of thirty-three in December 2002, and this included the majority of the Optare Solo buses running with Stagecoach in Lancashire. Lettered for route F4 is 47023, PO51WLP, an example soon to be replicated for the bus modeller. *Bob Downham*

46378	TQ	N182CMJ	Iveco TurboDaily 59.12	Alexander AM	B29F	1996	
46379	TQ	N183CMJ	Iveco TurboDaily 59.12	Alexander AM	B29F	1996	
46381	TQ	N190GFR	Iveco TurboDaily 59.12	Mellor	B27F	1996	
46382	TQ	N463HRN	Iveco TurboDaily 59.12	Mellor	B27F	1996	
46383	TQ	K171CAV	Iveco TurboDaily 59.12	Marshall C31	B25F	1992	
46385	TQ	K173CAV	Iveco TurboDaily 59.12	Marshall C31	B25F	1992	
46386	TQ	L950EOD	Iveco TurboDaily 59-12	Mellor Duet	B26D	1993	
46388	TQ	L318BOD	Iveco TurboDaily 59-12	Mellor Duet	B26D	1993	
46389	TQ	L945EOD	Iveco TurboDaily 59-12	Mellor Duet	B26D	1994	
46390	TQw	K718UTT	Iveco TurboDaily 59-12	Mellor Duet	B29F	1993	
46391	TQw	L947EOD	Iveco TurboDaily 59-12	Mellor Duet	B26D	1994	
46392	TQ	L948EOD	Iveco TurboDaily 59-12	Mellor Duet	B26D	1994	
46393	TQ	L949EOD	Iveco TurboDaily 59-12	Mellor Duet	B26D	1994	
46396	TQ	N189GFR	Iveco TurboDaily 59.12	Mellor	B27F	1996	
46398	TQ	N188GFR	Iveco TurboDaily 59.12	Mellor	B27F	1996	
46399	TQ	N464HRN	Iveco TurboDaily 59.12	Mellor	B27F	1996	

46602-46612			Iveco Daily 49.10		Mellor		B17F	1997	46612 is a mobile control room 46602/3/4/8/9/ are ancillary

46602	LLu	R602KDD		46606	SNu	R606KDD		46608	TQu	R608KDD	46610 CTu R610KDD
46603	PRu	R603KDD		46607	SZu	R607KDD		46609	TQu	R609KDD	46612 PMu R612KDD
46604	TQu	R604KDD									

47001-47015			Optare Solo M850		Optare		N26F	2001

47001	LE	KX51CRU	47005	LE	KX51CSO	47009	LE	KX51CSZ	47013	LE	KX51CTO
47002	LE	KX51CRV	47006	LE	KX51CSU	47010	LE	KX51CTE	47014	LE	KX51CTU
47003	LE	KX51CRZ	47007	LE	KX51CSV	47011	LE	KX51CTF	47015	LE	KX51CYV
47004	LE	KX51CSF	47008	LE	KX51CSY	47012	LE	KX51CTK			

Another depot to deploy Optare Solo buses is Leamington Spa where fifteen are used on town services. Seen in the Spa town is 47014, KX51CTU. *Richard Godfrey*

47016-47024

			Optare Solo M850		Optare			N27F	2001	
47016	PR	PO51WLF	**47019**	PR	PO51WLJ	**47021**	PR	PO51WLL	**47023**	PR	PO51WLP
47017	PR	PO51WLG	**47020**	PR	PO51WLK	**47022**	PR	PO51WLN	**47024**	PR	PO51WLR
47018	PR	PO51WLH									

47025	HP	YL02FKY	Optare Solo M850	Optare	N27F	2002	
47026	NU	YG52DHM	Optare Solo M850	Optare	N27F	2002	On loan from Warwickshire CC
47027	NU	YG52DFY	Optare Solo M850	Optare	N27F	2002	On loan from Warwickshire CC
47028	NU	YG52DFZ	Optare Solo M850	Optare	N27F	2002	On loan from Warwickshire CC

47801-47804

			Optare Alero		Optare			N12F	2002	
47801	AR	YR02YRY	**47802**	AR	YR02YTA	**47803**	SY	YU02GRK	**47804**	SY	YU02GRX

47900	CB	GAZ4381	Optare MetroRider MR17 (CNG)	Optare	B29F	1999	
47901	CBu	GAZ4382	Optare MetroRider MR17 (CNG)	Optare	B29F	1999	
47924	AEw	K184YDW	Optare MetroRider MR01	Optare	B31F	1992	Cardiff Buses, 2001
47927	MRw	K187YDW	Optare MetroRider MR01	Optare	B31F	1992	Cardiff Buses, 2001
47972	CBw	K972HUB	Optare MetroRider	Optare	B29F	1993	
47975	PE	M975WWR	Optare MetroRider	Optare	B29F	1995	
47976	PEu	M976WWR	Optare MetroRider	Optare	B29F	1995	
47977	PE	M977WWR	Optare MetroRider	Optare	B29F	1995	
47978	PE	M978WWR	Optare MetroRider	Optare	B29F	1995	
47979	PE	M959VWY	Optare MetroRider	Optare	B29F	1995	
47988	PE	M808WWR	Optare MetroRider	Optare	B29F	1995	
47989	PE	M809WWR	Optare MetroRider	Optare	B29F	1995	
47990	CB	M810WWR	Optare MetroRider	Optare	B29F	1995	

48001	CEt	A247GAO	Dodge Commando G13	Reeve Burgess	TV	1983	MoD, 1999 (30KB44)
48002	CNw	B101ETX	Dodge Commando G13	Wadham Stringer Vanguard	TV	1984	MoD, 1999 (99KM47)
48003	CNw	B109ETX	Dodge Commando G13	Wadham Stringer Vanguard	TV	1984	MoD, 1999 ( )
48007	SYt	B916JVK	Dodge Commando G13	Wadham Stringer Vanguard	TV	1984	MoD, 1997 (31KF09)
48009	SEt	C168BNX	Dodge Commando G13	Wadham Stringer Vanguard	TV	1985	MoD, 1996 ( )
48010	KGt	C249UNV	Dodge Commando G13	Wadham Stringer Vanguard	TV	1986	MoD, 1998 (31KC84)

48011	CBt	C307KER	Dodge Commando G13	Wadham Stringer Vanguard	TV	1985	MoD, 1998, (81KC85)
48012	CXt	C508UNV	Dodge Commando G13	Wadham Stringer Vanguard	TV	1985	MoD, 1998 ( )
48013	SCt	C918AHN	Dodge Commando G13	Wadham Stringer Vanguard	TV	1985	MoD, 1998 (31KC55)
48014	xx	RBZ4245	Dodge Commando G13	Wadham Stringer Vanguard	TV	1985	MoD, 1999 ( )
48015	PRt	RBZ5459	Dodge Commando G13	Wadham Stringer Vanguard	TV	1985	MoD, 1999 (C973KWL)
48016	xx	HBZ5492	Dodge Commando G13	Wadham Stringer Vanguard	TV	1985	MoD, 2000 ( )
48017	KLt	RIL5085	Dodge Commando G13	Wadham Stringer Vanguard	TV	1985	MoD, 2000 (31KC17)
48018	xx	XSU906	Dodge Commando G13	Wadham Stringer Vanguard	TV	1905	MnD, 1999 ( )
48020	HLt	D155HHN	Dodge Commando G13	Wadham Stringer Vanguard	TV	1986	MoD, 1998 ( )
48021	SCt	D216HHN	Dodge Commando G13	Wadham Stringer Vanguard	TV	1986	MoD, 1998 (81KF09)
48022	SCt	D157HHN	Dodge Commando G13	Wadham Stringer Vanguard	TV	1986	MoD, 1998 (80KF95)
48023	WGt	D235MEA	Dodge Commando G13	Wadham Stringer Vanguard	TV	1986	MoD, 1996 ( )
48024	WPt	D240SNC	Dodge Commando G13	Wadham Stringer Vanguard	TV	1987	MoD, 1998 (92KF94)
48025	xx	D241MEA	Dodge Commando G13	Wadham Stringer Vanguard	TV	1986	MoD, 1996 ( )
48026	SYt	D298YTY	Dodge Commando G13	Wadham Stringer Vanguard	TV	1987	MoD, 1997 (81KF23)
48027	BYt	D305YTY	Dodge Commando G13	Wadham Stringer Vanguard	TV	1986	MoD, 1997 (80KF36)
48028	CNw	D34PAX	Dodge Commando G13	Wadham Stringer Vanguard	TV	1986	MoD, 1999 ( )
48029	CYt	D375DCK	Dodge Commando G13	Reeve Burgess	TV	1987	MoD, 2000 (80KF50)
48030	RUt	D39FBD	Dodge Commando G13	Wadham Stringer Vanguard	TV	1987	MoD, 2001 ( )
48033	HEt	D431SNC	Dodge Commando G13	Wadham Stringer Vanguard	TV	1986	MoD, 2000 (80KF93)
48034	PEt	D443GAV	Dodge Commando G13	Wadham Stringer Vanguard	TV	1987	MoD, 1998, (81KF04)
48035	xx	D452UGB	Dodge Commando G13	Wadham Stringer Vanguard	TV	1986	MoD, 1999 (80KF72)
48036	RUt	D467SNC	Dodge Commando G13	Wadham Stringer Vanguard	TV	1987	MoD, 1999 ( )
48037	HEw	D474SNC	Dodge Commando G13	Wadham Stringer Vanguard	TV	1986	MoD, 2000 (80KF32)
48038	HEt	D475SNC	Dodge Commando G13	Wadham Stringer Vanguard	TV	1986	MoD, 2000 (80KF26)
48039	CEt	D513XAO	Dodge Commando G13	Wadham Stringer Vanguard	TV	1986	MoD, 1999 (80KF60)
48040	CBt	D595GAV	Dodge Commando G13	Wadham Stringer Vanguard	TV	1987	MoD, 2000, (80KF23)
48041	CBt	D601GAV	Dodge Commando G13	Wadham Stringer Vanguard	TV	1987	MoD, 2000, (80KF29)
48042	ATt	D676GDC	Dodge Commando G13	Wadham Stringer Vanguard	TV	1986	MoD, 2001 ( )
48043	BDt	D692ENV	Dodge Commando G13	Wadham Stringer Vanguard	TV	1987	MoD, 1998 ( )
48044	LEt	D765ENV	Dodge Commando G13	Wadham Stringer Vanguard	TV	1987	MoD, 1999 (93KF06)
48045	NNt	D780ENV	Dodge Commando G13	Wadham Stringer Vanguard	TV	1987	MoD, 2000 ( )
48046	CTt	D891DWP	Dodge Commando G13	Wadham Stringer Vanguard	TV	1987	MoD, 2000 (93KF07)
48047	SUt	D918KPT	Dodge Commando G13	Wadham Stringer Vanguard	TV	1986	MoD, 1997 (80KF58)
48048	MDt	D932TWE	Dodge Commando G13	Wadham Stringer Vanguard	TV	1987	MoD, 1998 (93KF03)
48049	WPt	D933TWE	Dodge Commando G13	Wadham Stringer Vanguard	TV	1986	MoD, 1998 (81KF14)
48050	OXt	D935TJO	Dodge Commando G13	Wadham Stringer Vanguard	TV	1987	MoD, 2000 (92KF96)
48051	GYt	D935TWE	Dodge Commando G13	Wadham Stringer Vanguard	TV	1986	MoD, 1998 (80KF72)
48052	CHt	D953TWE	Dodge Commando G13	Wadham Stringer Vanguard	TV	1986	MoD, 1998 (80KF72)
48053	CTt	HIL8410	Dodge Commando G13	Wadham Stringer Vanguard	TV	1986	MoD, 2000 (81KF02)
48054	NUt	4828VC	Dodge Commando G13	Wadham Stringer Vanguard	TV	1986	MoD, 1999 (80KF81)
48055	HEt	D56SNE	Dodge Commando G13	Wadham Stringer Vanguard	TV	1986	MoD, 1998 (80KF54)
48056	CHt	E250AKU	Dodge Commando G13	Wadham Stringer Vanguard	TV	1987	MoD, 1998 (93KF53)
48057	HEw	E260CVR	Dodge Commando G13	Wadham Stringer Vanguard	TV	1986	MoD, 2000 (93KF86)
48058	HEw	E269CVR	Dodge Commando G13	Wadham Stringer Vanguard	TV	1986	MoD, 2000 (80KF76)
48059	HEw	E293PDC	Dodge Commando G13	Wadham Stringer Vanguard	TV	1987	MoD, 1998 (93KF69)
48060	ANt	E301FSO	Dodge Commando G13	Reeve Burgess	TV	1988	USAF, 1999 (88B9957)
48061	NNt	E32RNV	Dodge Commando G13	Wadham Stringer Vanguard	TV	1988	MoD, 1998 (31KC49)
48062	BDt	E36RRP	Dodge Commando G13	Wadham Stringer Vanguard	TV	1988	MoD, 2000 ( )
48063	BBt	E685FTM	Dodge Commando G13	Wadham Stringer Vanguard	TV	1988	MoD, 1999 ( )
48064	CHt	E800ERR	Dodge Commando G13	Wadham Stringer Vanguard	TV	1987	MoD, 1996 ( )
48065	SSt	E875GRG	Dodge Commando G13	Wadham Stringer Vanguard	TV	1988	MoD, 2001 ( )
48066	LLt	RUT842	Dodge Commando G13	Wadham Stringer Vanguard	TV	1987	MoD, 2000 (94KF00)
48067	BAt	VLF578	Dodge Commando G13	Wadham Stringer Vanguard	TV	1987	MoD, 2000 (93KF81)
48068	ARt	E920HCD	Dodge Commando G13	Wadham Stringer Vanguard	TV	1987	MoD, 2000 (?, E789CHS)
48069	HEt	E968CVM	Dodge Commando G13	Wadham Stringer Vanguard	TV	1987	MoD, 1998 (93KF41)
48070	HEt	D41SNE	Dodge Commando G13	Wadham Stringer Vanguard	TV	1987	MoD, 1998 (80KF70)
48072	ANt	F187LSA	Dodge Commando G13	Reeve Burgess	TV	1988	USAF, 1999 (88B9946)
48074	PRt	F344ECK	Dodge Commando G13	Wadham Stringer Vanguard	TV	1989	MoD, 2000 (93KF72)
48076	ESt	F481DMS	Dodge Commando G13	Reeve Burgess	TV	1989	USAF, 1999 (88B9954)
48077	NUt	G313BJO	Dodge Commando G13	Wadham Stringer Vanguard	TV	1989	MoD, 2000 ( )
48078	SUt	G675XTN	Dodge Commando G13	Wadham Stringer Vanguard	TV	1990	USAF, 2000 (90B2063)
48079	SSt	G736XTN	Dodge Commando G13	Reeve Burgess	TV	1990	MoD, 2001 ( )
48080	EXt	G806YTA	Dodge Commando G13	Wadham Stringer Vanguard	TV	1989	USAF, 1999 (90B2051)
48081	EXt	G818YTA	Dodge Commando G13	Wadham Stringer Vanguard	TV	1989	USAF, 1999 (90B2040)
48082	EXt	G847LNP	Dodge Commando G13	Wadham Stringer Vanguard	TV	1990	USAF, 2000 (90B2044)
48083	GRt	HIL6075	Dodge Commando G13	Wadham Stringer Vanguard	TV	1989	USAF, 2000 (90B2068)
48201	SY	GJ02LVT	Renault Trafic	Rohill	M15	2002	
48202	SY	GJ02LVU	Renault Trafic	Rohill	M15	2002	

The new numbering system places all the coaches in the 5xxxx series with 50xxx itself being double-deck coaches; 51xxx articulated coaches and 52xxx the ubiquitous Volvo B10M. New arrivals are the first B12s and these start the 53xxx series. Pictured in London's Park Lane is Oxford Tube's T40UBE, now numbered 50040. *Richard Godfrey*

50034-50066

MAN 24.350 HOCL -R   Jonckheere Monaco   C53/15DT   1999-2000

50034	OX	T34DFC	**50041**	OX	T41BBW	**50048**	OX	T48BBW	**50055**	OX	T55UBE
50035	OX	T35DFC	**50042**	OX	T42BBW	**50049**	OX	T49BBW	**50056**	OX	T56BBW
50036	OX	T36DFC	**50043**	OX	T43BBW	**50050**	OX	T50UBE	**50057**	OX	T57BBW
50037	OX	T37BBW	**50044**	OX	T44UBE	**50051**	OX	T51BBW	**50058**	OX	T58BBW
50038	OX	T38BBW	**50045**	OX	T45BBW	**50052**	OX	T52BBW	**50059**	OX	T59BBW
50039	OX	T39BBW	**50046**	OX	T46BBW	**50053**	OX	T53BBW	**50060**	OX	T60UBE
50040	OX	T40UBE	**50047**	OX	T47BBW	**50054**	OX	T54BBW	**50066**	OX	W66BBW

51061	AY	YSV730	Volvo B10MA-55	Jonckheere Mistral 35	AC72F	1996
51062	AY	VCS391	Volvo B10MA-55	Jonckheere Mistral 35	AC72F	1996
51063	WSu	P563MSX	Volvo B10MA-55	Plaxton Première Interurban	AC71F	1996
51064	WSu	P564MSX	Volvo B10MA-55	Plaxton Première Interurban	AC71F	1996
51070	AY	WLT720	Volvo B10MA-55	Plaxton Première Interurban	AC71F	1996
51071	AY	UIB3543	Volvo B10MA-55	Plaxton Première Interurban	AC71F	1996
51073	CC	495FFJ	Volvo B10MA-55	Plaxton Première Interurban	AC71F	1996
51074	CC	VLT37	Volvo B10MA-55	Plaxton Première Interurban	AC71F	1996
51075	CC	896HOD	Volvo B10MA-55	Plaxton Première Interurban	AC71F	1996
51076	CC	MSU466	Volvo B10MA-55	Plaxton Première Interurban	AC71F	1996
51092	AS	T640KCS	Volvo B10MA-55	Jonckheere Modulo	AC72F	1999
51093	AS	T641KCS	Volvo B10MA-55	Jonckheere Modulo	AC72F	1999
51094	AS	T642KCS	Volvo B10MA-55	Jonckheere Modulo	AC72F	1999
51095	CC	T95JHN	Volvo B10MA-55	Jonckheere Modulo	AC72F	1999
51096	HLu	T96JHN	Volvo B10MA-55	Jonckheere Modulo	AC72F	1999
51097	CC	T97JHN	Volvo B10MA-55	Jonckheere Modulo	AC72F	1999
51098	AY	WLT978	Volvo B10MA-55	Plaxton Première Interurban	AC71F	1996
51099	AY	WLT809	Volvo B10MA-55	Plaxton Première Interurban	AC71F	1996

As we go to press the final articulated coaches in England are being exchanged with vehicles at West Scotland. Seen at work in Glasgow is 51071, UIB3543, a Volvo B10MA with Plaxton Première Interurban bodywork. The chassis chosen by Stagecoach for these vehicles incorporates a trailing rear unlike most articulated buses where the traction is provided to the axle on the trailer section. *Mark Doggett*

52001	KL	OIW5804	Volvo B10M-61	Van Hool Alizée	C53F	1983	Arriva (Heysham Travel), 2000
52002	ME	VKB708	Volvo B10M-61	Van Hool Alizée	C53F	1985	Arriva (Heysham Travel), 2000
52004	KYt	C330DND	Volvo B10M-61	Van Hool Alizée	TV	1986	Hardie's Coaches, 1994
52005	GY	PSU443	Volvo B10M-61	Van Hool Alizée	C53F	1986	Shearings, 1991
52006	ANt	D548MVR	Volvo B10M-61	Van Hool Alizée	C53F	1987	Shearings, 1991
52007	GY	PSU764	Volvo B10M-61	Van Hool Alizée	C53F	1987	Shearings, 1991
52008	GY	PS2743	Volvo B10M-61	Van Hool Alizée	C53F	1987	Shearings, 1991
52009	GY	D551MVR	Volvo B10M-61	Van Hool Alizée	C53F	1987	Shearings, 1991
52010	GY	SKY32Y	Volvo B10M-61	Van Hool Alizée	C53F	1987	Shearings, 1991
52011	BQt	D553MVR	Volvo B10M-61	Van Hool Alizée	C53F	1987	Shearings, 1991
52013	DEt	E644UNE	Volvo B10M-61	Van Hool Alizée	TV	1988	

52020-52024   Volvo B10M-62   Jonckheere Deauville 45   C49FT   1994

52020	LEu	498FYB	52022	NS	WLT890	52023	NS	630DYE	52024	KG	L159LBW
52021	BD	L156LBW									

52026-52030   Volvo B10M-62   Berkhof Excellence 1000LD   C51FT   1995

52026	SR	M103XBW	52027	AL	NSU133	52029	AN	LSK545	52030	AL	GSU341

52031-52038   Volvo B10M-62   Berkhof Excellence 1000LD   C51FT   1996

52031	LEu	WSU293	52033	BD	3063VC	52036	BD	9737VC	52038	PH	MSU463
52032	BD	6253VC	52035	BD	9258VC	52037	NUu	4012VC			

52051	GY	IIL1321	Volvo B10M-61	Plaxton Paramount 3200 III	C51FT	1987	
52056	KL	YDG616	Volvo B10M-61	Plaxton Paramount 3500 III	C48FT	1987	
52057	KL	JPU817	Volvo B10M-61	Plaxton Paramount 3500 III	C53F	1987	
52058	SR	283URB	Volvo B10M-60	Plaxton Paramount 3500 III	C53F	1987	
52059	CNt	HSV196	Volvo B10M-61	Plaxton Paramount 3500 III	TV	1988	

Pictured in Inverness, Interurban 52312, N582XSA is seen in the latest Stageocach Express styling. Sixty-seven Volvo B10Ms are allocated to suburban work in the Bluebird part of the East Scotland where the vehicles cover many kilometres between towns. *Murdoch Currie*

52061-52065

52061-52065		Volvo B10M-61		Plaxton Paramount 3200 III	C53F	1988		
52061	LLu	E131ORP	**52063**	CE	E133ORP	**52064**	CE	E134ORP	**52065**	LLu	E135ORP
52062	LLu	E132ORP						

52067	BQ	BSK744	Volvo B10M-61	Plaxton Paramount 3200 III	C57F	1988	Gray, Fochabers, 1996
52069	KKt	WLT416	Volvo B10M-60	Plaxton Paramount 3500 III	TV	1989	
52070	LLu	IIL3507	Volvo B10M-60	Plaxton Paramount 3500 III	C51F	1989	
52071	EXt	HSV195	Volvo B10M-61	Plaxton Paramount 3500 III	TV	1988	
52072	CE	WLT980	Volvo B10M-61	Plaxton Paramount 3500 II	C48F	1988	
52073	BJ	G344FFX	Volvo B10M-60	Plaxton Expressliner	C53F	1990	
52075	LLu	VLT104	Volvo B10M-60	Plaxton Expressliner	C53F	1990	
52076	KKt	G387PNV	Volvo B10M-60	Plaxton Expressliner	TV	1990	
52077	SEu	G520LWU	Volvo B10M-60	Plaxton Paramount 3500 III	C49FT	1990	
52078	GY	G525LWU	Volvo B10M-60	Plaxton Paramount 3500 III	C52F	1990	
52079	SR	WLT874	Volvo B10M-60	Plaxton Paramount 3500 III	C51F	1990	
52080	SR	VCS376	Volvo B10M-60	Plaxton Paramount 3500 III	C51F	1990	
52082	AN	G531LWU	Volvo B10M-60	Plaxton Paramount 3500 III	C51F	1990	
52084	SR	MIL4693	Volvo B10M-60	Plaxton Paramount 3500 III	C51F	1990	
52086	KKt	H149CVU	Volvo B10M-60	Plaxton Expressliner	TV	1990	
52087	PH	WLT830	Volvo B10M-60	Plaxton Expressliner	C53F	1990	
52088	KKt	YSV735	Volvo B10M-60	Plaxton Paramount 3500 III	C53F	1991	
52090	MRt	TSU638	Volvo B10M-61	Plaxton Paramount 3500 III	TV	1987	
52091	MD	H181EGU	Volvo B10M-60	Plaxton Paramount 3500 III	C49FT	1991	Wallace Arnold, 1995
52092	MD	H182EGU	Volvo B10M-60	Plaxton Paramount 3500 III	C49FT	1991	Wallace Arnold, 1995
52095	GY	J456FSR	Volvo B10M-60	Plaxton Paramount 3500 III	C51F	1991	
52096	SR	UWP105	Volvo B10M-61	Plaxton Paramount 3500 III	C53F	1991	
52097	SR	UM7681	Volvo B10M-61	Plaxton Paramount 3500 III	C53F	1991	
52098	LL	J120AHH	Volvo B10M-60	Plaxton Expressliner	C46FT	1991	
52099	LL	J121AHH	Volvo B10M-60	Plaxton Expressliner	C46FT	1991	
52103	FH	VLT54	Volvo B10M-60	Plaxton Premiére 350	C49FT	1992	
52104	FH	866NHT	Volvo B10M-62	Plaxton Premiére 350	C51FT	1995	

52106-52114 Volvo B10M-60 Plaxton Première 350 C48FT 1992 Wallace Arnold, 1994

52106	PR	J702CWT	52109	CB	ACZ7491	52111	ETw	ACZ7493	52113	ETt	TSU639
52107	ETw	ACZ7489	52110	CB	ACZ7492	52112	ETw	ACZ7494	52114	ETw	TSU640
52108	CB	ACZ7490									

52115	GY	927GTA	Volvo B10M-60	Plaxton Expressliner	C49FT	1992
52116	BJ	K758FYG	Volvo B10M-60	Plaxton Première 350	C50FT	1992
52117	BJ	K759FYG	Volvo B10M-60	Plaxton Première 350	C50FT	1992
52118	BJ	TSU641	Volvo B10M-60	Plaxton Première 350	C50FT	1992
52119	FH	TSU642	Volvo B10M-60	Plaxton Première 350	C50FT	1992

52120-52124 Volvo B10M-60 Plaxton Première Interurban BC51F 1993

| 52120 | BD | K150DNV | 52122 | BD | K152DNV | 52123 | PE | K153DNV | 52124 | PE | K154DNV |
| 52121 | BD | K151DNV | | | | | | | | | |

| 52130 | BQ | HSK760 | Volvo B10M-60 | Plaxton Expressliner 2 | C49FT | 1993 |

52131-52140 Volvo B10M-60 Plaxton Première Interurban BC51F 1993

52131	IS	TSV718	52134	FH	TSV721	52137	FH	127ASV	52139	FH	VLT272
52132	IS	TSV719	52135	PH	TSV722	52138	FH	128ASV	52140	FH	VLT245
52133	PR	TSV720	52136	FH	126ASV						

52141-52147 Volvo B10M-60 Plaxton Première Interurban BC53F 1993

| 52141 | DA | K571DFS | 52143 | HL | K573DFS | 52145 | WP | K575DFS | 52147 | HL | K577DFS |
| 52142 | BQ | K572DFS | 52144 | RO | K574DFS | 52146 | HL | K576DFS | | | |

52155-52162 Volvo B10M-60 Plaxton Première Interurban BC51F 1993

| 52155 | PE | L155JNH | 52157 | PE | L157JNH | 52159 | CB | L159JNH | 52161 | NN | L161JNH |
| 52156 | PE | L156JNH | 52158 | CB | L158JNH | 52160 | NN | L160JNH | 52162 | KG | L162JNH |

52168-52177 Volvo B10M-60 Plaxton Première Interurban BC51F 1993

52168	IS	VLT154	52171	IS	UOT648	52174	FH	WLT526	52176	AN	XRC487
52169	FH	GSU950	52172	CB	L582JSA	52175	IS	NSU132	52177	AN	ESU435
52170	FH	L580JSA	52173	CJ	WLT415						

52178-52190 Volvo B10M-60 Plaxton Première Interurban BC51F 1993

52178	GS	L578HSG	52182	CN	L582HSG	52185	DE	L585HSG	52188	KY	L588JSA
52179	CB	L579HSG	52183	SA	L583HSG	52186	BR	L586HSG	52189	CB	L589JSA
52180	BR	L580HSG	52184	SA	L584HSG	52187	DE	L587HSG	52190	CB	L590JSA
52181	PT	L581HSG									

52193	FH	BSK756	Volvo B10M-62	Plaxton Expressliner 2	C49F	1993
52194	ANt	NUF276	Volvo B10M-62	Plaxton Expressliner 2	TV	1993
52195	PR	L125NAO	Volvo B10M-62	Plaxton Expressliner 2	C46FT	1994
52196	PR	L126NAO	Volvo B10M-62	Plaxton Expressliner 2	C46FT	1994
52197	BEt	L127NAO	Volvo B10M-62	Plaxton Expressliner 2	TV	1994

52207-52213 Volvo B10M-62 Plaxton Première Interurban BC51F 1993

| 52207 | CH | L637LDT | 52209 | CH | L639LDT | 52211 | CH | L641LDT | 52213 | MD | L643LDT |
| 52208 | CH | L638LDT | 52210 | CH | L640LDT | 52212 | MD | L642LDT | | | |

52214-52220 Volvo B10M-62 Plaxton Première 350 C53F* 1995 *52220 convertible to C49FT

| 52214 | AN | M404BFG | 52216 | PN | M406BFG | 52218 | EX | CSU978 | 52220 | MR | M410BFG |
| 52215 | WWu | M405BFG | 52217 | NS | SYC52 | 52219 | NS | CSU992 | | | |

52227-52244 Volvo B10M-62 Plaxton Première Interurban BC51F 1994

52227	BQ	HSV194	52232	AN	CSU920	52237	BQ	M537RSO	52241	IS	M541RSO
52228	PH	TSV778	52233	FH	CSU921	52238	FH	M538RSO	52242	FH	M542RSO
52229	PH	TSV779	52234	BQ	CSU922	52239	PH	M539RSO	52243	IS	M543RSO
52230	AN	TSV780	52235	BQ	CSU923	52240	FH	M540RSO	52244	BQ	145CLT
52231	AN	TSV781	52236	BQ	M536RSO						

Interurban 52212, L642LDT, is seen leaving Chesterfield on service 747 to Manchester. The Interurban was built by Plaxton to Stagecoach requirements and differs considerably from the Premiere coach whose body shape it uses. The interior of the vehicle includes many features normally found only on buses, such as drivers screen and cash trays, while many of the coach features have been excluded. As such the type is treated as a bus with high-back seating. *Mark Doggett*

52245-52259

Volvo B10M-62   Plaxton Premiére Interurban   BC51F   1994

52245	DE	M945TSX	52249	GS	M949TSX	52253	GS	M953TSX	52257	MD	M940TOX
52246	DE	M946TSX	52250	GS	M950TSX	52254	KY	M954TSX	52258	KY	M944TSX
52247	DEw	M947TSX	52251	GS	M951TSX	52255	KY	M955TSX	52259	WP	M942TSX
52248	GS	M948TSX	52252	SA	M952TSX	52256	KY	M956TSX			

52260-52265

Volvo B10M-62   Plaxton Premiére Interurban   BC51F   1994

52260	DS	M160CCD	52262	AA	M162CCD	52264	AA	M164CCD	52266	EX	M166CCD
52261	CC	M161CCD	52263	RO	M163CCD	52265	EX	M165CCD			

52267	LL	M164SCK	Volvo B10M-62	Plaxton Expressliner 2	C46FT	1994
52268	PR	M165SCK	Volvo B10M-62	Plaxton Expressliner 2	C46FT	1994
52269	MD	M808JTY	Volvo B10M-62	Plaxton Expressliner 2	C44FT	1995

52271-52278

Volvo B10M-62   Plaxton Expressliner 2   C49FT   1994-95

52271	FH	M911WJK	52273	WWu	M913WJK	52275	WWu	M915WJK	52277	WWu	M917WJK
52272	AN	147YFM	52274	WWu	M914WJK	52276	WWu	M916WJK	52278	WWu	M918WJK

52281	PT	N91RVK	Volvo B10M-62	Plaxton Expressliner 2	C44FT	1996

52282-52294

Volvo B10M-62   Plaxton Premiére Interurban   BC51F   1996

52282	GW	N142XSA	52285	AS	N145XSA	52289	BQ	N149XSA	52292	IS	N152XSA
52283	DS	N143XSA	52287	AS	N247XSA	52290	BQ	N150XSA	52293	BQ	N153XSA
52284	DS	N144XSA	52288	AN	N148XSA	52291	IS	N151XSA	52294	BQ	N154XSA

52295-52302

Volvo B10M-62   Plaxton Expressliner 2   C49FT   1995

52295	KKu	N445XVA	52297	PR	N447XVA	52299	WWu	N449XVA	52301	PR	N451XVA
52296	KKu	N446XVA	52298	WWu	N448XVA	52300	WWu	N450XVA	52302	RU	N452XVA

52306-52310

Volvo B10M-62   Plaxton Expressliner 2   C44FT   1995

52306	CJ	DSV943	52308	RU	N618USS	52309	CJ	FSU739	52310	CJ	703DYE
52307	CJ	WLT447									

Unusual with Stagecoach is the arrival of a pre-used coaches. Here 52396, P281XYS, stands at Victoria bus station having worked a duplicate duty for National Express. The Volvo B10M carries a Plaxton Première 350 body and joined Stagecoach in 1998 from Crawfords of Neilston. It is normally found on the X94 service between Cheltenham and Gloucester. *Dave Heath*

52312	BQ	N582XSA	Volvo B10M-62			Plaxton Premiére Interurban		BC51F	1996		
52313	BQ	N583XSA	Volvo B10M-62			Plaxton Premiére Interurban		BC51F	1996		
52314	BQ	N584XSA	Volvo B10M-62			Plaxton Premiére Interurban		BC51F	1996		

52328-52332 — Volvo B10M-62 — Plaxton Expressliner 2 — C46FT — 1995

| 52328 | PR | N128VAO | **52330** | LL | N130VAO | **52331** | LL | N131VAO | **52332** | LL | N132VAO |
| 52329 | PR | N129VAO | | | | | | | | | |

52341-52346 — Volvo B10M-62 — Plaxton Premiére Interurban — BC51F — 1996

| 52341 | EX | P801XTA | **52343** | EX | P803XTA | **52345** | EX | P805XTA | **52346** | EX | P806XTA |
| 52342 | EX | P802XTA | **52344** | EX | P804XTA | | | | | | |

52348-52360 — Volvo B10M-62 — Plaxton Premiére Interurban — BC51F — 1996

52348	AS	P148ASA	**52352**	DE	P152ASA	**52355**	AY	P255ASA	**52358**	CC	P158ASA
52349	AS	P149ASA	**52353**	DE	P153ASA	**52356**	DE	P156ASA	**52359**	KK	13CLT
52350	AY	P150ASA	**52354**	KY	P154ASA	**52357**	HL	P157ASA	**52360**	KK	P160ASA
52351	HL	P151ASA									

52361-52367 — Volvo B10M-62 — Plaxton Premiére Interurban — BC51F — 1996

| 52361 | KY | P568MSX | **52365** | SA | P565MSX | **52366** | KY | P566MSX | **52367** | KY | P567MSX |
| 52362 | KY | P569MSX | | | | | | | | | |

52368-52373 — Volvo B10M-62 — Plaxton Premiére Interurban — BC51F — 1996

| 52368 | NN | P168KBD | **52370** | NN | P170KBD | **52372** | BD | P172KBD | **52373** | BD | P173KBD |
| 52369 | NN | P169KBD | **52371** | BD | P171KBD | | | | | | |

52378-52381 — Volvo B10M-62 — Plaxton Premiére Interurban — BC51F — 1996

| 52378 | HL | P178PRH | **52379** | HL | P179PRH | **52380** | KY | P180PRH | **52381** | HL | P181PRH |

Stagecoach provide several coaches in Flightlink colours for their National Express role. Pictured at Hanley bus station is Preston's 52268, M165SCK, which has an Expressliner II body. The Expressliner II was a similarly modified Plaxton coach to the initial Expressliner but based on the Premiere 350. *Cliff Beeton*

52382	PH	P622ESO	Volvo B10M-62	Plaxton Expressliner 2	C44FT	1997	
52385	PH	P625NSE	Volvo B10M-62	Plaxton Expressliner 2	C44FT	1997	
52386	PH	P626NSE	Volvo B10M-62	Plaxton Expressliner 2	C44FT	1997	
52387	PH	P627ESO	Volvo B10M-62	Plaxton Expressliner 2	C44FT	1997	
52392	CT	P92URG	Volvo B10M-62	Plaxton Expressliner 2	C44FT	1996	
52396	GR	P281XYS	Volvo B10M-62	Plaxton Première 350	C57F	1997	Crawford, Neilston, 1998

52397-52400   Volvo B10M-62   Plaxton Première Interurban   BC51F   1997

52397	CW	P107FRS	52398	CB	P108FRS	52399	CW	P109FRS	52400	GR	P110FRS

52401-52404   Volvo B10M-62   Plaxton Première Interurban   BC51F   1996

52401	CN	P771TTG	52402	CN	P772TTG	52403	CN	P773TTG	52404	CN	P774TTG

52405-52414   Volvo B10M-62   Plaxton Première Interurban   BC51F   1997

52405	PRu	P977UBV	52408	PR	P108DCW	52410	PR	P110DCW	52413	PR	P113DCW
52406	PR	P978UBV	52409	PR	P109DCW	52412	PR	P112DCW	52414	PR	P114DCW
52407	PR	P979UBV									

52415-52424   Volvo B10M-62   Plaxton Première Interurban   BC51F   1997

52415	CB	R115OPS	52418	GW	R118OPS	52421	AS	R121OPS	52423	DE	R113OPS
52416	GW	R116OPS	52419	KK	R119OPS	52422	DE	R112OPS	52424	KY	R114OPS
52417	BR	R117OPS	52420	KY	R120OPS						

52425	AS	R103LSO	Volvo B10M-62	Plaxton Première Interurban	BC51F	1997	
52426	AS	R104LSO	Volvo B10M-62	Plaxton Première Interurban	BC51F	1997	
52427	DS	R105LSO	Volvo B10M-62	Plaxton Première Interurban	BC51F	1997	

For the 1998 delivery of coaches Stagecoach chose products from the Belgium builder Jonckheere. For suburban express work the Modulo was selected while, for longer journeys, the Mistral 50 was the choice. Modulo S672RWJ, now numbered 52632, is pictured at Chesterfield while operating the Sheffield to Manchester service, prior to their recent transfer to Scotland in December 2002. *Mark Doggett*

52434-52439   Volvo B10M-62   Plaxton Expressliner 2   C46FT   1997

| 52434 | RU | R34AKV | 52436 | RU | R36AKV | 52438 | RU | R38AKV | 52439 | RU | R39AKV |
| 52435 | RU | R35AKV | 52437 | RU | R37AKV | | | | | | |

52440-52443   Volvo B10M-62   Plaxton Première Interurban   BC51F   1997

| 52439 | GS | R539GSF | 52441 | SA | R541GSF | 52442 | KY | R542GSF | 52443 | GS | R543GSF |

52444-52447   Volvo B10M-62   Plaxton Expressliner 2   C46FT   1997

| 52444 | RU | R454FCE | 52445 | PE | R455FCE | 52446 | PE | R456FCE | 52447 | RU | R453FCE |

52450-52454   Volvo B10M-62   Plaxton Expressliner 2   C49FT   1997

| 52450 | CT | R550JDF | 52452 | CT | R552JDF | 52453 | CT | R553JDF | 52454 | CT | R554JDF |
| 52451 | CT | R551JDF | | | | | | | | | |

52456-52458   Volvo B10M-62   Plaxton Première Interurban   BC51F   1997

| 52456 | KK | R636RSE | 52458 | KY | R638RSE | 52459 | KY | R639RSE | 52460 | DE | R640RSE |
| 52457 | KY | R637RSE | | | | | | | | | |

52462-52465   Volvo B10M-62   Plaxton Première Interurban   BC51F   1997

| 52462 | DS | R82SEF | 52463 | BQ | R83SEF | 52464 | AY | R84SEF | 52465 | CC | R85SEF |

52474-52486   Volvo B10M-62   Plaxton Première Interurban   BC51F   1996-97

52474	KG	R174DNH	52478	KG	R178DNH	52481	BD	R181DNH	52484	BD	R184DNH
52475	KG	R175DNH	52479	KG	R179DNH	52482	BD	R182DNH	52485	BD	R185DNH
52476	KG	R176DNH	52480	KG	R180DNH	52483	BD	R183DNH	52486	BD	R186DNH
52477	KG	R177DNH									

Most of the Jonckheere Mistral 50s are liveried for either National Express or Citylink duties. Pictured in Canterbury is 52655, V905DPN from Dover. As we go to press the 020 route is receiving ten new B12M coaches with the displaced coaches being transferred into south Wales where enhancements to the X3/X4 services with be implemented. *Richard Godfrey*

52490	PR	R120VFR	Volvo B10M-62	Jonckheere Mistral 50	C46FT	1998	
52491	CE	R791PAO	Volvo B10M-62	Plaxton Premiere Interurban	BC51F	1997	
52492	CE	R792PAO	Volvo B10M-62	Plaxton Premiere Interurban	BC51F	1997	
52493	MD	R663TKU	Volvo B10M-62	Plaxton Expressliner 2	C44FT	1997	
52494	MD	R664TKU	Volvo B10M-62	Plaxton Expressliner 2	C44FT	1997	

52495-52504

Volvo B10M-62   Plaxton Première Interurban   BC51F   1997

52495	BR	R775CDW	52499	BR	R779CDW	52501	BR	R781CDW	52503	BR	R783CDW
52496	BR	R776CDW	52500	BR	R780CDW	52502	BR	R782CDW	52504	BR	R784CDW
52498	BR	R778CDW									

52510	CC	S860VAT	Volvo B10M-62	Plaxton Première 320	C51F	1998	Plaxton demonstrator, 2002
52601	MD	S173SVK	Volvo B10M-62	Jonckheere Mistral 50	C44FT	1998	
52602	MD	S174SVK	Volvo B10M-62	Jonckheere Mistral 50	C44FT	1998	
52603	LL	S133KRM	Volvo B10M-62	Jonckheere Mistral 50	C44FT	1998	
52604	LL	S134KRM	Volvo B10M-62	Jonckheere Mistral 50	C44FT	1998	

52605-52612

Volvo B10M-62   Jonckheere Modulo   BC51F   1998

52605	BQ	S655JSE	52607	BQ	S657JSE	52609	FH	S659JSE	52611	BQ	S661JSE
52606	BQ	S656JSE	52608	FH	S658JSE	52610	BQ	S660JSE	52612	BQ	S662JSE

52613	PR	S269KHG	Volvo B10M-62	Jonckheere Modulo	BC51F	1998	
52614	PR	S270KHG	Volvo B10M-62	Jonckheere Modulo	BC51F	1998	
52615	PR	S905JHG	Volvo B10M-62	Jonckheere Mistral 50	C46FT	1998	
52616	PR	S906JHG	Volvo B10M-62	Jonckheere Mistral 50	C46FT	1998	

52617-52620

Volvo B10M-62   Jonckheere Mistral 50   C49FT   1988

52617	PE	S457BCE	52618	PE	S458BCE	52619	PE	S459BCE	52620	PE	S460BCE

52621	DO	S901CCD	Volvo B10M-62	Jonckheere Mistral 50	C49FT	1998	
52622	LL	S902CCD	Volvo B10M-62	Jonckheere Mistral 50	C49FT	1998	
52623	LL	S903CCD	Volvo B10M-62	Jonckheere Mistral 50	C49FT	1998	

The remaining Leyland Tiger coaches can be found in North West England and at Grimsby. Seen in Kendal on school duties is 59024, CKC624X, one of a pair with Duple Dominant express bodywork used primarily on such duties. It is seen heading out to Dungion Ghyll, a distance of some 32 kilometers. *Bob Downham*

52626-52633

Volvo B10M-62 — Jonckheere Modulo — BC51F — 1998

52626	LL	S796KRM	52628	LL	S798KRM	52630	MD	S670SDT	52632	CH	S672RWJ
52627	LL	S797KRM	52629	CE	S799KRM	52631	WP	S671SDT	52633	CH	S673RWJ

52635	MD	S665SDT	Volvo B10M-62	Jonckheere Mistral 50	C44FT	1998
52638	BQ	S808BTT	Volvo B10M-62	Jonckheere Modulo	BC51F	1998

52641-52649

Volvo B10M-62 — Jonckheere Mistral 50 — C44FT — 1999

52641	RU	T661OBD	52643	RU	T663OBD	52645	MD	KSU462	52648	MD	T668XTV
52642	RU	T662OBD	52644	MD	KSU461	52647	PH	T667XTV	52649	MD	T669XTV

52654-52659

Volvo B10M-62 — Jonckheere Mistral 50 — C49FT — 1999

52654	TH	V904DPN	52656	DO	V906DPN	52658	DO	V908DDY	52659	TH	V909DDY
52655	DO	V905DPN	52657	DO	V907DDY						

52666	AN	X676NSE	Volvo B10M-62	Jonckheere Mistral 50	C44FT	2001
52667	AN	X677NSE	Volvo B10M-62	Jonckheere Mistral 50	C44FT	2001
52668	AN	X678NSE	Volvo B10M-62	Jonckheere Mistral 50	C44FT	2001
52669	AN	X679NSE	Volvo B10M-62	Jonckheere Mistral 50	C44FT	2001

53001-53010

Volvo B12M — Plaxton Paragon Expressliner — C46FT — 2002

53001	DO	GU52WSX	53004	DO	GU52WTA	53007	DO	GU52WTE	53009	DO	GU52WTG
53002	DO	GU52WSY	53005	DO	GU52WTC	53008	DO	GU52WTF	53010	DO	GU52WTJ
53003	DO	GU52WSZ	53006	DO	GU52WTD						

Stagecoach own a collection of interesting vehicles mostly from operations that are now part of the group. More modern buses, such as Titan 10001 and Olympian prototype 14100 are candidates likely to join them in the future. Seen with the Bluebird motif, of which Stagecoach is now joint owner, 59922, BMS222 provides a spot of nostalgia. *Murdoch Currie*

59014	CE	PSU787	Leyland Tiger TRCTL11/3RZ	Duple Caribbean 2	C49FT	1986	
59015	ME	EKA215Y	Leyland Tiger TRCTL11/2R	Duple Dominant IV Express	C49F	1982	Arriva Heysham Travel, 2000
59020	ME	EKA220Y	Leyland Tiger TRCTL11/2R	Duple Dominant IV Express	C49F	1982	Arriva Heysham Travel, 2000
59024	KL	CKC624X	Leyland Tiger TRCTL11/2R	Duple Dominant IV Express	C49F	1982	Arriva Heysham Travel, 2000
59026	KL	CKC626X	Leyland Tiger TRCTL11/2R	Duple Dominant IV Express	C49F	1982	Arriva Heysham Travel, 2000
59035	GY	SKY31Y	Leyland Tiger TRCTL11/3R	Eastern Coach Works B51	C51F	1983	
59037	GY	PJI4316	Leyland Tiger TRCTL11/2R	Duple Dominant IV	C47F	1983	
59045	KL	WAO645Y	Leyland Tiger TRCTL11/2R	Alexander TE	BC49F	1983	
59059	GY	B52DWE	Leyland Tiger TRCTL11/2RH	Alexander TE	BC49F	1984	
59060	GY	B53DWJ	Leyland Tiger TRCTL11/2RH	Alexander TE	BC49F	1985	
59087	GY	PYE841Y	Leyland Tiger TRCTL11/3R	Duple Laser	C53F	1983	

59105	EX	M105CCD	Dennis Javelin 11SDL2133	Plaxton Premiere Interurban	BC47F	1995	
59106	EX	M106CCD	Dennis Javelin 11SDL2133	Plaxton Premiere Interurban	BC47F	1995	
59108	EX	M108CCD	Dennis Javelin 11SDL2133	Plaxton Premiere Interurban	BC47F	1995	
59130	EX	M950JBO	Dennis Javelin 11SDL2133	Plaxton Premiere Interurban	BC47F	1994	
59143	PR	L143BFV	Dennis Javelin 11SDL2129	Plaxton Premiere Interurban	BC47F	1993	
59152	PR	L152BFV	Dennis Javelin 11SDL2133	Plaxton Premiére Interurban	BC47F	1993	
59154	PR	L154BFV	Dennis Javelin 11SDL2133	Plaxton Premiere Interurban	BC47F	1993	
59160	PR	L160CCW	Dennis Javelin 11SDL2133	Plaxton Premiére Interurban	BC47F	1993	
59161	PR	L161CCW	Dennis Javelin 11SDL2133	Plaxton Premiére Interurban	BC47F	1993	

Special event vehicle - (initial owners shown and traditional vintage body codes used)

59922	ESu	BMS222	Leyland Royal Tiger PSU1/15	Alexander	C41C	1952	Alexander
59931	ESu	FES831W	Volvo B58-61	Duple Dominant IV	BC50F	1981	Gloagtrotter, Perth
59939	ESu	HDV639E	Bristol MW6G	Eastern Coach Works	C39F	1967	Western National
59943	ESu	GRS343E	Albion Viking VK43AL	Alexander Y	C40F	1967	Alexander Northern
59950	WSu	YSD350L	Leyland Leopard PSU3/3R	Alexander AY	B41F	1973	Western SMT

| 80001 | ST | RV52OGL | Transbus Enviro 300 | Transbus | N45F | 2002 | On demonstration. |
| 80002 | BY | | MAN 14.220 HOCL - NR | East Lancashire Myllennium | N38F | 2003 | On demonstration. |

Vehicle allocations

East Scotland (ES)

Aberdeen (Hillview Road) - Bluebird (AN)

Outstations - Alford; Ballater; Braemar; Inverurie; Stonehaven and Strathdon.

Leyland Olympian	14409	14410	14411	14415	14418	14451	14489	14496
	14497	14498	14962	14963	14964			
Volvo Olympian	16198	16199	16248	16249	16250			
Volvo B10M bus	20108	20109	20141	20142	20143	20144	20145	20151
	20152	20153	20191	20192	20193	20194	20195	20197
MAN/ALX300	22109	22110	22112	22701	22702	22703	22704	22705
	22706	22707	22708	22709	22710	22711		
Volvo B6	31492	31493						
Dart	32101	32103	32801	32802	32803	32804	32805	32811
Mercedes-	40050	41507	41511					
Volvo B10M coach	52029	52176	52177	52214	52230	52231	52232	52272
	52288	52666	52667	52668	52669			
Ancllliary	48060	48072	52006	52082	52194			

Aberhill (Methilhaven Road, Methil) - Fife (AL)

Titan	10560	10574	10577	10587	10593	10654	10751	10867
	10873	10944	11013	11050				
Volvo Citybus DD	15210	15211	15248	15250	15259	15260	15271	15276
	15294	15298						
Volvo Olympian	16421	16422	16423	16424	16425	16426	16427	16428
	16429							
Volvo B10M bus	20307	20314	20328	20330	20331			
Dart	32201	32210	32215	32216	23241	32343	32344	32346
Mercedes-Benz	40072	40073	40074	40103	40586	40587	40591	
Volvo B10M coach	52027	52030						

Banchory (Dykehead Garage, Blackhall) - J W Coaches (BJ)

Mercedes-Benz	40194	40195	40198	40203	40593	41512	41801
Volvo B10M	52073	52116	52117	52118			

Buchan (Grange Road, Balmoor, Peterhead) - Bluebird (FH)

Outstations - Fraserburgh and Mintlaw

Leyland Olympian	14463	14485	14488					
Volvo B6	30267	30268	30679	30680	30681			
Dart	32102	32104	32106					
Dart SLF	33477	33478						
Mercedes-Benz	40044							
Volvo B10M coach	52103	52104	52119	52134	52136	52137	52138	52139
	52140	52169	52170	52174	52193	52233	52238	52240
	52242	52271	52608	52609				

Cowdenbeath (Broad Street) - Fife (CJ)

Titan	10571	10586	10591	10601	10626	10801	10820	10825
	10858	10902	11084	11097	11119			
Volvo Citybus DD	15275	15282	15285	15286	15287	15296	15297	15299
Volvo B10M bus	20196	20301						
MAN/ALX300	22252	22253	22254	22255	22256	22257	22258	22259
	22260	22261	22262	22263	22264	22265	22269	22271
	22272	22273	22274	22276	22277			
Dart	32207	32208	32209					
Volvo B10M coach	52173	52306	52307	52309	52310			

Dunfermline (St Leonard's Street) - Fife (DE)

Titan	10566	10921	10922					
Leyland Olympian	14280	14460	14462	14706	14707	14718	14719	14720
	14721	14722	14723	14724	14725			
Volvo Citybus	15212	15290	15292					
Volvo Olympian	16035	16036						
Volvo B10M bus	20316	20323	20325	20326	20337	20338	20339	
Volvo B6	30651	30653	30654	30655	30656	30657	30658	30659
	30670	30671	30672					
Dart	32206	32304	32306	32307	32308			
Dart SLF	33414	33415	33416	33417	33418	33419		
Mercedes-Benz	40070	40071						
Volvo B10M coach	52185	52187	52245	52246	52352	52353	52356	52422
	52423	52460						
Ancillary vehicles	25739	52014						

Glenrothes (Flemington Road) - Fife (GS)

Titan	10622	10623	10636	10879	10802	10834	10935	11116
Volvo Citybus DD	15258	15272	15273	15274	15280	15283	15284	15289
	15291	15295						
Volvo B10M bus	20147	20148	20308	20324	20327			
MAN/ALX300	22266	22267	22268					
Dart	32122	32211	32342					
Mercedes-Benz	40080	40089	40095	40096	40097	40588		
Volvo B10M coach	52178	52248	52249	52250	52251	52253	52439	52443
Ancillary vehicle	14279							

Inverness (Burnett Road) - in Inverness (IS)

Outstation - Tain

Leyland Olympian	14456	14461	14490	14491	14492	14499		
Volvo Olympian	16200	16201	16202	16610				
Volvo B10M bus	20112	20118	20119	20146	20150	20154		
Volvo B6LE	31491							
Dart	32105	32806	32807	32808	32809	32810	32812	
Dart SLF	33437	33438	33439	33472	33473	33474	33475	33476
	33479							
Mercedes-Benz	40051	40052	40086	40088	40197	40534	50535	40536
Volvo B10M coach	52131	52132	52168	52171	52175	52241	52243	52291
	52292							

Kirkcaldy (Esplanade) - Fife (KY)

Titan	10555	10558	10582	10615	10791	10819	10945	10996
Leyland Olympian	14337	14448	14450	14701	14702	14703	14704	
	14705							
Volvo Citybus DD	15269	15279	15281					
Volvo B10M bus	20317	20318	20319	20320	20332	20334	20335	20336
	20341	20342						
Volvo B6	30426	30427	30428	30429	30430	30431	30652	30673
Dart	32202	32203	32204	32205	32212	32213	32348	32349
Mercedes-Benz	40270							
Volvo B10M coach	52188	52254	52255	52256	52258	52354	52361	52362
	52366	52367	52380	52420	52424	52442	52457	52458
	52459							
Ancillary vehicles	52004	52014						

Moray (Pinefield Depot, East Road, Elgin) - Bluebird (BQ)

Outstations - Buckie; Forres and Macduff

Volvo B10M bus	20107	20149						
Dart SLF	33469	33470	33471					
Mercedes-Benz	40041	40042	40043	40048	40049	40078	40079	40102
	40585	40589	40590	40636	40637	40640		
Volvo B10M coach	52067	52130	52142	52227	52234	52235	52236	42237
	52244	52289	52290	52293	52294	52312	52313	52314
	52463	52605	52606	52607	52610	52611	52612	52638
Ancillary vehicle	52011							

Perth (Ruthvenfield Road, Inveralmond) - in Perth (PH)

Outstations - Crieff and Spittalfield

Titan	11106	11114						
Leyland Olympian	14338	14408	14444	14452	14455	14457	14458	14467
	14468	14469	14470	14471	14486	14487		
Volvo B10M bus	20111	20113	20171	20172	20173	20174	20175	20176
	20177	20178	20179	20180				
MAN/ALX300	22712	22713	22714	22715	22716	22717	22718	22719
	22722							
Volvo B6LE	31494	31395	31496	31497	31498	31499		
Dart SLF	33428	34329	33430	33431	33432	33433	33434	33435
	33436							
Mercedes-Benz	40045	40046	40047	40542	41304	41509	41513	41517
	41950							
Volvo B10M coach	52038	52135	52228	52229	52239	52382	52385	52386
	52387	52647						
Ancillary vehicle	52087							

St Andrews (City Road) - Fife (SA)

Titan	10789	11007	11066	11093	11122			
Volvo Citybus	15270	15277	15288	15293				
Atlantean OT	15869							
Volvo Olympian	16430							
Volvo B10M bus	20302	20303	20304	20305	20306	20309	20310	20315
	20321	20322	20329	20340				
Mercedes-Benz	40075	40076						
Volvo B10M coach	52183	52184	52252	52365	52441	52462		

East Scotland unallocated/stored - (ES)

Special event vehicles	12107	19935	39925	59922	59931	59939	59943
Titan	10566	10572					
Dart	30269	32201	32246	32341	32347	32348	
Mercedes-Benz	40087	40090	40091	40594	41520		
Volvo B10M coach	52247						

West Scotland - (WS)

Ardrossan (Harbour Road) - Western, A1 Service (AS)

Routemaster	12060						
Leyland Olympian	14522						
Volvo Olympian	16068	16074	16846	16847	16848	16849	16850	16851
	16854	16855	16856	16858	16860		
Volvo B10M bus	20510	20511	20532	20536	20548	20556	20568	20569
Volvo B10B	21051						
Volvo B6	30325	30326	30332				
Dart	32138						
Mercedes-Benz	40060	40061	40068	40098	40611	40624	40625	40626
	40627	40632					
Volvo B10M arctic	51092	51093	51094				
Volvo B10M coach	52285	52287	52348	52349	52421	52425	52426

Arran (Brodick) - Western (AA)

Volvo B10M bus	20524	20526	20537	20538	20539	20595	20596
Mercedes-Benz	40054	40055	40059	40630	40631	40633	
Volvo B10M coach	52262	52264					

Ayr (Waggon Road) - Western, A1 Service, AA Buses (AY)

Titan	10005	10029	10209	10252	10999	11076	11081	11083
	11092						
Volvo Citybus	15247	15249					
Volvo B10M bus	20110	20114	20502	20504	20505	20513	20514	20516
	20517	20518	20519	20549	20565	20566	20567	20580
	20581	20582	20584	20586	20587		
Leopard	25769						
Volvo B6	30336	30675	30676	30677	30678		
Volvo B6LE	31366	31367	31368	31378	31379	31380	31381	31381
	31382	31383	31384	31385	31386		
Dart	32137	32145	32396	32397			
Dart SLF	33443	33444	33445	33446	33447	33775	33776	33777
	33778	33779	33780				
Mercedes-Benz	40602	40604	40605	40606	40607	40608	40638	
Volvo B10M arctic	51061	51062	51070	51071	51098	51099	
Volvo B10M coach	52265	52350	52355	52464			

Cumnock (Ayr Road) - Western (CC)

Titan	10874						
Leyland Olympian	14603						
Volvo Citybus B10M	15246						
Volvo Olympian	16039						
Volvo B10M bus	20265	20530	20531	20532	20533	20534	20535	20570
	20571	20572	20573	20574	20575	20576	20577	20578
	20579						
Mercedes-Benz	40056	40057	40064	40065			
Volvo B10M artic	51073	51074	51075	51076	51095	51097	
Volvo B10M coach	52351	52357	52358	52465	52640		

Dumfries (Eastfield Road) - Western (DS)

Outstation - Kirkcudbright

Titan	10246	10700					
Volvo Olympian	16037	16038	16040	16857			
Volvo B10M bus	20512	20583	20594	20597	20599		
Scania L113	28955						
Dart	32120	32390	32391	32392	32393	32394	32395	32398
Dart SLF	33088	33089	33772	33773			
Mercedes-Benz	40053	40062	40063	40066	40069	40099	40100	
Volvo B10M coach	52260	52283	52284	52427			

Dunoon (Argyll Road) - Western (DU)

Volvo B10M	20598					
National	25476					
Dart	32224	32381	32400	32401	32402	32405
Mercedes-Benz	40101	40603	40623			

Glasgow (Blochairn Road) - Glasgow (GW)

Leyland Olympian	14404	14412	14466	14521	14602	14604	14608	14612
	14616	14619	14622	14623	14625	14626	14627	14628
	14629	14638	14640	14647	14653	14654	14656	14657
	14662	14663						
Mercedes-Benz	40639							
Volvo B10M coach	52282	52416	52418					

Kilmarnock (Mackinlay Place) - Western (KK)

Titan	10208	10236	10843	10866	10950	11045		
Leyland Olympian	14601							
Volvo Olympian	16852	16853	16859	16861	16862	16863	16864	16865
	16866							
Volvo B10 bus	20503	20506	20507	20508	20509	20588	20589	20590
	20591	20591	20593					
MAN/ALX300	22601	22602	22603	22604	22605	22606		
National	25475							
Volvo B6	30312	30313	30318	30319	30320	30321	30322	30323
	30324	30327	30335	30337	30338	30339	30340	30341
	30674							
Volvo B6LE	31369	31370	31371	31372	31373	31374	31375	31376
	31377							
Dart SLF	34021	34025	34026	34063				
Mercedes-Benz	40058	40067	40530	40601	40609	40621	40628	40634
	40635	40985	40986	40987				
Volvo B10M coach	52359	52360	52419	52456				
Ancillary vehicles	52069	52076	52086	52088				

Rothesay (High Road, Port Bannatyne) - Western (RO)

Titan	10197	10273	10824	11079				
Volvo B10Mbus	20515							
Dart	32146	32225	32226	32380	32403	32404	32406	32407
	32408							
Mercedes-Benz	40629							
Volvo B10M coach	52144	52263						

Stranraer (Lewis Street) - Western (SR)

Outstation - Whithorn

Titan	10410	10762						
Volvo B10M bus	20521	20522	20585					
Leopard	25761	25771	25797					
Dart	32409							
Mercedes-Benz	40610	40612	40622					
Volvo B10M coach	52026	52058	52079	52080	52084	52096	52097	

West Scotland unallocated/stored - (WS)

Special event vehicles	19959	19982
Leopard	25728	
Dart	32382	
Mercedes-Benz	40082	40529

North East (NE)

Byker (Shields Road) - in Newcastle (BY)

Leyland Olympian	14181	14184	14186	14192	14194	14402	14403	14434
	14435	14520	14605	14611	14614	14642	14645	14646
	14676	14668	14669					
Scania DD	15301	15302	15303	15304	15305	15306	15307	15308
	15309	15310						
Volvo Olympian	16702	16706	16708	16709	16710	16711	16712	16713
	16714	16715	16716	16717	16718	16719	16720	16721
	16722	16723	16724	16725	16726	16727	16728	16729
	16730							
Volvo B10M bus	20120	20121	20122	20123	20124	20125	20126	20135
	20196	20550	20839	20840	20841	20842	20843	
Volvo B10B	21001	21002						
Volvo B10BLE	21101	21102	21103	21104	21105	21136	21137	21138
	21139	21140	21141	21142	21143	21144	21145	21146
	21147	21148	21149	21150	21151	21152	21153	21154
	21155	21156	21157	21158				
MAN/ALX300	22172	22174	22202	22203	22204	22205	22206	22207
	22208	22209	22210	22211				
Dart	32701	32714	32720	32744	32745	32751	32752	32753
	32768							
Mercedes-Benz	40092	40461	40462	40463	40464	40465	40466	40467
	40468	40485	40795					
Ancillary vehicles	40282	48027						

Darlington (Faverdale) - in Darlington (DA)

Titan	10634	10649	11022					
Leyland Olympian	14189	14652	14655	14658				
Atlantean	15818	15822	15826					
Volvo B10M bus	20261	20262	20273					
Volvo B6	30101	30102	30103	30104	30105	30106	30107	30108
	30238	30242	30243	30244	30245	30246	30247	30249
	30250	30254						
Dart	32655	32656	32567	32658	32659	32660	32661	32717
Mercedes-Benz	40791	40796						
Volvo B10M coach	52141							

Hartlepool (Brenda Road) - in Hartlepool (HP)

Leyland Olympian	14191	14639	14648	14651				
Atlantean	15827	15824	15828					
Volvo B10M bus	20256	20257	20258	20263	20264	20265	20266	20267
	20268	20269	20270	20271	20291	20292	20293	20294
	20295	20296	20297	20298	20299	20300		
Lynx	29112	29115	29125	29541	29542	29544	29545	29601
	29602	29603	29604	29605	29606			
Dart	32124	32301	32302	32303	32305	32615	32616	32617
Dart SLF	33482	33493	33484	33485	33486	33487		
Solo	47025							

Slatyford (Slatyford Lane) - in Newcastle (SY)

MAN ALX300	22190	22193	22195	22196	22197	22198	22199	22201
	22214	22215	22451	22452	22453	22454	22455	22456
	22462	22463	22464	22465	22466	22467	22468	22469
	22470	22471	22472	22473	22474	22475	22476	22477
	22478	22479	22480	22481	22482	22483	22484	22485
	22492	22493						

Scania SD	28901	28902	28903	28904	28905	28906	28907	28908
	28909	28910	28911	28912	28913	28914	28915	28916
	28017	20918	28919	28920	28921	28922	28923	28924
	28925	28926	28927	28928	28929	28930	28931	28932
	28933	28934	28935	28936	28937	28938	28951	28952
	28953	28954						
Dart	32723	32724	32725	32726	32727	32728		
Mercedes-Benz	40085	40093	40251	40277	40283	40286	40469	40470
	40471	40472	40473	40474	40475	40476	40477	40478
	40479	40480	40481	40482	40483	40484	40486	40525
	40620	40827	40828					
Alero	47803	47804						
Renault	48201	48202						
Ancillary	40254	40678	48007	48026				

South Shields (Dean Road) - in South Shields (SS)

Volvo Olympian	16701	16703	16704	16705	16707	16731	16732	16733
	16734	16735	16736	16737	16738	16739	16740	
Volvo B10M bus	20551	20552	20553					
Lynx	29101	29102	29103	29104	29105	29106	29108	29109
	29110	29111	29116	20117	29119	29120	29123	29124
	29126	29127						
Dart	32703	32709	32710	32711	32712	32715	32729	32740
	32741	32742	32743	32749	32759	32766	32767	32768
	32769	32783	32784	32785	32791	32792	32793	
Dart SLF	33101	33102	33825	33826	33827	33828	33829	
Mercedes-Benz	40094	40487	40488	40489	40491	40492	40493	40494
	40495	40496	40497	40498	40500	40642		
Ancillary vehicles	48065	48079						

Stockton-on-Tees (Church Road) - on Teeside (SC)

Titan	10643	10648	10659	10664	10666	10673	10675	10826
	10840	10849						
Leyland Olympian	14180	14185	14405	14615	14617	14618	14661	
Atlantean	15810	15811	15825	15830				
Volvo Olympian	16831	16832	16833	16834	16835	16836	16837	16838
	16839	16840						
Volvo B10M	20243	20244	20245	20246	20247	20248	20249	20250
	20251	20252	20253	20254	20255	20272	20554	
Volvo B10B	21031	21032	21033	21034	21035	21036	21037	21038
	21039	21040	21041	21042				
MAN ALX300	22656	22657	22658	22659	22660	22661	22662	22663
	22664	22665	22666	22667	22668	22669	22670	22671
	22672	22673	22674	22675				
Lynx	29107	29112	29607	29608	29609	29610	29611	29612
	29613	29614	29615	29616	29617	29618	29619	29620
	29621	29622	29623	29624	29625	29626	29627	29628
	29629	29630						
Dart	32746							
Dart SLF	33489	33490	33491	33492				
Mercedes-Benz	40792	40793	40794					
Ancillary vehicles	48013	48021	48022					

Sunderland (North Bridge Street) - in Sunderland (SU)

Leyland Olympian	14182	14183	14667	14670	14671	14672	14673	14674
	14675							
Volvo B10M bus	20101	20102	20103	20104	20105	20106	20115	20116
	20117	20695	20837	20838	20844			
MAN/ALX3000	22486	22487	22488	22489	22490	22491	22494	22495
	22727	22728	22729	22730	22731	22732	22733	22734
	22735	22736						
Dart	32112	32117	32121	32125	32127	32128	32129	32133
	32134	32620	32621	32622	32623	32624	32631	32632
	32633	32634	32637	32638	32702	32718	32722	32730
	32731	32732	32733	32734	32735	32736	32737	32738
	32739	32748	32750	32751	32760	32761	32762	32763

	32764	32765	32770	32773	32777	32778	32779	32780
	32781	32782	32786	32787	32788	32789	32790	32794
	32795							
Dart SLF	33118	33120	33121	33122	33123	33124	33125	33126
	33127	33128	33924					
Mercedes-Benz	40490	40499						
Ancillary vehicles	48047	48078						

North East unallocated/stored - (NE)

Titan	10668	10827	11026
Atlantean	15808		
Lynx	29113	29118	29121
Mercedes-Benz	40281	40284	40678
Group trainers	15905	15914	15917
Special event vehicles	10003	19912	19917

North West - (NW)

Barrow (Walney Road) - in Cumbria (BA)

Outstations - Coniston; Millom; Ulverston; Askam and Haverthwaite

Leyland Olympian	13296	13297	14177	14241	14242	14243	14245	14246
	14473	14474	14475	14480	14481			
Volvo B10M bus	20477	20478	20699	20702	20754	20755	20756	20757
	20758	20759	20760	20761	20762	20778	20780	20786
	20787							
Volvo B6	30310	30461	30846					
Mercedes-Benz	40004	40005	40016	40017	40018	40019	40020	40021
	40022	40023	40026	40034	40035	40327	40435	40646
	40652	40813	40814	40818	40834	40882	40883	40885
	40886	42000	42090	42091	42092	42093	42094	42095
	42096							
Ancillary vehicle	48067							

Carlisle (Willowholme Ind Est) - in Cumbria (CE)

Outstation - Penrith

Titan	10334							
Leyland Olympian	14203	14228	14229	14230	14231	14232		
Volvo B10M bus	20473	20715	20716	20717	20718	20719	20720	20721
	20722	20723	20724	20725	20726	20727	20728	20729
	20730	20731	20732	20733	20734	20735	20736	20737
	20738	20739	20741	20742	20743	20745	20746	20766
	20772	20773	20781	20783	20784	20785	20788	20789
	20790							
MAN/ALX300	22801	22802	22803	22804	22805	22806	22807	22808
	22809	22811	22812	22813	22814			
Lance	27201	27202	27203	27204	27205	27206	27207	27208
	27209	27210	27211	27212				
Volvo B6	30237	30309	30333	30334	30454	30455	30456	30458
	30460							
Mercedes-Benz	40039	40040	40329	40426	40645	40822	40823	40826
	40875	40876						
Volvo B10M coach	52063	52064	52072	52491	52492	52629		
Tiger	59014							
Ancillary vehicles	48001	48039						

Chorley (Eaves Lane) - in Lancashire (CY)

Leyland Olympian	14100	14117	14138	14179	14197	14198	14216	14219
	14244	14247	14249	14250	14260	14261	14262	14263
	14264							
Volvo Olympian	16634	16635	16636	16637	16638	16639	16646	16647
	16648	16649	16650	16651	16652	16653	16654	16655

	16656	16657	16658	16659	16660	16661		
Volvo B10M bus	20129	20130	20131	20132	20436	20451	20452	
Volvo B6	30241	30303	30306	30307	30724	30726		
Mercedes-Benz	40399	40418	40425	40819	40829	40833	40836	40878
	40884							
Ancillary vehicle	48029							

Kendal (Station Road) - in Cumbria (KL)

Outstations - Ambleside; Appleby; Grange and Kirkby Stephen

Titan	10512	11100	11091	11110				
Leyland Olympian	13117	14129	14175	14248	14251	14252	14945	
Volvo Olympian	16330	16331	16332	16334	16335	16336	16337	16338
	16339	16340						
Volvo B10M bus	20705	20774	20775	20776				
Tiger bus	25800							
Volvo B6	30270	30275	30276	30282				
Mercedes-Benz	40001	40002	40003	40007	40008	40009	40010	40011
	40012	40013	40613	40614	40615	40616	40617	40619
	40641	40651						
Volvo B10M coach	52001	52056	52057					
Tiger coach	59024	59026						
Ancillary vehicle	48017							

West Cumbria (Blackwood Road, Lillyhall) - in Cumbria (LL)

Leyland Olympian	14233	14234	14253	14254	14255	14257	14258	
Volvo Olympian	16624	16625	16626	16627				
Volvo B10M bus	20455	20456	20457	20458	20459	20708	20709	20710
	20711	20712	20713	20714	20753	20763	20764	20765
	20767	20768	20769	20770	20771	20777	20779	
Mercedes-Benz	40006	40014	40015	40024	40025	40027	40028	40029
	40030	40031	40033	40036	40037	40038	40328	40413
	40414	40421	40423	40649	40650	40810	40811	40812
	40832	40881	40887	40888				
Volvo B10M coach	52098	52099	52267	52330	52331	52332	52603	52604
	52626	52627	52628					
Ancillary vehicle	25753	40269	48066					

In 2001 a new depot was opened in Morecambe displacing the fomer municipal garage and the old Ribble depot in Lancaster. Lancaster is the southern end of the famous 555 service that links the city with Keswick in winter and Carlisle during the summer. High-back seated Olympians are the norm, represented by N340NPN which was pictured shortly after a recent repaint. *Bob Downham*

Morecambe (White Lund Estate) - in Lancaster (ME)

Outstations - Garstang and Ingleton

Titan	10056	10179	10254	10281	10311	10340	10684	10697
	10728	10729	10738	10809	10855			
Leyland Olympian	14174	14202	14204	14205	14206	14207	14208	14209
	14210	14235	14266	14267				
Volvo Olympian	16243	16244	16245	16628	16630	16631	16662	16663
	16664	16665	16666	16667	16668			
Volvo B10M bus	20417	20418	20419	20422	20423	20463	20540	20541
	20542	20543	20544	20545	20546	20547	20700	20701
	20703	20704	20706	20707	20744	20748	20749	20750
	20751	20752	20793	20794	20795			
MAN/ALX300	22721	22815	22816	22817	22818	22819	22821	22822
	22823	22824	22825	22826	22827			
Javelin bus	27035	27036	27037					
Volvo B6	30277	30456						
Mercedes-Benz	40412	40416	40417	40420	40422	40424	40427	40519
	40520	40645	40815	40816	40820	40825	40877	
Volvo B10M coach	52002	52106						
Tiger coach	59015	59020						
Ancillary vehicles	25704	25759						

Preston (Selbourne Street) - in Lancashire (PR)

Outstation: Fleetwood

Leyland Olympian	13213	14116	14134	14170	14176	14187	14188	14193
	14195	14196	14199	14201	14217	14220	14223	14256
	14259	14265	14266	14267	14278			
Volvo Olympian	16325	16326	16327	16328	16329	16629	16632	16633
	16640	16641	16642	16643	16644	16645	16669	16670
Volvo B10M bus	20127	20128	20133	20134	20424	20425	20430	20435
	20454	20474	20475	20476	*			
Volvo B6	30252	30255	30256	30271	30272	30273	30274	30278
	30281	30283	30301	30302	30304	30305	30308	30459
	30462	30662	30665	30668				
Mercedes-Benz	40267	40394	40395	40396	40397	40398	40401	40402
	40415	40419	40428	40441	40443	40445	40446	40447
	40452	40455	40647	40648	40824	40830	40831	40835
	42670	42672						
Solo	47016	47017	47018	47019	47020	47021	47022	47023
	47024							
Volvo B10M coach	52133	52195	52196	52216	52229	52268	52297	52328
	52329	52405	52406	52407	52408	52409	52410	52412
	52413	52414	52445	52490	52613	52614	52615	52616
Javelin interurban	59143	59160	59161	59192	59194			
Special event vehicles	39957	39995						
Ancilliry vehicles	48015	48074						

North West unallocated/stored - (NW)

Leyland Olympian	14102							
Bristol VR	15724	15731	15735					
Mercedes-Benz	40192	40263	40264	40265	40266	40268	40666	40667
	40670	40671	40675					
Volvo B10m coach	52061	52062	52065	52070	52075	52405		

Manchester (MA)

Glossop (York Street) - (GP)

Leyland Olympian	13080	13124	13125	13126	13132	13133	13135	13138
	13143	13145	13255	13260	13269			
Volvo B10M bus	20904	20905	20906	20907	20908	20909	20910	20918
	20961	20962	20963	20964				
MAN/ALX300	22169							
Mercedes-Benz	42550	42551	42552	42553	42562	42563	42564	42565
	42566							

Manchester (Hyde Road) - (HE)

Outstation: Chadderton

Leyland Olympian	13020	13021	13022	13023	13024	13025	13026	13027
	13028	13029	13031	13032	13033	13035	13036	13039
	13049	13053	13055	13056	13057	13058	13060	13065
	13070	13072	13074	13077	13082	13084	13087	13088
	13089	13094	13095	13114	13118	13119	13121	13122
	13137	13146	13150	13154	13165	13166	13167	13170
	13173	13179	13195	13196	13199	13207	13214	13216
	13224	14613	14631					
Scania	15313	15314	15315	15316	15317			
Volvo Olympian	16501	16502	16503	16504	16505	16511	16512	16513
	16744	16745	16746	16747	16748	16749	16751	16752
	16753	16754	16755	16756	16757	16758	16759	16760
	16761	16762	16763	16764	16765	16766		
Trident	17612	17613	17626	17627	17628	17631	17632	17633
	17641	17642	17643	17644	17645	17646	17647	17723
	17724	17725	17726	17727				
Volvo B10M bus	20653	20674	20677	20896	20897	20901	20902	
	20903	20912	20913	20914	20915	20916	20917	20919
	20920	20921	20922	20923	20924	20925	20926	20927
	20928	20929	20930	20931	20932	20933	20934	20935
	20936	20937	20938	20939	20940	20941	20942	20943
	20950	20951	20952	20953	20954	20955	20956	20957
	20965	20966	20967	20968	20969	20970	20971	20972
	20973	20974	20975	20976	20977	20978	20979	20983
	20984	20985	20986	20987	20988	20989	20990	
MAN/ALX300	22107	22108	22135	22136	22137	22138	22139	22140
	22146	22148	22149	22153	22154	22166	22167	22168
	22185	22186	22187					
Mercedes-Benz	42530	42531	42532	42541				
Ancilliry vehicles	15023	15855	25738	25785	40989	48033	48038	48055
	48057	48058	48059	48069	48070			

Manchester (Princess Road) - (PS)

Leyland Olympian	13067	13069	13086	13091	13110	13178	13181	13191
	13226	13236	13268	14239	14240			
Dominator	15012	15019	15020	15021	15024	15026	15029	15030
	15031	15032	15033	15034	15035	15036	15037	15038
	15039	15040						
Dragon	15180	15181	15182	15183	15184	15185	15186	15187
	15188	15189	15190	15191	15192	15193	15194	15195
	15196	15197	15198	15199				
Volvo Olympian	16767	16768	16769	16770	16771	16772	16773	16774
	16775	16776	16778	16779	16780	16781	16782	16786
	16787	16788	16789	16790	16791	16792	16793	16794
	16795	16796	16797	16798	16799	16800		
Trident	17617	17618	17651	17652	17653	17654	17655	17656
	17657	17658	17659	17660	17661	17662	17663	17664
	17665	17666	17667	17668	17669	17670	17671	17672

	17701	17702	17703	17704	17705	17706	17707	17708
	17709	17710	17711	17712	17713	17714	17715	17716
	17717	17718	17719	17720	17721	17730		
Volvo B10M bus	20857	20858	20859	20860	20861	20862	20863	20864
	20865	20866	20867	20868	20898	20899	20944	20945
	20946	20947	20948	20949	20958	20959	20960	20980
	20981	20982						
MAN/ALX300	22156	22157	22158	22159	22160	22161	22162	22163
	22164	22165	22173	22178	22179	22212	22213	22235
	22236	22237	22238					

Stockport (Daw Bank) - (ST)

Leyland Olympian	13147	13149	13153	13155	13156	13158	13164	13169
	13172	13174	13175	13176	13184	13185	13193	13197
	13198	13205	13208	13210	13212	13215	13221	13234
	13272	13277	13282	13283	13285	13289	13291	13294
	13295	13298	13300	13301	13304			
Volvo Olympian	16506	16507	16508	16509	16510			
Trident	17614	17615	17616	17619	17620	17621	17622	17623
	17624	17629	17634	17635	17636	17637	17638	17639
Volvo B10M bus	20845	20846	20847	20848	20849	20850	20851	20852
	20853	20854	20855	20856	20875	20876	20877	20878
	20879	20880	20881	20882	20893	20894	20991	20992
	20993	20994	20995	20996				
MAN/ALX300	22101	22102	22103	22104	22105	22106	22113	22114
	22115	22116	22117	22118	22119	22120	22121	22122
	22124	22125	22126	22127	22128	22129	22130	22131
	22132	22133	22134	22141	22142	22143	22144	22145
	22147	22150	22151	22152	22180	22181	22182	22183
	22184	22188	22189	22216	22217	22218	22219	22221
	22223	22224	22226	22227	22228	22229	22231	22232
	22233	22234	22239	22241	22242	22243	22244	22246
Transbus Enviro 300	80001							

Stockport (Charles Street) - (CS)

Dart	32048	32351	32352	32353	32354	32355	32356	32357
	32358	32359	32360	32361	32362	32363	32364	32365
	32366	32367	32368					
Dart SLF	34037	34038	34041					
Mercedes-Benz	40429	40430	40431	40432	40433	40434	42002	42003
	42004	42013	42014	42016	42017	42533	42534	42535
	42536	42537	42538	42539	42540	42542	42543	42544
	42545	42546	42547	42548	42549	42554	42556	42557
	42558	42559	42567	42568	42569			
	42570	42571	42572	42573				

Manchester unallocated - (MA)

Mercedes-Benz	40663	40660	40664	40556				
Olympian	13230							
Dominator	15001	15005	15006	15010	15011	15013	15014	15015
	15016	15017	15025	15027	15028			
Ancillary	48037	48057	48058	48059				

East Midlands - (EM)

Chesterfield (Stonegravels, Sheffield Road) - in Chesterfield (CH)

Leyland Olympian	14316	14318	14327	14329	14334	14347	14348	
Volvo Olympian	16453	16454	16455	16456	16457	16458	16459	16460
	16483	16484	16485	16486	16487	16488	16489	16490
	16491	16492	16493	16494	16495	16496	16497	16500
Volvo B10M bus	20439	20440	20441	20442	20443	20444	20493	20498
	20499							
Tiger	25821	25822	25823	25824	25825	25827	25828	
Dart	32111	32113	32114	32115	32147	32148	32415	32418
	32421	32422	32423	32425	32427	32818	32819	32820
Dart SLF	33401	33402	33403	33760	33761	33762	33764	33765
	33766	33767	33768	33838	33839	33840	33841	
Optare Excel	35000	35001	35002	35003	35004	35005	35006	
Mercedes-Benz	40746	40749	40750	40751	40752	40753	40754	40755
	40756	40757	40758	40759	40760	40761	40762	40763
	40764	40765	40797	40799	41715	41717	41719	42576
	42578	42579	42582	42587	42589			
Volvo B10M coach	52207	52208	52209	52210	52211	52632	52633	
Ancillary vehicles	48052	48056						

Grimsby (Victoria Street) - Grimsby Cleethorpes (GY)

Leyland Olympian	14871							
Dominator	15002	15003	15004	15007	15008	15009	15075	15076
	15077	15079	15080	15081	15084	15085	15092	15093
	15094							
Fleetline OT	15513	15514						
Trident	17673	17674	17675	17676	17677	17678	17679	17680
	17681	17682	17683	17684	17685	17686	17687	17688
Lance	27301	27302	27303	27304	27701	27702	27703	27704
	27705	27706	27707	27708	27709			
Dart	32419	32420						
Dart SLF	33404	33405	33406					
Mercedes-Benz	40767	40768	40769	40770	40771	40801	40802	40803
	40998	41802						
Volvo B10M coach	52005	52007	52008	52009	52010	52051	52078	52095
	52115							
Tiger coach	59035	59037	59059	59060	59087			
Ancillary vehicles	48051							

Kingston-upon-Hull (Foster Street, Stoneferry) - in Hull (HL)

Leyland Olympian	14303	14314	14322	14339	14341	14362	14363	14364
	14367	14379	14380	14621	14630	14632	14633	14634
	14635	14636	14637	14643	14644	14649	14664	14665
	14901	14905	14906	14907	14908	14909	14910	14911
	14912	14914	14915	14917	14918	14919	14920	14921
	14922	14923	14924	14925	14927			
Dominator	15041	15043	15044	15046	15047	15048	15049	15051
	15052	15059	15060	15061	15062			
Volvo Olympian	16471	16472	16473	16498	16499	16817	16818	16819
	16823	16824	16825	16826	16827	16828	16829	16830

Volvo B10M Bus	20274	20275	20276	20277	20278	20279	20280	20281
	20282	20283	20284	20285	20286			
Tiger	25829	25830	25832					
Volvo B6	30239	30279						
Dart	32066	32067	32068	32069	32071	32073	32080	32081
	32082	32083	32087	32089	32116	32118	32123	32713
Dart SLF	33001	33103	33104	33105	33107	33108	33109	33110
	33112	33113	33114	33115	33116	33117	33769	33770
	33771							
Mercedes-Benz	40798	41713	41714	41716	42355	42356	42357	42358
Volvo B10M coach	52143	52146	52147	52351	52357	52358	52379	52381
Ancillary vehicle	48020							

Mansfield (Sutton Road) - in Mansfield (MD)

Leyland Olympian	14315	14319	14324	14325	14326	14331	14332	14335
	14336	14340	14342	14343	14344	14345	14346	14349
	14350	14351	14352	14353	14354	14355	14356	14357
	14358	14478						
Volvo Olympian	16474	16475	16476	16477	16478	16479	16480	16481
	16482							
Tridents	17737	17738	17739					
Volvo B10M bus	20496	20497						
Volvo B6	30435	30436	30437	30438	30439	30440	30441	30442
	30443	30445	30446	30447	30448	30449	30450	30451
	30452	30453						
Dart	32416	32424						
Dart SLF	33831	33832	33833	33834	33835	33836	33837	33847
	33848	33849						
Mercedes-Benz	40744	40745	40748	40772	40773	40774	40775	40776
	42577	42583	42584	42585	42590			
Volvo B10M Coach	52212	52213	52257	52269	52493	52494	52601	52602
	52630	52635	52644	52645	52648	52649		
Ancillary vehicles	48048	52091	52092					

Worksop (Hardy Street) - in Bassetlaw (WP)

Leyland Olympian	14320	14321	14323	14333	14359	14360	14361	
Volvo Olympian	16461	16462	16463	16464	16465	16466	16467	16468
	16469							
Volvo B10M bus	20412	20413	20414	20491	20492	20494	20495	
Dart	32417	32426	32819					
Dart SLF	34001	34002	34003	34004	34005	34006	34007	34008
	34009							
Optare Excel	35007	35008	35009	35010	35011	35012	35013	35014
	35015							
Mercedes-Benz	40736	40737	40738	40739	40740	40741	40742	40743
	40777	40778	40779	40780	40781	40800	40804	41718
Volvo B10M coach	52145	52259	52631					
Ancillary vehicle	48024							

East Midlands unallocated/stored (EM)

Leyland Olympian	14320	14322					
Leopard	25775						
Tiger	25826	25830	25831	25833			
Dart	32520						
Mercedes-Benz	40749	40990	40991	40994	40995	40998	40999
Volvo B10M arctic	51096						

East (EA)

Bedford (St Johns) - (BD)

Outstations - Biggleswade; Chown's Mill; Huntingdon; Northampton and Rushden

Leyland Olympian	14000	14001	14022	14023	14024	14030	14031	14032
	14034	14035	14036	14037	14038	14039	14040	14041
	14042	14044	14046	14048	14049	14055	14056	14061
	14062	14063	14064	14065	14472	14476	14477	14479
	14482	14483	14484	14493	14494	14495	14508	14509
	14510	14511	14512	14708	14709	14710	14713	14948
	14949	14950						
Volvo Olympian	16527	16569	16570	16571	16583	16584	16585	16586
Volvo B6	30401	30402	30403	30404	30405	30406	30407	30408
	30409	30410	30411	30412	30413	30414	30415	30416
	30417	30418	30419	30420	30421	30422	30423	30424
	30425	30551	30552	30553	30554			
Mercedes-Benz	40302	40303	40304	40317	40318	40319	40320	40321
	40322	40323	40324	40325	40326	40332	40334	40335
	40336	40337	40338	40350	40351	40367	40368	40369
	40370	40371	40372					
Volvo B10M coach	52021	52032	52033	52035	52036	52120	52121	52122
	52371	52372	52373	52481	52482	52483	52484	52485
	52486							
Ancillary vehicle	40984	41998	48043	48062				

Cambridge (Cowley Road) - in Cambridge (CB)

Outstations: Ely; Haverhill; Kings Lynn; Littleport; Longstowe; Newmarket; Royston and St Ives.

Leyland Olympian	14513	14514						
Volvo Olympian	16004	16005	16006	16007	16008	16009	16010	16011
	16012	16013	16014	16015	16018	16019	16020	16021
	16022	16023	16024	16025	16026	16431	16432	16433
	16434	16435	16436	16437	16533	16541	16542	16543
	16544	16545	16551	16552	16553	16554	16556	16563
	16564	16565	16566	16567	16572	16573	16574	16575
	16576	16577	16578	16579				
Trident	17691	17692	17693	17694	17695	17696	17697	
MAN/ALX300	22278	22301	22302	22303	22304	22305	22306	22307
	22308	22309	22310	22311	22312	22313	22314	22315
	22316	22317	22318	22319	22320	22321	22322	22323
	22324	22325	22326	22327	22328	22329	22330	22331
	22332	22333	22334	22335	22336	22337	22338	22339
	22340	22457	22458	22459	22460	22461		
Volvo B6	30555	30556	30837	30838				
Dart	32756	32757	32758					
Dart SLF	33802	33814						
MetroRider	47900	47990						
Volvo B10M coach	52158	52159	52172	52179	52189	52190		
	52398							
Special event vehicles	19952	19953						
Ancillary vehicle	48011	48040	48041	52108	52109			

Corby (Station Road) - (CX)

Titan	10556	10559	10565	10569	10576	10584	10588	10590
	10830	11034	11096	11099	11117			
Mercedes-Benz	40354	40356	40357	40359	40360	40361	40362	40363
	40364	40365	40366	40382				
Ancillary vehicle	41983							

Kettering (Northampton Road) - (KG)

Outstations - Chown's Mill; Desborough; Thrapston and Wellingborough

Olympian	14002	14020	14021	14025	14026	14027	14028	14029
	14033	14043	14045	14054	14057	14058	14059	14060
	14067	14068	14069	14070	14946	14947		
Volvo Olympian	16209	16210	16211	16212	16213	16214	16215	16216
	16217	16218						
Mercedes-Benz	40306	40307	40308	40309	40310	40311	40312	40313
	40314	40315	40316	40339	40340	40341	40342	40343
	40344	40345	40346	40347	40348	40349	40383	
Volvo B10M coach	52024	52162	52474	52475	52476	52477	52478	52479
	52480							
Ancillary vehicle	48010							

Northampton (Rothersthorpe Avenue) - (NN)

Outstations - Chown's Mill; Daventry;and Milton Keynes

Leyland Olympian	14004	14005	14006	14007	14008	14009	14010	14011
Volvo Olympian	16221	16222	16223	16224	16225	16226	16227	16228
	16229	16230	16231	16555	16671	16672	16673	16674
	16675	16676	16677	16678	16679	16680	16681	16682
	16683	16684	16685	16686	16687	16688	16689	16690
	16691	16692	16693	16694	16695	16696	16697	16698
	16699							
Dart SLF	33396	33399	33453	33454	33455	33456	33457	33458
	33459	33460	33461	33462	33463	33464		
Mercedes-Benz	40301	40305	40373	40374	40375	40376	40377	40378
	40379	40380	40381					
Volvo B10M coach	52160	52161	52368	52369	52370			
Ancillary vehicle	48045	48061	52300					

Peterborough (Lincoln Road) - in Peterborough - (PE)

Outstations: Crowland;; Lincoln; March; Market Deeping; Oundle; Stamford and Wisbech.

Leyland Olympian	14047	14506	14507	14523	14524	14525		
Volvo Olympian	16232	16528	16529	16530	16531	16532	16534	16535
	16536	16537	16538	16539	16540	16546	16547	16548
	16549	16550	16557	16558	16559	16561	16562	16568
	16580	16581	16582	16587	16588	16589	16590	16591
	16592	16593						
Dart	32650	32651	32652	32707	32708	32754	32755	32771
	32772	32774	32775	32776				
Dart SLF	33322	33323	33324	33393	33394	33395	33397	33398
	33604	33806	33813	33815	33816	33817	33817	33818
	33819	33820						
MetroRider	47975	47976	47977	47978	47979	47988	47989	
Volvo B10M coach	52123	52124	52155	52156	52157	52445	52446	52617
	52618	52619	52620					
Ancillary vehicle	48034							

East unallocated/stored - (EA)

MetroRider	47901	47972		
Mercedes-Benz	40352	40353	40355	40358
Volvo B10M coach	52107	52110	52114	

South Midlands - (SM)

Banbury (Canal Street) - Midland Red (BB)

Olympian	14936							
Volvo B6LE	31319	31320	31353	31361	31362	31365	31852	31853
	31854							
Dart	32704	32705	32706					
Mercedes-Benz	40162	40163	41525	42588				

Ancillary vehicle 48063

Leamington (Station Approach) - Midland Red (LE)

Leyland Olympian	14365	14369	14373	14374	14375	14377	14378	14392
	14515	14516	14517					
Volvo Olympian	16027	16028	16029	16030	16031	16032	16033	16598
	16599	16600	16614	16615	16616	16617	16618	16619
	16620							
Volvo B10M bus	20201	20202	20217	20218	20219	20220	20401	20402
	20557	20558	20559	20560	20803	20804	20808	
Mercedes-Benz	40134	40135	40136	40137	40138	40139	40140	40141
	41518	41521	42586					
Optare Solo	47001	47002	47003	47004	47005	47006	47007	47008
	47009	47010	47011	47012	47013	47014	47015	

Ancillary vehicle 48044 52020

Nuneaton (Newtown Road) - Midland Red (NU)

Olympian	14382	14386						
Volvo B10M bus	20205	20206	20207	20208	20209	20210	20211	20212
	20213	20214	20215	20216	20226	20227	20809	20814
National	25402							
Volvo B6LE	31327	31328	31329	31332	31334	31350	31351	31352
	31354	31355	31356	31357	31363	31364		
Dart	32001	32002	32004	32005	32006	32007	32008	
Dart SLF	33650	33651	33652	33653	33654	33655	33763	33821
	33822							
Mercedes-Benz	40142	40143	40146	40147	40148	40149	40150	40152
	40161	40165	40166	40167	40168	40169	40170	40171
	40172							
Solo	47026	47027	47028					

Ancillary vehicle 48054 48077 52037

Oxford (Horspath Road, Cowley) - (OX)

Outstations: Bicester, Chipping Norton, Harwell, Horspath and Stortford.

Leyland Olympian	14933	14937						
Volvo Olympian	16438	16439	16440	16524				
Volvo B10M bus	20004	20005	20006	20007	20008	20009	20010	20011
	20012	20203	20204	20228	20694	20805	20812	20822
MAN/ALX300	22279	22913	22914	22915	22916	22917	22918	22919
	22920	22921	22922	22923	22924	22925	22926	22927
	22928	22929	22930	22931	22932	22933	22934	22935
	22936	22937	22938	22940	22941	22942	22943	22944
	22945	22946	22947	22948				
Lance	27901	27902	27903					
Volvo B6LE	31330	31331	31333					
Dart	32051	32052	32053	32054	32056	32057	32058	32059
	32061	32062	32063	32064	32610	32611	32612	32613
	32614							
Mercedes-Benz	42371	42372	42374	42375	42376	42383		

MAN DD coach	50034	50035	50036	50037	50038	50039	50040	50041
	50042	50043	50044	50045	50046	50047	50048	50049
	50050	50051	50052	50053	50054	50055	50056	50057
	50058	50059	50060	50066				
Ancillary vehicle	25421	25453	48050					

Rugby (Railway Terrace) - Midland Red (RU)

Leyland Olympian	14371	14387	14930	14931	14932	14935	14942	14943
	14944							
Volvo B10M bus	20221	20223	20224	20225	20813	20816	20821	20823
National	25405							
Volvo B6LE	31321	31322	31323	31324	31325	31326		
Dart	32003							
Mercedes-Benz	40153	40154	40155	40156	40157	40158	40159	40160
	40654	41504	41505	41506				
Volvo B10M coach	52302	52308	52434	52435	52436	52437	52438	52439
	52444	52447	52641	52642	52643			
Ancillary vehicle	48030	48036						

Witney (Corn Street) - Oxford (WY)

Outstation: Chipping Norton

Volvo Olympian	16514	16515	16516	16517	16518	16519	16520	16521
	16522	16523	16525	16526				
Dart	32625	32626	32627	32628	32629	32630		
Mercedes-Benz	40126	40656	40657	40658	40659	41515	41523	42373
	42375	42377	42378	42379	42380	42381	42382	

South Midlands unallocated/stored - (SM)

Olympian	16072	16076	16078	16079	16140	16141	16144	
Volvo B10M bus	20820	20822						
National	25472							
Mercedes-Benz	40106	40107	40108	40110	40127	40128	41510	41522
	42624							
Volvo B10M coach	52020	52031	52037					

Three Plaxton Verde-bodied Dennis Lance buses operate with Stagecoach Oxford and are based at Chipping Norton. From the trio, 27902, N902PFC, is seen in Woodstock preparing for the trip to Oxford.
Richard Godfrey

Wales and West (WW)

Aberdare (Cwmbach New Road, Cwmbach) - Red & White (AE)

Volvo B10M bus	20352	20353						
Volvo B6	30253	30664	30669	30701	30702	30703	30706	30707
	30708	30721	30729	30732				
Dart	32078	32960						
Mercedes-Benz	40594	40643	40714	41326	41403	41404	41421	41424

Brynmawr (Warwick Road) - Red & White (BR)

Volvo B10M bus	20001	20385	20387	20388	20406	20420	20421	20873
Volvo B6	30704	30705	30725					
Dart SLF	33554	33556	33557	33558				
Mercedes-Benz	40541	40567	40568	40570	40571	40576	40577	40712
	40715							
Volvo B10M coach	52180	52186	52417	52495	52496	52498	52499	52500
	52501	52502	52503	52504				

Caerphilly (Bedwas House Ind Est, Bedwas) - Red & White (CL)

Dart	32235	32237	32238	32239	32240	32241	32242	32243
	32244	32245	32247	32248	32249	32250	32254	32255
	32256	32257	32259	32269	32967	32986	32987	
Dart SLF	33605	33606	33607	33608	33609	33610	33611	33612
	33613	33614	33615	33616	33617	33618	33619	33620

Chepstow (Bulwark Road) - (CW)

Titan	10592	10602	10606	10686	10699	10702	10719
Volvo B10M bus	20403	20405	20869	20870	20887	20889	20892
Volvo B6	30240	30251	30831	30832			
Mercedes-Benz	40546						
Volvo B10M coach	52397	52399					

Winter in Cheltenham and route 94 is the home to a batch of 11.3m long Darts with Plaxton bodywork. When delivered in 2000 they were the first Super Pointer darts for the group and have since been joined by further examples working in the South East.
Bill Potter

Cheltenham (Lansdown Ind Est, Gloucester Road) - in Cheltenham (CT)

Leyland Olympian	14609							
Trident	17722	17728	17729					
Volvo B6	30660	30661	30663	30844	30847			
Dart SLF	33501	33502	33503	33504	33505	33506	33507	33508
	33509	33510	33511	33512	33513	33926	33927	33928
	33929	33930	33938	33939	33940	33941	33953	33954
	33955	33956	33957	33958	33959	33961	33962	
Mercedes-Benz	40718	40719	40723	40724	40728	40729	40730	40731
	40732	40736						
Volvo B10M coach	52392	52450	52451	52452	52453	52454		
Ancillary vehicles	46610	48046	48053					

Cwmbran (St David's Road) - Red & White (CN)

Titan	10492	10542	10589	10619	10646	10651	10662	10665
	10905							
Volvo Olympian	16444	16445	16446	16447				
Volvo B10M bus	20368	20369	20370	20389	20390	20391	20392	20404
	20407	20408	20886					
Volvo B6	30710	30728	30833	30836				
Mercedes-Benz	40144	40145	40537	40538	40539	40543	40544	40547
	40555	40556	40557	40558	40559	40566	40569	40572
	40575	40578	40579	40580	40581	40582	40583	40584
	40618	40708	40709	40710	40713	41151	41309	41315
	41317	41322	41323	41324	41405	41408	41412	41413
	41414	41415	41416	41417	41419	41420	41422	41423
	41425	41429	41430					
Volvo B10M coach	52182	52401	52402	52403	52404			
Ancillary vehicle	30835	41981	52059					

Gloucester (London Road) - in Gloucester (GR)

Leyland Olympian	14273	14281	14283	14284	14285	14287	14289	14291
	14292	14500	14501					
Volvo Olympian	16442							
Volvo B10M bus	20817	20818	20819					
Volvo B6	30711	30712	30723	30839	30840	30841	30842	30843
	30845							
Dart SLF	33601	33602	33603	33944	33945	33946	33947	33948
	33949	33950	33951	33952	33960	33966	33967	33968
	33969	33970	33971	33972	33973	33974	33975	33976
	33977							
Mercedes-Benz	40733	40734	41152	41153	41158	41159	41161	41167
	41171	41311						
Volvo B10M coach	52396	52400						
Ancillary vehicles	27034	27934	48083					

Merthyr Tydfil (Merthyr Industrial Estate, Dowlais) - Red & White (MR)

Outstation: Brecon

Volvo B10M bus	20350	20351	20354	20355	20356	20357	20358	20359
	20360	20361	20362	20363	20364	20365	20366	20367
	20697	20698	20806	20807	20810	20811	20815	
Dart	32233	32258	32964	32966	32970	32990	32997	
Dart SLF	33561							
Mercedes-Benz	40548	40561	40562	40563	40564	40565	40573	40574
	41401	41402	41406	41407	41409	41410	41411	
Ancillary vehicle	52090							

Porth (Aberrhondda Road) - Red & White (PT)

Volvo B10M bus	20871	20872	20874	20883	20884	20885	20890	20891
MB O405/Prisma	23950	23951						
Dart	32257	32965	32968	32969	32983	32984	32985	32988
	32989	32991	32992	32993	32994	32995	32996	32998
	32999							
Dart SLF	33559	33621	33622	33623	33624	33625	33626	33627
Mercedes-Benz	40554	41150	41154	41155	41156	41157	41160	41162
	41163	41164	41165	41166	41168	41169	41170	41418
	41426	41427	41428					
Volvo B10M coach	52181	52281						

Ancillary vehicle:	52071

Ross-on-Wye (Platform 62, Business Park) - in Wye and Dean - (RY)

Volvo Olympian	16203	16204	16205	16206	16207	16208	16441
Volvo B6	30248	30709					
Dart SLF	33978	33979	33980				
Mercedes-Benz	41503	41516					

Stroud (London Road) - in the Cotswolds - (SZ)

Leyland Olympian	14274	14275	14282	14286	14288	14293	14502	14610
Volvo B10M bus	20824	20825	20826	20827	20828			
Dart	32901	32902	32903	32936	32937			
Dart SLF	33809	33810	33811	33812				
Mercedes-Benz	40720	40721	40722	40725	40726	40727	40735	41308
	41330	41803	41804	41805	41806			

Ancillary vehicle	46607	48068

Swindon (Eastcott Street) - in Swindon (SN)

Outstation - Chippenham and Cirencester

Titan	10838	11112						
Leyland Olympian	14271	14272	14464	14465	14624	14641	14650	14659
Volvo Olympian	16443	16449	16450	16451				
Volvo B10M bus	20682	20683	20684	20685	20686	20687	20688	20689
	20694	20697	20698					
Dart	32085	32086	32126	32130	32234	32236	32132	32313
	32317	32319	32320					
Dart SLF	33808	33904	33905	33906	33907	33908	33909	33910
	33911	33912	33913	33914	33915	33916	33917	33918
	33924	33925	33942	33943				

Ancillary vehicle	27032	32318	46606

Unallocated (Wales & West) - (WW)

Titan	10606	10686	10699	11108				
Olympian	14290							
Volvo B6	30706	30707						
Mercedes-Benz	40546	40644	40723	40724	40725	40729	40733	40734
	41150	41154	41322					
Iveco	46606							
MetroRider	47924	47927						
Dodge	48002	48003	48028					
Volvo B10M coach	52273	52274	52275	52276	52277	52278	52298	52299
	52300							

South West (SW)

Exeter (Belgrave Road) - (EX)

Outstations: Cullompton; Ottery St Mary; Sidmouth and Tiverton

Scania	15322	15323	15325	15326	15328	15329		
Volvo Olympian	16016	16017	14164	16401	16402	16403	16602	16603
	16604							
Trident	17734	17735	17736					
Volvo B10M bus	20479	20480	20481	20482	20801	20802		
Scania N112	28701	28702	28703	28704	28705	28706		
Volvo B6	30700							
Volvo B6BLE	31701	31702	31703	31704	31705	31706	31707	31708
	31709	31710	31711	31712	31713	31714		
Dart	32099	32139	32140	32141	32251	32261	32263	32264
	32271	32328	32330	32332	32333	32335	32410	32411
	32432	32433	32434	32435	32436	32437	32438	32439
	32440	32441	32442	32443	32444	32599	32618	32639
	32640							
Dart SLF	33158	33159	33160	33200	33201	33202	33751	33774
	33801	33803	33807	33823	33824			
Mercedes-Benz	40226	40227	40228	40229	40230	40231	40232	40233
	40234	40235	40236	40237	40238	40239	40240	40241
	40242	40243	40244	40245	40246	40247	40248	40249
	40250	40508	40512	40979	40981	42101	42102	42103
	42104	42105	42107	42108	42109	42110	42112	42113
	42114	42115	42116	42117	42118			
Iveco	46300	46301	46302	46303	46304	46305	46306	46307
	46308	46309	46310	46311	46312	46314	46315	46316
	46317	46318	46319	46321	46327	46329	46331	46332
	46333	46334						
Volvo B10M coach	52218	52265	52266	52341	52342	52343	52344	52345
	52346							
Javelin interurban	59105	59106	59108	59130				
Special event vehicles	19992							
Ancillary vehicles	48080	48081	48082	52071				

Exmouth (Imperial Road) - (EH)

Titan	11032	11067						
Volvo B10M bus	20347							
Dart	32251	32252	32253	32260				
Dart SLF	33781	33782	33783	33804	33805			
Iveco	46320	46322	46323	46324	46325	46326	46328	46330

Torquay (Regent Close, Shiphay) - (TQ)

Scania	15324	15327						
Volvo Olympian	16164	16404	16405	16406	16407	16408	16409	16410
	16411	16412	16413	16414	16415	16416	16417	16418
	16419	16420	16448	16601				
Dart	32014	32015	32016	32017	32018	32019	32020	32021
	32022	32619	32636					
Mercedes-Benz	40506	40507	40509	40510	40511	40513	40514	40515
	40516	40517	40518	40545	40560	40685	40691	40692
	40693	40694	40695	40696	40697	40698	40699	40701
	40702	40703	40704	40705	40706	40707	40980	40982
Iveco	46365	46366	46367	46368	46369	46370	46371	46372
	46373	46374	46375	46376	46377	46378	46379	46381
	46382	46383	46385	46386	46388	46389	46392	46393
	46396	46398	46399					
Ancillary vehicles	46313	46604	46608	46609				

South West unallocated/Stored - (SW)

Titan	10462	10469	10473	10585	10660	10859		
National	25493							
Dart	32079	32084	32251	32261	32271			
Mercedes-Benz	40549	40550	40551	40553	40554	40711	40716	40717
Iveco	46335	46339	46344	46363	46390	46391	46604	

London - (LN)

Barking (Longbridge Road) - In London (BK)

Trident	17063	17064	17065	17066	17067	17068	17069	17070
	17071	17072	17073	17075	17076	17077	17078	17079
	17080	17359	17360	17361	17362	17363	17364	17365
	17366	17367	17368	17369	17370	17371	17372	17373
	17374	17375	17376	17377	17378	17379	17380	17381
	17382	17383	17384	17385	17386	17387	17388	17389
	17390	17391	17392	17393	17394			
Dart SLF	34021	34022	34023	34024	34027	34036	34039	34040
	34062	34076	34124	34125	34126	34127	34128	34129
	34130	34131	34132	34133	34134	34135	34136	34137
	34138	34198	34199	34202	34254	34255	34256	34257
	34258	34259	34260	34261	34262	34263	34264	34265
	34266	34267	34268	34269	34270	34271	34272	34273
	34274	34275	34276	34277	34278	34279	34280	34281
	34282	34283	34284	34285	34286	34287	34288	34328
	34329	34330	34331	34332	34333	34334	34335	34336
	34337	34338	34339	34340	34341	34342	34343	34344
	34345	34346	34347	34348	34352	34353		
Ancillary vehicle	26012	26019	26027	26031	26033			

Bow (Fairfield Road) - In London (BW)

Routemaster	12098	12300	12392	12399	12402	12415	12429	12435
	12437	12444	12450	12451	12462	12470	12481	12488
	12493	12495	12527	12592	12607	12624	12657	12665
	12668	12696	12709	12719	12738	12743	12749	
Olympian	16044	16045	16046	16047	16048	16049	16050	16051
	16052	16053	16054	16055	16056	16057	16058	16059
	16060	16061	16062	16063	16064	16065	16066	16067
	16068u	16069	16071	16073	16075	16077	16081	16146
	16148							
Trident	17039	17040	17041	17042	17043	17044	17045	17046
	17047	17048	17049	17146	17192	17194	17237	17238
	17239	17240	17241	17242	17244	17245	17246	17466
	17486	17487	17488	17489	17490	17491	17492	17493
	17494	17495	17496	17497	17498	17499	17500	17501
	17535	17536						

Bromley (Hastings Road) - In London (TB)

Olympian	16122	16123	16124	16125	16126	16127u	16130	16133
	16175	16178						
Trident	17230	17231	17232	17233	17234	17235	17236	17279
	17280	17281	17282	17283	17284	17285	17286	17287
	17288	17289	17290	17324	17334	17335	17336	17337
	17338	17339	17340	17341	17342	17343	17344	17345
	17346	17347	17348	17349	17351	17352	17353	17354
	17355	17356	17357	17358				
Dart SLF	34028	34029	34061	34067	34068	34069	34070	34096
	34204	34217	34218	34219	34220	34221	34222	34223
	34224	34225	34226	34227	34228	34229	34230	34231
	34232	34233	34234	34235	34236	34240	34245	34248
Ancillary vehicle	26003	26011	26024	26028				

Catford (Bromley Road) - In London (TL)

Olympian	16084	16085	16086	16087	16090	16092	16096	16097
	16099	16103	16104	16106	16110	16157		
Trident	17139	17143	17148	17150	17151	17152	17153	17154
	17155	17156	17157	17158	17160	17223	17224	17225
	17226	17227	17228	17229	17317	17318	17319	17320
	17321	17322	17323	17325	17326	17327	17328	17329
	17330	17331	17332	17333	17350	17467	17468	17469
	17470	17471	17472	17473	17474	17475	17476	17477
	17478	17479	17480	17481	17482	17483	17484	17485
	17523	17524	17525	17526	17527	17528	17529	17530
	17531	17532	17533	17534	17567	17568	17569	17570
	17571	17572	17573	17574	17575	17576	17577	17578
	17579	17580	17581	17582	17583	17584	17585	17586
	17587	17588	17589	17590	17591			
Dart	34043	34044	34045	34047	34048	34059	34071	34074
	34094	34109	34200	34201	34203	34205	34206	34207
	34208	34209	34210	34211	34237	34238	34239	34241
	34242	34243	34244	34246	34247	34249	34250	34251
	34252	34253	34303	34304	34305	34306	34307	34308
	34309	34310	34311	34312				
Ancillary vehicle	26014	26016	26017					

Leyton (High Road) - In London (T)

Trident	17001	17002	17003	17004	17005	17006	17007	17008
	17009	17010	17011	17012	17013	17014	17015	17016
	17017	17018	17019	17020	17021	17022	17023	17024
	17025	17026	17027	17028	17029	17030	17031	17032
	17033	17034	17035	17036	17037	17038	17050	17051
	17052	17053	17054	17055	17056	17057	17058	17059
	17060	17061	17062	17180	17181	17182	17183	17184
	17185	17186	17187	17188	17189	17190	17191	17409
	17410	17411	17412	17413	17414	17415	17416	17417
	17418	17419	17420	17421	17422	17423	17424	17425
	17426	17427						
Dart SLF	34289	34290	34291	34292	34293	34294	34295	34296
	34297	34298	34299	34300	34301	34302		
Ancillary vehicle	26021	26023	26025	26032				

Pictured in Eltham is Dart 34246, Y246FJN. At the time of the picture this 9-metre model was classed SLD, though later the letters SSD were used. It is reported an 's' suffix has been added locally to the number display.
Laurie Rufus

133

Plumstead (Pettman Crescent) - In London (PD)

Olympian	16070	16082	16083	16088	16089	16091	16092	16093
	16095	16098	16099	16100	16101	16102	16105	16107
	16108	16109	16113	16114	16131	16132	16134	16135
	16136	16137	16138	16139	16143	16145	16147	16149
	16150	16151	16152	16155	16158	16159	16160	16161
	16162	16163	16165	16166	16167	16168	16169	16170
	16171	16172	16173	16174	16176	16177		
Trident	17099	17100	17101	17102	17103	17104	17105	17107
	17108	17109	17110	17112	17113	17115	17116	17117
	17118	17119	17120	17121	17122	17123	17125	17126
	17127	17128	17130	17131	17133	17134	17138	17140
	17141	17142	17145	17149	17159	17161	17162	17163
	17164	17166	17193	17195	17214	17215	17216	17217
	17218	17219	17220	17221	17222	17261	17262	17263
	17264	17265	17266	17267	17269	17270	17271	17272
	17273	17274	17275	17276	17277	17278	17302	17303
	17304	17305	17306	17307	17308	17309	17310	17311
	17312	17313	17314	17315	17316			
Citaro Artic	23001	23002	23003	23004				
Dart SLF	34042	34064	34065	34066	34072	34073	34075	34077
	34078	34079	34080	34081	34082	34083	34084	34085
	34086	34087	34088	34212	34213	34214	34215	34216
	34313	34314	34315	34316	34317	34318	34319	34320
	34321	34322	34323	34324	34325	34326	34327	
Mercedes-Benz	42001	42005	42006	42007	42008	42009	42010	42011
	42012	42015	42018					
Ancillary vehicle	26010	26013	26015	26026	26034	26035		

Romford (North Street) - In London (NS)

Olympian	16001	16002	16003	16041	16042	16043	16111	16112
	16115	16116	16117	16118	16119	16120	16121	16153
	16154	16156						
Trident	17106	17114	17124	17132	17135	17136	17137	17144
	17211	17212	17213	17268	17292	17293	17294	17295
	17296	17297	17298	17299	17300	17301	17428	17429
	17430	17431	17432	17433	17434	17435	17436	17437
	17438	17439	17440	17441	17442	17443	17444	17445
	17446	17447	17448	17449	17450	17451	17452	17453
	17454	17455	17456	17457	17458	17459	17460	17461
	17462	17463	17464	17465				
Dart SLF	34035	34060	34089	34090	34091	34092	34093	34095
	34107	34108	34110					
Volvo B10M coach	52022	52023	52217	52219				
Special event vehicle	10001							
Ancillary vehicle	26001							

Stratford (Waterden Road) - In London (SD)

Trident	17111	17170	17171	17172	17173	17174	17175	17176
	17177	17178	17179	17196	17197	17198	17199	17200
	17201	17202	17395	17396	17397	17398	17399	17400
	17401	17403	17404	17405	17406	17407	17408	17502
	17503	17504	17505	17506	17507	17508	17509	17510
	17511	17512	17513	17514	17515	17516	17517	17518
	17519	17520	17521	17522	17537	17538	17539	17540
	17541	17542	17543	17544	17545	17546	17547	17548
	17549	17550	17551	17552	17553	17554	17555	17556
	17557	17558	17559	17560	17561	17562	17563	17564
	17565	17566						

Dart SLF							
33351	33352	33353	33354	33355	33356	33357	33358
33359	33360	33361	34030	34031	34032	34033	34034
34046	34049	34050	34051	34052	34053	34054	34055
34056	34057	34058	34058	34097	34098	34099	34100
34101	34102	34103	34104	34105	34106	34111	34112
34113	34114	34115	34116	34117	34118	34119	34120
34121	34122	34123	34139	34140	34141	34142	34143
34144	34145	34146	34147	34148	34149	34150	34151
34152	34153	34154	34155	34164	34165	34166	34167
34168	34169	34170	34171	34172			

Upton Park (Redclyffe Road) - In London (U)

Routemaster	12013	12080	12086	12090	12127	12156	12161	12185
	12189	12199	12272	12286	12303	12311	12445	12456
	12496	12497	12541	12550	12565	12581	12610	12616
	12639	12641	12642	12661	12670	12671	12705	12723
	12748	12760						
Trident	17081	17082	17083	17084	17085	17086	17087	17088
	17089	17090	17091	17092	17093	17094	17095	17096
	17097	17098	17129	17147	17165	17167	17168	17169
	17203	17204	17205	17206	17207	17208	17209	17210
	17243	17247	17248	17249	17250	17251	17252	17253
	17254	17255	17256	17257	17258	17259	17260	17291
Dart	34156	34157	34158	34159	34160	34161	34162	34163
	34173	34174	34175	34176	34177	34178	34179	34180
	34181	34182	34183	34184	34185	34186	34187	34188
	34189	34190	34191	34192	34193	34194	34195	34196
	34197							
Scania N113	28615	28616	28617	28618	28619	28620	28621	28622
	28623	28624	28625	28626	28627	28628	28629	28630
Ancillary vehicle	26002	26018	26020	26022	26029	26030		

Stagecoach has been highly praised for its Routemaster operation. Seen at Holborn Circis is 12399, JJD399D, from the RML class. *Richard Godfrey*

South East - (SE)

Aldershot (Halimote Road) - Hants and Surrey (AT)

Outstations - Haslemere and Petersfield

Leyland Olympian	14370	14376	14985	14987	14988	14989		
Volvo Olympian	16305	16319	16320	16351	16352	16353	16391	
Volvo PS	20446	20447	20460	20461	20618	20635		
Dart	32041	32075	32107	32312	32316	32412	32413	32522
	32523	32529	32530	32534	32567	32572	32575	32584
	32585	32586	32587	32588				
Dart SLF	33020	33029	33031	33032	33033	33034	33035	34010
	34011	34012	34013	34015	34016	34017	34018	34019
	34020							
Mercedes-Benz	40112	40113	40114	40115	40118	40119	40120	40123
	40125	40129	40130	40132	40686	40687	40905	40906
	40907	40908	40909	40910	40911	40912	40913	40914

Special event vehicle   19913

Andover (Livingstone Road) - Hampshire Bus (AR)

Leyland Olympian	14717	14957	14974	14986				
Volvo Olympian	16279	16293	16294	16295	16393	16394		
Volvo B10M bus	20438	20445	20606	20607	20608	20615	20616	20617
	20631							
Dart	32521	32528	32544	32545	32551			
Mercedes-Benz	49116	40117	40122	40124	40131	40901	40902	40915
	40920	40921	40922	40924				
Alero	47801	47802						

Ashford (Brunswick Road) East Kent (AD)

Titan	10348	10596					
Leyland Olympian	14803	14806	14828				
Volvo Olympian	16285						
Volvo B10M bus	20644	20645	20659				
MAN	22191	22192	22194				
Dart	33017	33018	33019	33021	33022	33023	33024
Mercedes-Benz	40898	40946	40948	40949	40950	40951	40952

Special event vehicle   19946

Basingstoke (Rankine Road, Daneshill) - Hampshire Bus (BE)

Leyland Olympian	14951	14952	14954	14958				
Bristol VR	15760	15761	15762	15763				
Volvo Olympian	16262	16268	16269	16366	16367	16379	16380	
Volvo B10M bus	20627	20643	20648	20649	20651	20652	20662	20663
	20665	20667	20668	20669	20670			
Dart	32009	32010	32011	32012	32013	32092	32315	32321
	32322	32459	32460	32461	32462	32463	32526	32531
	32533	32547	32549	32573	32574	32578	32581	32582
Dart SLF	33030	33036	33037	33038	33039	33040		

Canterbury (Bus Station, St Georges Lane) - East Kent (CA)

Titan	10244	10647	11121	11125				
Leyland Olympian	14714	14807	14808	14809	14976	14977	14978	14980
	14982							
Scania N113	15311	15312	15340	15345	15353	15357	15358	15359
	15362	15363	15365	15368				
Volvo Olympian	16264	16265	16266	16267	16270	16271	16272	16273
	16274	16275	16283	16284	16296	16297	16298	16360
	16361	16362	16370					
Trident	17402	17689	17690					
Volvo B10M bus	20612	20614	20619					
MAN	22004	22005	22006	22007	22008	22009		
Dart	32458	32465						
Mercedes-Benz	40935	40936	40937	40938	40939	40940	40941	40942
	40943	40947						

Chichester (Southgate) - Sussex Coastline (CR) - Sussex Bus (SB)

Sussex Coastline

Leyland Olympian	14817	14818	14970	14971	14972	14975		
Volvo Olympian	16281	16282						
Volvo B10M bus	20601	20621	20623	20626	20628	20629	20829	20830
Dart	32546	32552	32553	32554	32555	32556	32557	32580
Mercedes-Benz	40690	40820	40895	40897	40903	40904	40917	40918

Sussex Bus

Volvo Citybus	15201	15206			
Volvo B10M bus	20602	20603	20604	20605	
Dart	32524	32532	32537	32543	
Mercedes-Benz	40164	40655	40891	40893	

Dover (Russell Street) - East Kent (DO)

Leyland Olympian	14979	14981	14983	14984				
Volvo Olympian	16299	16363	16364	16368	16369	16386	16387	16389
	16390							
Volvo B10M bus	20633	20637	20638	20639	20640	20661	20676	
Mercedes-Benz	40953	40954	40955	40956	40957	40959	40960	40961
	40962	40963	40964	40965	40966	40967		
Volvo B10M coach	52621	52622						
	52623	52655	52656	52657	52658			
Volvo B12M coach	53001	53002	53003	53004	53005	53006	53007	53008
	53009	53000						

Note: when 53001-10 enter service some of the B10M coaches will be transferred elsewhere.

Folkestone (Kent Road, Cheriton) - East Kent (FO)

Leyland Olympian	14384	14811	14812	14813	14814	14821	14822	14829
	14830							
Volvo Olympian	16287	16365	16371	16372	16375	16376	16377	16378
Volvo B10M bus	20613	20622	20624	20625				
Dart	32467							
Mercedes-Benz	40958	40968	40969	40970	40972	40973	40974	40975
	40976							

Hastings (Beaufort Road, Silverhill, St Leonards) - East Kent (HS)

Leyland Olympian	14801	14802	14804	14805				
Volvo Citybus	15205	15207	15208	15209				
Scania N113	15335	15337	15343	15356	15360	15361		
Volvo Olympian	16315	16316	16317	16318	16382	16383	16384	16385
	16388							
Volvo B10M bus	20190	20313	20609	20620	20646	20647	20650	20654
	20660	20675	20678	20679	20680			
Dart	32311	32327	32457	32464	32466	32501	32502	32503
	32505	32506	32508	32509	32510	32512	32513	32514
	32515	32516	32519	32601	32602	32603	32604	32605
	32606	32607	32608					
Special event vehicle	19909							

Lewes (Eastgate Street) - Sussex Coastline (LS)

Outstation: Eastbourne; Seaford and Uckfield

Volvo Olympian	16313	16314	16354	16355	16356	16357	16358	16359
	16373	16374	16392					
Volvo B10M bus	20664							
Dart	32065	32090	32091	32093	32094	32095	32097	32098
	32414	32456						
Mercedes-Benz	40889	40944	40971					

Portsmouth (Langstone Point) - Sussex Coastline (PM)

Leyland Olympian	14973							
Volvo Citybus	15202	15203	15204					
Volvo Olympian	16278	16302	16306	16307	16322	16323	16324	16341
	16342	16343	16344	16395	16397	16399		
Volvo B6LE	31043	31044	31045	31046	31047	31048	31049	31050
	31051	31052						
Dart	32070	32074	32108	32109	32429	32430	32446	32447
	32448	32449	32450	32451	32452	32453	32454	32455
	32571	32716	32719					
Dart SLF	33053	33054	33056	33057	33058	33059	33061	33062
	33063	33064	33065	33066	33067	33068	33069	33071
	33072							

Thanet (Margate Road, Westwood) - East Kent (TH)

Leyland Olympian	14715	14716	14810	14815	14819	14823	14824	14825
	14826	14827						
Scania N113	15330	15331	15332	15333	15334	15336	15338	15339
	15341	15342	15344	15346	15347	15348	15349	15350
	15351	15352	15354	15355	15364	15366	15367	15369
	15370	15371						
Volvo Olympian	16241	16242	16246	16247	16286	16301	16381	
Volvo B10M bus	20311	20312	20641	20642				
Dart	32088	32221	32222	32223				
Mercedes-Benz	40925	40926	40927	40928	40929	40930	40931	40932
	40933	40934	40977					
Volvo B10M coach	52215	52220	52654					

Winchester (The Broadway) - Hampshire Bus (WI)

Outstations - Alton; Bishops Waltham and Petersfield

Leyland Olympian	14816	14953	14955	14956	14959	14960	14961	14990
Volvo Olympian	16260	16261	16263	16276	16277	16288	16289	16290
	16291	16292	16303	16304	16396	16398		
Volvo B10M bus	20189	20198	20462	20632	20634			
Volvo B6	30141	30142	30800	30801	30802	30803		
Dart	32047	32076	32309	32310	32314	32323	32324	32325
	32326	32536	32538	32539	32542	32550	32565	32569
Dart SLF	33014	33015	33016	33025	33026	33027	33028	
Mercedes-Benz	40689	40894	40896					

Worthing (Library Place) - Sussex Coastline (WG)

Outstation - Henfield

Volvo Olympian	16308	16309	16310	16311	16312	16345	16346	16347
	16348	16349	16350					
Volvo B10M bus	20831	20832	20833	20834	20835	20836		
Lance	27404	27405	27406	27407	27408			
Dart	32077	32096	32527	32541	32558	32559	32560	32561
	32562	32563	32564	32566	32568	32570	32576	32577
	32579							
Dart SLF	33002	33003	33004	33005	33006	33007	33008	33009
	33010	33011	33012	33013	33119			
Mercedes-Benz	40688	40890	40899	40923	40945			

South East unallocated - (SE)

Titan	10180	10190	10511	10645	10670	11124
Leyland Olympian	14372					
Bristol VR	15741					
Dart	32518	32548	32583			
Dart SLF	34014					
Loan to East Midland	32504	32511	32517	32520		
Mercedes Benz	40121	40661	40662	40892	40916	

Special event bus	19945				
Ancillary vehicles	15751	25710	46612	52197	

Previous UK Registrations

126ASV	K566GSA	CSU922	M534RSO
127ASV	K567GSA	CSU923	M535RSO
128ASV	K568GSA	CSU978	M408BFG
13CLT	P159ASA	CSU992	M409BFG
145CLT	M544RSO	D382XRS	D382XRS, WLT528
147YFM	M912WJK	D384XRS	D384XRS, WLT512
283URB	E561UHS	D548MVR	D548MVR, TSV780
3063VC	N43MJO	D551MVR	D551MVR, CSU921
400DCD	GM7642 (HK), N977RCD	D553MVR	D553MVR, CSU923
4012VC	N47MJO	DSV943	N616USS
401DCD	GM4964 (HK), N978RCD	E644UNE	E644UNE, UOT648
402DCD	GM6631 (HK), N979RCD	E920HCD	?
403DCD	GM7558 (HK), N24PWV	EDS50A	WLT560
404DCD	GM6717 (HK), N23PWV	ESU435	L587JSA
405DCD	R705DNJ	FSU739	N619USS
406DCD	GM6788 (HK), N998RCD	G344FFX	G344FFX, WLT809
407DCD	GM7990 (HK), N997RCD	GSO1V	C471SSO
408DCD	R118VPU	GSO6V	D376XRS
410DCD	P610SEV	GSO7V	D377XRS
411DCD	P611SEV	GSO8V	D378XRS
412DCD	R712XAR	GSU341	M107XBW
413DCD	P613SEV	GSU950	L579JSA
414DCD	M404OKM	H181EGU	H654UWR, ?
415DCD	M405OKM	HSK760	K910TKP
416DCD	M406OKM	HSV194	M527RSO
417DCD	M407OKM	HSV195	E905UNW
418DCD	M408OKM	HSV196	E315OEG
419DCD	R119VPU	IIL1321	D51ORH
420DCD	R120VPU	IIL3507	F410DUG
421DCD	R115VPU	J713DAP	J713CYG, 472YMF
422DCD	R116VPU	J715DAP	J715DAP, YLJ332
423DCD	R117VPU	JPU817	D207LWX
424DCD	W426NFG	K574DFS	K574DFS, VLT37
495FFJ	P973UBV	K714ASC	K714ASC, YEL4T
498FYB	L155LBW	K758FYG	J758CWT, 83CBD
511OHU	E789CHS	K759FYG	J759CWT, VT255
6253VC	N42MJO	K921OWV	NDZ3021
630DYE	L158LBW	K922OWV	NDZ3022
647DYE	N336HGK	K923OWV	NDZ3023
685DYE	N337HGK	L100JLB	L110JSA
703DYE	N620USS	L156LBW	L156LBW, VLT225
83CBD	R703DNH	L159LBW	L159LBW, 83CBD
866NHT	J439HDS	L338KCK	L338KCK, 418DCD
896HOD	P975UBV	L345KCK	L345KCK, 415DCD
9258VC	N45MJO	L346KCK	L346KCK, 416DCD
927GTA	J909NKP	L347KCK	L347KCK, 417DCD
9737VC	N46MJO	L392LNA	KAG932E (Kenya)
A14RBL	B176FFS	L424TJK	L604VCD, 404DCD
ABV669A	927GTA	L425TJK	L605VCD, 405DCD
ACZ7489	J739CWT	L426TJK	L606TDY, 406DCD
ACZ7490	J740CWT	L427TJK	L607TDY, 407DCD
ACZ7491	J741CWT	L582JSA	L582JSA, 703DYE
ACZ7492	J742CWT	L608TDY	L608TDY, 408DCD
ACZ7493	J743CWT	L619TDY	L619TDY, 419DCD
ACZ7494	J744CWT	L620TDY	L620TDY, 420DCD
B43MAO	B155WRN	L621TDY	L621TDY, 421DCD
BSK744	F424GCB, TSV777, F213JWD	L622TDY	L622TDY, 422DCD
BSK756	L81YBB	L623TDY	L623TDY, 423DCD
C330DND	C330DND, CSU921	L942RJN	L212YAG
C383SAO	C473SSO	LDS201A	607DYE
C384SAO	C474SSO	LFF875	456CLT
C472SSO	C472SSO, GSV2V	LSK545	M106XBW
CSU920	M532RSO	M151FGB	M1ABO
CSU921	M533RSO		

Cherished index marks from older buses, particularly the Routemasters, are often used on other vehicles, most frequently coaches. Here we list those numbers which are currently in use alongside are the numbers that vehicle has displyed in the past. Articultaed Interurban 51076, seen here in Glasgow, currently displays MSU466 though when new was P976UBV. *Mark Doggett*

M343NOD	GJ155(HK)	N421PWV	GU5924(HK)
M379TJA	KAG602M (Kenya)	N422PWV	GU5116(HK)
M510FWV	M490BFG, 400DCD	N446TOS	N2SBL
M511FWV	M401BFG, 401DCD	N618USS	N618USS, 705DYE
M512FWV	M402BFG, 402DCD, M512FWV, 472YMF	N731XDV	GM8040(HK)
M610APN	M610APN, 410DCD	N732XDV	GM5334(HK)
M611APN	M611APN, 411DCD	N733XDV	GM6788(HK)
M612APN	M612APN, 412DCD	N734XDV	GM9182(HK)
M613APN	M613APN, 413DCD	N735XDV	GM5431(HK)
M614APN	M614APN, 414DCD	N736XDV	GM5376(HK)
M680TDB	KAG933E (Kenya)	N737XDV	GM6331(HK)
M681TDB	KAH560B (Kenya)	N738XDV	GM7131(HK)
M682TDB	KAG931E (Kenya)	N739XDV	GM8269(HK)
M683TDB	KAG544H (Kenya)	N740XDV	GM8240(HK
M684TDB	KAG542J (Kenya)	N742XDV	GM6090(HK)
M685TDB	KAG770V (Kenya)	N743XDV	GM7606(HK)
M686TDB	KAG060M (Kenya)	N744XDV	GM5868(HK)
M687TDB	KAG292E (Kenya)	NDZ3017	W427NFG
M688TDB	KAG543J (Kenya)	NDZ3018	W428NFG
M689TDB	KAG471T (Kenya)	NDZ3019	W425NFG
M690TDB	KAG522X (Kenya)	NDZ3020	R114VPU
M691TDB	KAG405W (Kenya)	NDZ3021	T191MVM
M692TDB	KAG025X (Kenya	NDZ3022	T192MVM
M693TDB	KAG601M (Kenya)	NDZ3023	T194MVM
M694TDB	KAG470T (Kenya)	NFX667	K716PCN
M695TDB	KAG544J (Kenya)	NIB4138	B114WUV
M696TDB	KAG264R (Kenya)	NIB5232	B100WUV
M699TDB	KAG472T (Kenya)	NIB5233	B93WUV
M911WJK	M911WJK, WLT444	NIB5455	B106WUV
MHS4P	C464SSO	NSU132	L585JSA
MHS5P	C465SSO	NSU133	M104XBW
MIL4693	G535LWU	NUF276	L83YBB
MSU463	N48MJO	OIW5804	WCN643Y
MSU466	P976UBV	OIW7025	GLP427T

OSK784	H657UWR	UIB3543	P671LWB
OU51WLK	OU51WLL	UM7681	J919LEM
OU51WLL	OU51WLK	UOT648	L581JSA
OV51AMO	OU51KAO	USK625	WLT980
P299AYJ	HC8802(HK)	UWP105	J917LEM
P301AYJ	HB7989(HK)	VCS370	G529LWU
P302AYJ	HC5075(HK)	VCS391	N562SJF
P330AYJ	HC5122(HK)	VKB708	B483UNB
P343AYJ	HC9501(HK)	VLJ332	M403BFG
P426AYJ	HC9965(HK)	VLT104	VLT104
P434AYJ	HC5014(HK)	VLT14	V476KJN
P435AYJ	HC5778(HK)	VLT154	L588JSA
P457AYJ	HB5013(HK)	VLT245	K570GSA
P458AYJ	HB8862(HK)	VLT255	N331HGK
P466AYJ	HB5506(HK)	VLT272	K569GSA
P479AYJ	HC4904(HK)	VLT37	P974UBV
P758FOD	HB9296(HK)	VLT54	J430HDS
P760FOD	HC5574(HK)	WLT415	L583JSA, FSU739, L583JSA
P762FOD	HB4996(HK)	WLT416	F252OFP
PJI4316	UHE37Y	WLT439	G569ESD
PRX189B	417DCD	WLT444	M911WJK
PS2743	D550MVR, CSU920	WLT447	N617USS
PSU443	D547MVR, TSV779	WLT461	V475KJN
PSU764	D549MVR, TSV781	WLT491	V474KJN
PSU787	C495LJV	WLT512	N332HGK
R71NPN	HM6567(HK)	WLT526	L584JSA
R95NPN	HM2185(HK)	WLT528	N353HGK
R119NPN	HM653(HK)	WLT538	E159XHS
R132NPN	HM1895(HK)	WLT546	TBC1X
R133NPN	HM547HK)	WLT575	X374NNO
R144NPN	HM8456(HK)	WLT682	N334HGK
R177NPN	HM536(HK)	WLT720	P670LWB
R178NPN	HM2053(HK)	WLT774	E158XHS
R196NPN	HM1495(HK)	WLT809	P199OSE
R270NPN	HM1738(HK)	WLT830	H150HVU
R559DRP	R559DRP, WLT528	WLT874	G528LWU
RIB4309	B110WUV	WLT890	L157LBW
S173JVK	1JVK	WLT898	S210WHK
S174JVK	2JVK	WLT908	N335HGK
SHH124M	SCS355M	WLT978	P198OSE
SKY32Y	D552MVR, CSU922, D552MVR	WLT980	G105DWR
SYC52	M407BFG	WSU293	N41MJO
TSU638	H402DEG	WVT618	L618TDY
TSU639	J752CWT	XFF813	WLT898
TSU640	J753CWT	XFF814	WLT890
TSU641	K760FYG	XIA857	PKP548R, XIA256
TSU642	K761FYG	XRC487	L586JSA
TSV718	K561GSA	XSL596A	289CLT
TSV719	K562GSA	XSU612	R812HCD
TSV720	K563GSA	XSU682	P832FVU
TSV721	K564GSA	XYK976	K719PCN
TSV722	K565GSA	YDG616	D206LWX
TSV778	M528RSO	YLJ332	M403BFG, 403DCD, M553FWV
TSV779	M529RSO	YSV730	N561SJF
TSV780	M530RSO	YSV735	H406DAV
TSV781	M531RSO	YTS820A	599CLT
UIB3076	EGT458T		

Stagecoach SUPERTRAM

South Yorkshire Supertram Ltd, 11 Arundel Gate, Sheffield, S1 2PN.

101-125		Siemens		Duewag		AB88T	1993-94		
101	104	107	110	113	116	118	120	122	124
102	105	108	111	114	117	119	121	123	125
103	106	109	112	115					

Depot: Nunnery, Sheffield

The Supertram operation in Sheffield has sucessfully provided transport over the current route, but national funding for an extension is slow to materialise. Pictured with the additional dark blue skirt is 105 while 120 displays an overall advertisement. *Mark Doggett*

STAGECOACH NEW ZEALAND

Stagecoach Wellington, 45 Onepu Road, Kilbirnie, Wellington, New Zealand
Cityline Hutt Valley, Waterloo Interchange, Oxford Terrace, Lower Hutt
Stagecoach Auckland, 451 Mount Eden Road, Mount Eden, Auckland
Runciman Motors, 4 Masefield Street, Upper Hutt

2	NA4281	Isuzu MR113	Coachwork International	B28F	1987	
5	NA3943	Isuzu MR113	Coachwork International	BC28F	1987	
6	SK700	Isuzu ECR570	Demac	C45F	1986	
8	NY58	Isuzu ECR570	Coachwork International	BC45F	1988	
9	MQ8716	Isuzu ECR570	Coachwork International	BC49F	1986	
10	JR48	Ford R1114	New Zealand Motor Bodies	BC48F	1980	
11	ON223	Isuzu ECR570	Austral	B45F	1989	
12	PT2685	Hino RG197	Coachwork International	B37D	1991	
13	JR47	Ford R1114	New Zealand Motor Bodies	BC48F	1980	
15	JZ7041	Ford R1114	New Zealand Motor Bodies	BC48F	1981	
16	OB1552	Isuzu ECR570	Coachwork International	BC49F	1988	
17	JR2616	Mercedes-Benz 0303	New Zealand Motor Bodies	B41D	1980	
18	JW8024	Mercedes-Benz 0303	New Zealand Motor Bodies	B41D	1980	
19	LE4641	Hino BX341	New Zealand Motor Bodies	BC48F	1983	
21	MC609	Isuzu ECR570	New Zealand Motor Bodies	BC49F	1985	

22-26

		Volvo B10M-56		Alexander PS		BC41F	1993	Stagecoach Hong Kong, 1996

22	UO8044	23	UO7966	24	UO7989	25	UO8020	26	UO8000

27-35

		MAN 10-100		Designline		BC28F	1990	

27	OU3699	29	OZ8661	31	OZ8664	33	OZ8666	35	OZ8668
28	OZ8699	30	OZ8660	32	OZ8665	34	OZ8667		

37-57

		Mercedes-Benz 709D		Alexander Sprint		B25F	1996	

37	UN5515	42	UN5521	46	UO3110	50	UP7144	54	UP8933
38	UN5517	43	UN5522	47	UO3112	51	UP7145	55	UP8934
39	UN5518	44	UO3084	48	UP4829	52	UP8928	56	UP8944
40	UN5519	45	UO3085	49	UP4840	53	UP8929	57	UP8945
41	UN5520								

58	ABT884	Denning Landseer		Austral		C	1988	

61-70

		Volvo B6LE		Plaxton Pointer		NC26D	1998	Citybus, Hong Kong, 2002

61	AKS536	63	AKS533	65	AKS534	67	AKS508	69	AKS535
62	AKS504	64	AKS511	66	AKS532	68	AKS510	70	AKS509

124	XP6840	Bristol VRT/SL3/6LXC	Eastern Coach Works	B43/31F	1981	Bluebird Buses, 1998
125	XL1789	Bristol VRT/SL3/6LXC	Eastern Coach Works	B43/31F	1981	Bluebird Buses, 1998
126	ZD4016	Bristol VRT/SL3/6LXB	Eastern Coach Works	B35/25F	1980	Stagecoach Cumberland, 2000
127	ZF9123	Bristol VRT/SL3/6LXB	Eastern Coach Works	B35/25F	1980	Stagecoach Cumberland, 2000
128	ZF9122	Bristol VRT/SL3/6LXB	Eastern Coach Works	B35/25F	1980	Stagecoach Cumberland, 2000

141-170

		MAN SL202		Coachwork International		B45D	1986-89	

141	NF2109	147	NH2755	153	NL9414	159	NL9540	165	NZ8003
142	NF2117	148	NI5642	154	NL9420	160	NL9566	166	NZ8266
143	NH2634	149	NI5704	155	NL9466	161	OB1550	167	OG8397
144	NH2652	150	NI5718	156	ZP1073	162	NT9387	168	OG8398
145	NH2754	151	NL9377	157	NL9461	163	PA6879	169	OG8399
146	NH2756	152	NL9393	158	NL9531	164	NZ8004	170	OG8551

Nine MAN 10-100 minibuses with Designline bodies are in service with the New Zealand Cityline operation. Awaiting their next duty are 27, OU3699 and 33, OZ8666. *Ken MacKenzie*

171-180

| | | | | | | MAN 16.200 UOCL | | | Coachwork International | B39D | 1989-91 |

171	ON525	173	PL5272	175	PL5274	177	PL5823	179	PP5206
172	PL5003	174	PL5273	176	PL5822	178	PL5824	180	PP5205

181	PP5219	MAN 16.240 UOCL	Coachwork International	B41D	1991

201-234

Volvo B58 BBC4ELO2002 — Hawke Coachwork — B40D — 1981-84

201	KA9102	211	KA9110	217	NA87	222	KD7488	227	KH4274
204	JM7127	212	KA9111	218	KA7233	223	KD7485	229	KH4358
207	JY5832	213	KA9184	219	KA7234	224	KD7486	232	KJ8245
208	JY5831	214	KA9185	220	KA7235	225	KH4273	233	KJ8244
209	KA9103	216	KA9192	221	KD7490	226	KD7487	234	LQ2643
210	KA9109								

235-254

Volvo B58 BBC4ELO2002 — Hawke — B40D — 1985

235	LW6465	239	MB7635	243	ME9235	247	MJ2016	251	MJ2168
236	MA8821	240	MB7638	244	ME9236	248	MJ2015	252	MJ2169
237	MA5210	241	MB7636	245	ME2504	249	MJ2014	253	MJ2171
238	MA5209	242	MB7637	246	MJ2012	250	MJ2013	254	MJ2172

255-268

Volvo B58 BBC4ELO2002 — Hawke — B40D — 1986

255	MO1322	258	SC2911	261	MS1706	264	MS1703	267	MS1812
256	MO1321	259	MO1397	262	MS1705	265	MS1814	268	MS1815
257	MO1391	260	MS1707	263	XG2300	266	MS1813		

270	MC6399	Hino AC140	Micanta		1985	
290	PD1036	Renault S75	Coachwork International	B23F	1990	
291	PD1037	Renault S75	Coachwork International	B23F	1990	
292	PD1038	Renault S75	Coachwork International	B23F	1990	
293	PE5096	Renault S75	Coachwork International	B23F	1990	
294	RM4511	Toyota Hiace	Toyota	M15	1992	Wellington, 1993

The 2003 Stagecoach Bus Handbook

Stagecoach maintain the Wellington trolleybus network. As we go to press the first re-bodied trolleybus is expected to re-enter service, and after evaluation the future of the vehicles will be considered. Representing the Volvo B58s is 242, MB7637. *Ken MacKenzie*

401-416

				Leyland Leopard PSU3C/2R		Hawke Coachwork			B40D	1976-77		

401	HZ2712	406	HE2656	408	HQ3899	410	PW8450	413	IL4518
402	HI1974	407	HE2657	409	HQ3907	412	IL4519	416	IK7801
403	GA6806								

417-478

Leyland Leopard PSU3E/2R — Hawke Coachwork — B40D — 1978-79

417	IU9434	425	IX3781	441	JA1185	455	JF1910	469	JA1184
418	IU9433	427	IX3783	442	JA1198	456	JF1911	474	JD181
419	IU9432	428	IX3782	444	JC2568	457	JF1913	476	JD199
421	IX7733	435	IU9931	448	JD183	458	JF1914	477	JF1902
423	IX3304	436	IU9932	451	JD197	462	IX7767	478	JF1912
424	IX3302	439	JC2430	452	JF1903	464	ADN679		

481	LA5234	Leyland Leopard PSU3E/2R	Hawke Coachwork	B49D	1983	Invercargill, 1992
482	JT684	Leyland Leopard PSU3E/2R	Hawke Coachwork	B47D	1982	Cesta Travel, 1993

501-520

MAN 11.190 HOCL - R — Designline — B39D — 1994-95

501	SS5537	505	TB6105	509	SY1641	513	TA2667	517	TB6042
502	SS5538	506	SW4400	510	SY1631	514	TA2691	518	TB6050
503	ST7109	507	SW4435	511	SZ5917	515	TA2714	519	TB6056
504	SX7724	508	SW4436	512	SZ5918	516	TB6023	520	TB6057

521-554

MAN 11.190 HOCL — Designline — B39D — 1995

521	TB6106	528	TE2325	535	TG5856	542	TG5879	549	TJ2515
522	TB6107	529	TE2326	536	TG5857	543	TG5896	550	TJ2516
523	TD2564	530	TE2327	537	TG5871	544	TG5897	551	TR1643
524	TD2593	531	TF6235	538	TG5872	545	TG5898	552	TR1644
525	TD2594	532	TF6236	539	TG5876	546	TG5899	553	TR1645
526	TD2630	533	TF6237	540	TG5877	547	TH5837	554	TR1646
527	TD2631	534	TG5855	541	TG5878	548	TH5838		

Leyland Leopard s still provide sterling service and type PSU3E/2R number 418, IU9433, shows off its Hawke Coachwork as it rests in Wellington. Of interest is the number of destination and information displays.
Ken MacKenzie

601-626

MAN 11.190 HOCL   Designline   N39D   1995-96

601	TJ2541	607	UB490	612	XY8784	617	UB483	622	UF5846
602	TJ2542	608	UB491	613	UB500	618	UB482	623	XT1245
603	UB487	609	UB492	614	UB499	619	UB484	624	UF5850
604	UB488	610	UB497	615	UB498	620	UB485	625	UF5851
605	TU1498	611	UB495	616	UF5845	621	UF5849	626	UF5852
606	UB489								

627-658

MAN 11.190 HOCL   Designline Ashburton   N39D   1996-97

627	UF5853	634	UH7205	641	UH7218	647	UL5044	653	UL5060
628	UF5854	635	UH7206	642	UH7212	648	UL5045	654	UL5042
629	UF5855	636	UH7207	643	UH7219	649	UL5046	655	UO9429
630	UF5856	637	UH7208	644	UH7220	650	UL5051	656	UO9427
631	UF5857	638	UH7215	645	UH7213	651	UL5052	657	UO9433
632	UF5858	639	UH7216	646	UH7214	652	UL5053	658	UT5625
633	UH7204	640	UH7217						

701-740

MAN 11.190 HOCL   Designline Ashburton   N39D   1998

701	XG2082	709	XI9041	717	XJ5244	725	XL3262	733	XL9778
702	XG2081	710	XI9042	718	XJ5245	726	XL3264	734	XL9779
703	XG2083	711	XI9043	719	XJ5246	727	XL3265	735	XN4432
704	XG2084	712	XI9044	720	ZD6442	728	XL3266	736	XN4433
705	XG2085	713	XI9045	721	XJ5247	729	XL9773	737	XN4436
706	XG2087	714	XJ5241	722	XJ5249	730	XL9774	738	XN4437
707	XG2088	715	XJ5242	723	XJ5250	731	XL9775	739	XN4438
708	XG2089	716	XJ5243	724	XL3261	732	XL9777	740	XN4439

Designline Ashburton bodied a batch of MAN 11.190s in 1998, the MAN product being well received in the country. The type is allocaed to Auckland, where 750, ZE2402 is seen. *Ken MacKenzie*

741-780   MAN 11.190 HOCL   Designline Ashburton   N39D   1998-99

741	XN8101	**749**	XO7306	**757**	XS4093	**765**	XT7869	**773** XW4119
742	XN8102	**750**	ZE2402	**758**	XS4094	**766**	XT7870	**774** XY1872
743	XN8103	**751**	XP6952	**759**	XS4097	**767**	XW4111	**775** XY1873
744	XN8106	**752**	XP6953	**760**	XS4098	**768**	XW4112	**776** XY1874
745	XN8107	**753**	XP6954	**761**	XS4100	**769**	XW4113	**777** XY1875
746	XN8108	**754**	XP6955	**762**	XT7864	**770**	XW4114	**778** XY1877
747	XO7305	**755**	XP6958	**763**	XT7867	**771**	XW4115	**779** XY1878
748	XO7304	**756**	XP6959	**764**	XT7868	**772**	XW4118	**780** XY1880

801-835   MAN 16.230 HOCL   Fairfax Industries   N51D   2000

801	ZI7441	**808**	ZI7448	**815**	ZI7455	**822**	ZI7462	**829** ZI7469
802	ZI7442	**809**	ZI7449	**816**	ZI7456	**823**	ZI7463	**830** ZI7470
803	ZI7443	**810**	ZI7450	**817**	ZI7457	**824**	ZI7464	**831** ZI7471
804	ZI7444	**811**	ZI7451	**818**	ZI7458	**825**	ZI7465	**832** ZI7472
805	ZI7445	**812**	ZI7452	**819**	ZI7459	**826**	ZI7466	**833** ZI7473
806	ZI7446	**813**	ZI7453	**820**	ZI7460	**827**	AGR422	**834** ZI7474
807	ZI7447	**814**	ZI7454	**821**	ZI7461	**828**	ZI7468	**835** ZI7475

1012	IX3950	Mercedes-Benz O303	NZ Motor Bodies	B51D	1978
1033	JD616	Mercedes-Benz O303	NZ Motor Bodies	B51D	1979
1036	JD800	Mercedes-Benz O303	NZ Motor Bodies	B51D	1979
1040	JD1323	Mercedes-Benz O303	NZ Motor Bodies	B51D	1979
1070	NY9392	Mercedes-Benz O303	NZ Motor Bodies	B51D	1980
1074	JQ9731	Mercedes-Benz O303	NZ Motor Bodies	B51D	1980
1096	LA5164	Mercedes-Benz O303	NZ Motor Bodies	B51D	1980

1101-1139   MAN 22.240   Coachwork International   B53D   1998

1101	PG8701	1109	PI9549	1117	PS2953	1125	YY8717
1102	PG8702	1110	PM772	1118	PS2954	1126	PT7114
1103	PG8703	1111	PM773	1119	PS2955	1127	PT7115
1104	PG8704	1112	PM774	1120	PS2956	1128	PT7116
1105	PG8705	1113	PM775	1121	PT6621	1129	PT7117
1106	PG8706	1114	PN8766	1122	PT6849	1130	PT7118
1107	PI9547	1115	PS3379	1123	PT6850	1131	PX3609
1108	SR1039	1116	PS3380	1124	PT6851	1132	PX3610

1133	PX3611
1134	TD2660
1135	PX3613
1136	PX3614
1137	PX3615
1138	PX3616
1139	PX3617

1140	WR2559	Mercedes-Benz O305	Fairfax Industries	B53D	1997
1141	XU8299	Mercedes-Benz O305	Fairfax Industries	B53D	1999
1142	YC6102	Mercedes-Benz O305	Fairfax Industries	B53D	1998
1143	YE4656	Mercedes-Benz O305	Fairfax Industries	B53D	1999
1144	YE4658	Mercedes-Benz O305	Fairfax Industries	B53D	1999
1145	YH5811	Mercedes-Benz O305	Fairfax Industries	B53D	1999
1146	YS5352	Mercedes-Benz O305	Designline Ashburton	B53D	2000
1147	YP8055	Mercedes-Benz O305	Designline Ashburton	B53D	2000
1200	ST7217	MAN 11.190	Fairfax Industries	B41F	1994
1201	SN7897	MAN 11.190	Coachwork Auckland	B39F	1994

1202-1241   Nissan Scorpion SBR180   Fairfax Industries   N41D   1995-96

1202	SP4125	1210	TE8727	1218	TK2701	1226	TO2604
1203	SR7404	1211	TE8775	1219	TK2732	1227	TP3843
1204	SR7403	1212	TE8776	1220	TK2731	1228	TS119
1205	ZE5673	1213	TG2853	1221	TM8033	1229	TS118
1206	SZ8401	1214	TI3484	1222	TM8050	1230	ZO3592
1207	TB6204	1215	TI3485	1223	TM8049	1231	TU7223
1208	TB2659	1216	TI3511	1224	TM7788	1232	TU7222
1209	TE8726	1217	TI3540	1225	TO2605	1233	TU7221

1234	TY882
1235	TY8997
1236	TY8998
1237	UA8873
1238	UA8872
1239	UD4659
1240	UE3261
1241	UE3262

1296	WP7444	MAN 10.160	Designline Ashburton	N37F	1997
1297	WP7445	MAN 10.160	Designline Ashburton	N37F	1997
1299	MF7517	Volvo B10M	Coachwork Auckland	B46D	1985
1300	MF7516	Volvo B10M	Coachwork Auckland	B46D	1985

1301-1360   MAN 12.223 HOCL-R   Coachwork International   B53D   2002

1301	AMT745	1313	ATK361	1325	AWZ519	1337	AQL357
1302	ANF929	1314	ATK362	1326	AQB435	1338	ATP945
1303	APP362	1315	ATK364	1327	AQB436	1339	ARR725
1304	APP365	1316	ATK365	1328	AQB438	1340	ARR728
1305	APP366	1317	ATK366	1329	AQL344	1341	ARD600
1306	APP369	1318	APT947	1330	AQL345	1342	ARR730
1307	ASJ557	1319	AZE116	1331	AQL352	1343	ASA164
1308	ASH467	1320	AZE115	1332	AQL351	1344	ASA165
1309	ASU457	1321	AZE112	1333	AQL356	1345	ASA168
1310	ASU458	1322	AYP208	1334	ARD190	1346	ASA170
1311	ATB792	1323	AYP204	1335	ARD196	1347	ATZ463
1312	ATB794	1324	AWZ520	1336	ARD197	1348	ATZ472

1349	ATZ473
1350	AUM732
1351	AUM734
1352	AUW481
1353	AUW486
1354	AUW487
1355	AUW491
1356	AUW497
1357	AWZ508
1358	AWZ509
1359	AWZ511
1360	AWZ512

Recent arrivals are low-floor MAN 12.223 buses. The latest styling is shown on the first ot the batch of sixty, 1301, AMT475, seen in the rain shortly after delivery.
Ken Mackenzie

149

Thirty-four MAN articulated buses made up of SG220 and SG240 models are divided between many of the depots where they provide large capacity. The five Bristol VR double-deck buses are retained for tourist duties. Allocated to Shore and Orewa, 2030, OT6354 shows off the Coachwork International styling.
Ken MacKenzie

1506-1551 Mercedes-Benz O305 NZ Motor Bodies B45D 1977-78

1506	IQ4498	1521	IU7096	1536	IX3258	1542	IX3957	1547	JA1474
1507	IQ4499	1527	IU8160	1538	IX3260	1543	IX4152	1549	JA2161
1509	IU3476	1533	IX2459	1539	XC8762	1544	IX4153	1550	JA2162
1511	IU3478	1534	TD2661	1540	IX3955	1545	IX4154	1551	NR8964
1512	IU3479	1535	IX2562	1541	IX3956	1546	JA1473		

1552-1600 Mercedes-Benz O305 NZ Motor Bodies B45D 1979

1552	RE7374	1561	JD795	1572	IB8098	1582	JQ3496	1592	JL2163
1553	JD140	1562	JD796	1573	IB8099	1584	JL879	1593	SJ1700
1554	JD241	1565	JD1678	1574	JB8100	1585	JL1404	1594	TC5184
1555	JD612	1566	PS2957	1575	JG5928	1587	JL1406	1595	JN1685
1556	JD790	1567	MF7509	1576	JG5929	1588	JL1407	1598w	TR354
1557	JD791	1568	JG4613	1577	JG5930	1589	JL1408	1599	JN2205
1558	JD792	1569	JG4614	1578	UK5492	1591	PE1593	1600	JN2206
1559	JD793	1570	YL6611	1579	JG6298				

1601-1661 MAN SL200 Hawke Coachwork B-- D 1981-83

1601	KI6723	1613	KN4858	1626	KQ1183	1638	KT8186	1650	KT9106
1602	KI6724	1614	KN4859	1627	KQ1184	1639	KT8187	1651	KX8648
1603	KI6725	1615	KN4860	1628	KQ1185	1640	KD3568	1652	KX8647
1604	KI6726	1616	KN4881	1629	KQ1186	1641	KD3569	1653	KX8646
1605	KI6727	1617	KN4882	1630	KS1252	1642	KD3570	1654	KX8645
1606	KJ1587	1618	KN5551	1631	KS1253	1643	KD3571	1655	KX8644
1607	KJ1588	1620	KN5547	1632	KS1254	1644	KD3572	1656	KX9350
1608	KJ1589	1621	KN5548	1633	KS1255	1645	KT8916	1657	KX9351
1609	KJ1590	1622	KN5549	1634	KS1256	1646	KT8917	1658	KX9352
1610	KJ1591	1623	KN5550	1635	KS1257	1647	RE7408	1659	KX9353
1611	KJ1592	1624	KQ1181	1636	KT8184	1648	KT8919	1660	KX9394
1612	KJ1593	1625	KQ1182	1637	KT8185	1649	KT8920	1661	KD9603

1662	RD5280	MAN SL200	Coachwork International	B-- D	1985

The 2003 Stagecoach Bus Handbook

1663-1670   MAN SL200   Hawke Coachwork   B-- D   1984

1663	LT964	1665	LX1166	1667	LX4260	1669	LX4258	1670	LX4257
1664	LT965	1666	LX1165	1668	LX4259				

1671-1688   MAN SL200   Coachwork International   B-- D   1985

1671	MA6604	1675	MD1200	1678	MD1203	1681	MF7341	1686	MH6117
1672	MA7121	1676	MD1201	1679	MF7339	1682	MF7607	1687	MH6118
1673	MA7122	1677	MD1202	1680	MF7340	1685	MH6116	1688	MH6119
1674	MA7123								

1689-1757   MAN SL202   Coachwork International   B-- D   1986-89

1689	MA6224	1703	MW3305	1717	NF6910	1731	NS2855	1745	OC4045
1690	MT7457	1704	MW3306	1718	NF6909	1732	NS2853	1746	OC4046
1691	WN5440	1705	MW3307	1719	NF6912	1733	NS3202	1747	OD3724
1692	OC4173	1706	MY4759	1720	NK9509	1734	NS3201	1748	NX1748
1693	MJ8299	1707	MY4758	1721	NK9508	1735	NO3078	1749	NY8741
1694	MW3300	1708	MY4756	1722	NL528	1736	NO3081	1750	NX1750
1695	MW2339	1709	MU3567	1723	YW9657	1737	NO3079	1751	NY8742
1696	MW3301	1710	MU3569	1724	NL530	1738	NX1738	1752	OF313
1697	MW3302	1711	MU3568	1725	NF5886	1739	NX1739	1753	OF314
1698	MW2380	1712	NF2699	1726	NF5887	1740	NY9889	1754	OF315
1699	ZK8188	1713	NF2698	1727	NF5885	1741	NY9890	1755	OF316
1700	MW2382	1714	NF1525	1728	NS1647	1742	OC4042	1756	OD3725
1701	ZE2405	1715	NF4958	1729	NS1648	1743	OC5480	1757	OD3726
1702	MW3304	1716	NF6911	1730	YY8711	1744	OC4044		

1801-1867   Nissan Scorpion SLF180   Fairfax Industries   N35D   1996-97

1801	UN7501	1814	WK5488	1832	UZ3649	1844	WD4127	1856	WG1059
1802	UN7502	1821	US7577	1833	UZ7785	1845	WD4126	1857	WG8781
1803	UN7503	1822	UU3597	1834	UZ7786	1846	WD4185	1858	WG8782
1804	UN7504	1823	US7576	1835	UZ7787	1847	WD4187	1859	WJ3305
1805	UN7505	1824	UW6598	1836	WA4292	1848	WD4186	1860	WJ3304
1806	UN7506	1825	UW6597	1837	WA4291	1849	WE6195	1861	WJ3302
1807	UN7507	1826	UX2881	1838	WA4290	1850	WE6196	1862	WJ3301
1808	UN7508	1827	UX2882	1839	WA4289	1851	WE6197	1863	WJ9156
1809	UN7509	1828	UX9327	1840	WA2443	1852	WE6198	1864	WJ9155
1810	UN7510	1829	UX9328	1841	WA2445	1853	WG5359	1865	WK8984
1811	UN7511	1830	UX9330	1842	WA2444	1854	WF6426	1866	XQ2361
1812	ZK1561	1831	UZ3648	1843	WA2442	1855	WG5360	1867	WK8986
1813	UN7513								

Allocated to Waterloo is number 8, NY58, one of six Isuzu ECR570 buses operated by Stagecoach. On this example the Coachwork International body is fitted with high-back seating.
Ken MacKenzie

1868-1892   Nissan Scorpion SLF180   Fairfax Industries   N38D   1997-98

1868	WM5722	**1873**	WO2149	**1878**	WO2145	**1883**	WU6684	**1888**	WG8922
1869	WM5723	**1874**	WO2148	**1879**	WR2862	**1884**	WW3947	**1889**	WI9316
1870	WM5724	**1875**	WT657	**1880**	WS696	**1885**	WX4593	**1890**	WL5655
1871	WM5725	**1876**	WO2147	**1881**	WS697	**1886**	WX7647	**1891**	XM9633
1872	WO2150	**1877**	WO2146	**1882**	WT9909	**1887**	WX7648	**1892**	XN7643

2001-2020   MAN SG220   Hawke Coachwork   AB76D   1983

2001	KS1258	**2005**	LC7015	**2009**	LC7936	**2013**	KL6812	**2017**	KD9596
2002	LA5936	**2006**	LC7016	**2010**	KL6786	**2014**	KD4078	**2018**	KD9597
2003	LA5937	**2007**	LC7017	**2011**	KL6787	**2015**	KD4077	**2019**	KD9598
2004	KR6018	**2008**	LC7018	**2012**	KL6788	**2016**	KD9594	**2020**	PE1592

2021-2034   MAN SG240   Coachwork International   AB76D   1988-90

2021	NY8743	**2024**	NY9893	**2027**	OW6753	**2030**	OT6354	**2033**	OT6350
2022	NY9891	**2025**	OW6752	**2028**	OT6352	**2031**	OT6351	**2034**	OT6349
2023	NY9892	**2026**	PB8184	**2029**	OT6353	**2032**	OW6754		

5907	1055IC	Hino BG300		Emslie	C41F	1980
6009	JZ6948	Bedford NFM/6BD1		NZ Motor Bodies	B37D	1981
6890	MI8415	Hino RK176		NZ Motor Bodies	B45D	1985

7193-7253   Hino RK176   Coachwork International   B47D*   1987-88   *6890/7193/7-7200 are B45D

7193	NA6078	**7201**	NK8507	**7237**	NA7358	**7245**	NL7826	**7250**	NL7831
7197	NA6060	**7231**	NA7353	**7238**	NA7359	**7246**	NL7827	**7251**	NA7832
7198	NA6947	**7232**	NA7350	**7239**	NA7361	**7247**	NL7828	**7252**	NA7833
7199	NA6946	**7233**	NA7351	**7242**	XU7670	**7248**	NL7829	**7253**	NL7834
7200	NA6945	**7236**	NA7357	**7244**	NL7825	**7249**	NL7830		

7255-7556   Hino RK177   Coachwork International   B47D   1988-89

7255	NL7823	**7266**	NL8272	**7278**	NX9487	**7538**	OB4207	**7547**	OE7912
7256	NL7790	**7267**	NL7793	**7279**	NX9488	**7539**	OB4208	**7548**	OE7917
7258	NL7796	**7268**	NL8264	**7532**	NX9510	**7540**	OB4215	**7549**	OG5328
7259	NL7797	**7269**	NL8265	**7533**	NX9509	**7542**	OB4213	**7551**	OG5327
7260	NL7799	**7270**	NL8266	**7534**	NX9507	**7543**	OB4212	**7553**	OG5341
7261	NL7794	**7271**	NL8273	**7535**	NX9508	**7544**	OB4214	**7554**	OG5342
7263	NL7791	**7273**	NL8267	**7536**	NX9516	**7545**	OE7913	**7555**	OG5343
7264	NL7792	**7274**	NL8268	**7537**	NX9517	**7546**	OE7916	**7556**	OG5344
7265	NL7798	**7276**	NX9485						

F17	ON350	Hino RB145	Coachwork International	1989
F18	JL646	Bedford VAM75	NZ Motor Bodies	1979
F19	JL643	Bedford VAM75	NZ Motor Bodies	1980
F20	JR3343	Bedford VAM75	NZ Motor Bodies	1981
F21	NN4726	Hino RK76	Coachwork International	1988
F22	ND8808	Hino RK176	Coachwork International	1987
F23	JB7766	Bedford VAM75	NZ Motor Bodies	1979
F24	OX4066	Hino BC144	Coachwork International	1990
F25	JL645	Bedford VAM75	NZ Motor Bodies	1979
F27	LO9830	Hino AM140	Hawke	1984
F30	WA9789	Isuzu LR312J	Isuzu (Japanese)	1988
F31	WH4333	Hino AC140	Hawke	1986

Ancillary vehicles

480	ADS121	Leyland Leopard PSU3E/2R	Hawke Coachwork	B49D	1978	Arts Festival promotion
1368	HL6982	Mercedes-Benz O305	NZ Motor Bodies	B--D	1975	

Previous UK Registrations:

XL1769	KWA215W	XP6840	KWA216W

CITYBUS

Citybus Ltd, 13/F 9 Des Voeux Road West, Hong Kong.

1	HK1931	AEC Routemaster R2RH	Park Royal	O33/28R	1964	London Buses, 1984
2w	ES4007	AEC Routemaster R2RH	Park Royal	O26/28R	1962	London Buses, 1984
7	EB1030	Leyland Olympian ONTL11/2R	Eastern Coach Works	O44/32F	1982	Badgerline, 1988
14w	DN1648	Leyland Olympian ONLXB/1R	Roe	O47/29F	1982	West Yorkshire PTE, 1987
15	DN779	Leyland Olympian ONLXB/1R	Roe	O47/29F	1982	West Yorkshire PTE, 1987
17	DN3750	Leyland Olympian ONLXB/1R	Roe	O47/29F	1982	West Yorkshire PTE, 1987
18	DN4435	Leyland Olympian ONLXB/1R	Roe	O47/29F	1982	West Yorkshire PTE, 1987
105	DU5866	Leyland Olympian ONTL11/3RSp	ECW/Ben Hop(1995)	C55/41F	1985	Leyland demonstrator, 1987

106-117

Leyland Olympian ONCL10/5RZ   Alexander RH   BC53/41F   1989

106	EE5853	109	EF1671	112	EF3592	114	EF8967	116	EF8850
107	EF1962	110	EF587	113	EF6118	115	EF9671	117	EF9412
108	EF2067	111	EF1523						

118-128

Leyland Olympian ONCL10/5RZ   Alexander RH   BC53/41F   1990

118	EL7207	121	EF7565	125	EM7306	127	EM6616	128	EM5408
119	EL9367	123	EL8119	126	EM2375					

130-179

Leyland Olympian ON3R49C18Z4*   Alexander RH   BC53/41F   1990* 145/7 fitted with Gardner engines

130	ER1374	140	ES3710	150	ES8691	160	ET1190	170	EX258
131	ER9169	141	ES1962	151	ET1989	161	ES8820	171	EV4813
132	ER7389	142	ET1026	152	ET778	162	ET1746	172	EW4971
133	ER6824	143	ES3771	153	ET2205	163	HR7642	173	EW9757
134	ER6587	144	ES7623	154	EV3020	164	EW9215	174	EW8815
135	ER9371	145	ES4877	155	ET1163	165	EX441	175	EW8584
136	ER9289	146	ES5389	156	ET623	166	EW8656	176	EW9231
137	ER8952	147	ET1848	157	EW3034	167	EW9698	177	EV4854
138	ER8635	148	ET1613	158	ET160	168	EW9357	178	EV6091
139	ES2467	149	ET550	159	ET1023	169	EX166	179	EW5449

The Ocean Park leasure area is connected to Central by a bus service which Citybus have provided since the days of open-top DMSs. Currently, the stock is Olympians, represented this year by 121, EF7565.
Malcolm King

180-204 — Leyland Olympian ON3R49C18Z4* Alexander RH — BC53/41F 1991-92 — * 204 type ON3R49G18Z4

180	FC3474	185	FC5301	190	FD8372	195	FD6686	200	FD8677
181	FB8714	186	FC4750	191	FD7919	196	FD8049	201	FD9105
182	FC3084	187	FC8295	192	FD7206	197	FD8768	202	FD8653
183	FC2566	188	FC6577	193	FD8109	198	FD8530	203	FD9084
184	FC6490	189	FD6912	194	FD8434	199	FD9162	204	FJ4074

205	FG9161	Leyland Olympian ON3R49C18Z4 Alexander RH	BC49/37F	1992

206-238 — Leyland Olympian ON3R49C18Z4 Alexander RH — B49/37F 1993

206	FS7207	213	FS4075	220	FS3991	227	FS3214	233	FS3544
207	FS6695	214	FS2692	221	FS6891	228	FS7921	234	FS7418
208	FS3596	215	FS3166	222	FS3055	229	FS6880	235	FS8420
209	FS4088	216	FS7159	223	FS4341	230	FS7682	236	FS6950
210	FS4022	217	FS7820	224	FS3026	231	FS3645	237	FS6873
211	FS8100	218	FS2678	225	FS8209	232	FS4481	238	FS2847
212	FS2841	219	FS7829	226	FS7274				

239-248 — Volvo Olympian YN3RV18Z4 Alexander RH — B49/36F 1994

239	GC7987	241	GC7306	243	GC7776	245	GC6617	247	GC9321
240	GC6664	242	GC6717	244	GC7665	246	GC7448	248	GC8753

300-314 — Leyland Olympian ONC3R56C18Z4/5RZ Alexander RH — BC57/45F 1992 — 301/4/6/10/12 CLP,1997-2001. Remainder operated on behalf of China, Light & Power.

300	FC3781	303	FC712	306	FC7431	310	FC8014	313	FC8248
301	FC1067	304	FC1714	307	FC7752	311	FC7256	314	FC7328
302	FC736	305	FC7535	309	FC8342	312	FC7233		

315	GE5135	Volvo Olympian YN3RC18Z4	Alexander RH	BC57/45F	1994	China Light & Power, 1997.
316	GE5021	Volvo Olympian YN3RC18Z4	Alexander RH	BC57/45F	1994	China Light & Power, 1997.

324-329 — Volvo Olympian — Alexander RH — B57/45D 1998

324	HV5025	326	HV5419	327	HV7618	328	HV9029	329	HV5031
325	HV5961								

330-340 — Leyland Olympian ONC3R56C18Z4/5RZ Alexander RH — BC57/45F 1992

330	FG4672	333	FG4101	335	FG5594	337	FG5912	339	FG5290
331	FK5095	334	FG4976	336	FG4769	338	FG5350	340	FK5226
332	FG3811								

341	EL7976	Leyland Olympian ON3R56C18Z5 Alexander RH (1993)	B57/42D	1990

342-395 — Leyland Olympian ON3R56C18Z5 Alexander RH — B57/42D 1993

342	FR2937	353	FS1819	364	FR5308	375	FR7570	386	FS5611
343	FR3093	354	FR5671	365	FS2231	376	FR6990	387	FS4861
344	FS7312	355	FR7062	366	FR6369	377	FR8386	388	FS6141
345	FR2618	356	FR3369	367	FR8472	378	FS6384	389	FS7009
346	FR3454	357	FR3501	368	FR5220	379	FR7911	390	FS6492
347	FR2763	358	FR2931	369	FR5468	380	FS5587	391	FS7669
348	FR3613	359	FR8225	370	FR5742	381	FS6392	392	FS9208
349	FR3055	360	FR6674	371	FR4546	382	FS5668	393	FS9252
350	FR7432	361	FR3912	372	FR4821	383	FS5030	394	FW5526
351	FR7947	362	FR3695	373	FR8415	384	FS6038	395	FW4489
352	FR3046	363	FR4162	374	FR8349	385	FS5383		

396-411 — Volvo Olympian YN3RC18Z4* Alexander RH — B57/42D 1993 — * 396 is type YN3RV18Z4

396	FX4273	400	FX5563	403	FX4838	406	FY5560	409	FZ1978
397	FX2865	401	FX4150	404	FX4555	407	FY5799	410	FZ352
398	FX2556	402	FY4982	405	FY6216	408	FY7146	411	FY8417
399	FX3423								

The workhorse of the Citybus fleet is the Volvo Olympian. The majority of the type have been bodied by Alexander shown here by 397, FX2865. More pictures of this Hong fleet can be found in the Honk Kong Bus Handbook available from the publishers. *Ken MacKenzie*

412-426   Volvo Olympian YN3RC18Z4   Alexander RH   B57/42D   1994

412	GF3853	415	GF1163	418	GE5272	421	GG1360	424	GG378
413	GF2158	416	GF7675	419	GE4513	422	GF8727	425	GH478
414	GF6558	417	GG1976	420	GG1443	423	GF9457	426	GE7657

427-484   Volvo Olympian YN3RV18V3   Alexander RH   B57/42D   1995

427	GM6872	439	GM7352	451	GL6714	463	GM5644	474	GM6832
428	GM8856	440	GM8361	452	GL8129	464	GM2650	475	GM6785
429	GM2809	441	GL8374	453	GL7657	465	GM5127	476	GM7027
430	GM3815	442	GL8643	454	GU1089	466	GM5896	477	GM8183
431	GM4350	443	GM5427	455	GL7626	467	GM6384	478	GM8267
432	GM2871	444	GL9161	456	GM2664	468	GM8486	479	GM6891
433	GM3523	445	GM427	457	GL7298	469	GM4803	480	GM6779
434	GM8303	446	GL7440	458	GM236	470	GM4689	481	GM7991
435	GM2972	447	GL7865	459	GM6398	471	GM4809	482	GM7118
436	GM6773	448	GL7047	460	GM3446	472	GM7332	483	GN5150
437	GM3255	449	GM3206	461	GM3538	473	GM6615	484	GP9991
438	GM6754	450	GL9583	462	GM4002				

485-504   Volvo Olympian YN3RV18V3   Plaxton Palatine 1   B57/42D   1996

485	GW1926	489	GX8049	493	GW7286	497	GX7802	501	GX7638
486	GW3302	490	GX7142	494	GW4321	498	GW3206	502	GW6799
487	GX7687	491	GW7519	495	GX7765	499	GX7655	503	GX3886
488	GX6968	492	GW7734	496	GW7120	500	GX8043	504	GX7008

505-510   Volvo Olympian YN3RC18Z4   Alexander RH   B57/42D   1995   Stagecoach HK, 1996

505	GK7584	507	GK3194	508	GK4058	509	GK9454	510	GW1534
506	GK2009								

511-585 Volvo Olympian Alexander RH BC57/42D* 1997 *some B57/42D, 520 B57/3?D

511	HA9347	526	HB2027	541	HC2271	556	HD1184	571	HD7581
512	HA6325	527	HA8771	542	HC9451	557	HD2072	572	HD7329
513	HA8502	528	HA9346	543	HD1150	558	HD2353	573	HD7404
514	HA3140	529	HB9187	544	HD4363	559	HD4385	574	HD9422
515	HA2477	530	HA9698	545	HC9180	560	HD8873	575	HE152
516	HA3567	531	HB2122	546	HC9107	561	HD4006	576	HD7252
517	HB1656	532	HB8762	547	HD156	562	HD674	577	HD7093
518	HB9800	533	HB9423	548	HD723	563	HD4364	578	HE7921
519	HA9714	534	HC429	549	HD392	564	HD2014	579	HD7684
520	HA9070	535	HB6578	550	HC9014	565	HD7626	580	HD9627
521	HA9804	536	HC2417	551	HD4492	566	HD1479	581	HD6589
522	HA9013	537	HC4449	552	HC9648	567	HD7489	582	HG5934
523	HA9820	538	HC1380	553	HC8950	568	HE457	583	HE3921
524	HB2181	539	HD1136	554	HC8604	569	HD9014	584	HE2740
525	HB2127	540	HC9271	555	HC9921	570	HD6896	585	HE2706

586-620 Volvo Olympian Plaxton Palatine B57/42D 1997

586	HM4450	593	HM994	600	HJ5553	607	HP1760	614	HP2060
587	HL4301	594	HJ5024	601	HJ5152	608	HP1193	615	HP5932
588	HL9870	595	HH5510	602	HM1052	609	HP1268	616	HR8031
589	HL3130	596	HH5548	603	HM3980	610	HP1368	617	HR7507
590	HH6240	597	HM219	604	HM1528	611	HP1298	618	HS5583
591	HM251	598	HL2784	605	HM1620	612	HP2274	619	HS6295
592	HM876	599	HL3432	606	HP1158	613	HR2194	620	HS4668

621-699 Volvo Olympian Alexander RH BC57/42D* 1998 *621-49 are B57/42D

621	HF1792	637	HU2851	653	HU2673	669	HU3668	685	HU6517
622	HF940	638	HT9566	654	HU3055	670	HU6805	686	HU9720
623	HE5271	639	HT9708	655	HU3162	671	HU3830	687	HU7791
624	HF1036	640	HT8675	656	HU3984	672	HU8656	688	HU9112
625	HF2057	641	HT8865	657	HU4392	673	HU6784	689	HU9262
626	HE8132	642	HT8541	658	HU2518	674	HU8326	690	HU9075
627	HF6829	643	HU164	659	HU3803	675	HU7692	691	HU9241
628	HJ5263	644	HT9711	660	HU3579	676	HV2258	692	HV1286
629	HF7633	645	HU3608	661	HU4373	677	HU9421	693	HU9603
630	HG3906	646	HU2982	662	HU2550	678	HU7527	694	HV4985
631	HF8016	647	HU3867	663	HU2560	679	HU9508	695	HV5580
632	HG3816	648	HU3759	664	HU3262	680	HV5362	696	HV6418
633	HF8902	649	HU3876	665	HU2980	681	HV7333	697	HV5277
634	HG120	650	HU2987	666	HU4048	682	HU9053	698	HV6196
635	HL3175	651	HU3048	667	HU3160	683	HV153	699	HV5166
636	HT8766	652	HU3818	668	HU6819	684	HU9447		

701-720 Dennis Dragon DDA2202 Duple Metsec B50/37F 1994 * 701 is now a trolleybus B49/36F

701	GD1492	705	GD5698	709	GD5150	713	GD6286	717	GE4025
702	GD1340	706	GD3176	710	GD8314	714	GD5727	718	GE3148
703	GD1405	707	GD1363	711	GD4855	715	GD4924	719	GE3031
704	GD3124	708	GD3392	712	GD5968	716	GE4348	720	GF8124

721-730 Dennis Dragon DDA2204 Duple Metsec B50/37F 1995

721	GS3491	723	GS5232	725	GS5902	727	GS5497	729	GS3908
722	GS6069	724	GS5550	726	GS3486	728	GS2819	730	GS2902

731-740 Dennis Dragon DDA2206 Duple Metsec B49/37F 1996-97

731	HB2811	733	HB4005	735	HB5201	737	HB3857	739	HB2965
732	HB5114	734	HB3380	736	HB8207	738	HB3972	740	HB7872

In addiiton to Alexander bodywork, Plaxton also supplied bodies on Olympians. Illustrating the Plaxton styling is 606, HP1158, pictured in Central while heading for Kennedy Town. *Ken MacKenzie*

801-830

Dennis Dragon DDA2301   Duple Metsec   B56/42D   1994-95

801	GJ6202	807	GG9906	813	GG9857	819	GJ4691	825	GL2614
802	GG9926	808	GG5800	814	GJ6038	820	GJ5015	826	GL5275
803	GH290	809	GG6484	815	GG9967	821	GJ5954	827	GL3631
804	GG8766	810	GG4674	816	GH392	822	GL4393	828	GL4465
805	GG9134	811	GL6432	817	GG9591	823	GL2448	829	GL4506
806	GH126	812	GH469	818	GG9178	824	GL4186	830	GL3812

831-860

Dennis Dragon DDA2302   Duple Metsec   B56/42D   1995

831	GS3278	837	GM6898	843	GP8055	849	GP6675	855	GR2793
832	GM5723	838	GN485	844	GN281	850	GP8266	856	GS4109
833	GM6324	839	GM9644	845	GM9634	851	GS4391	857	GS4432
834	GM7811	840	GM9789	846	GM9296	852	GS3740	858	GS3788
835	GM7339	841	GN371	847	GM8662	853	GR4432	859	GS3216
836	GM6583	842	GM9300	848	GP8260	854	GR2547	860	GS4173

861-880

Dennis Dragon DDA2303   Duple Metsec   BC55/42D   1997

861	HD1169	865	HD3198	869	HD937	873	HD1846	877	HD1873
862	HD953	866	HD902	870	HD935	874	HD3455	878	HD6044
863	HD1407	867	HD1759	871	HD1419	875	HD2541	879	HD1433
864	HD1555	868	HD1436	872	HD1562	876	HN6752	880	HD1989

Single-deck buses are now entirely low-floor and airconditioned with older models being tranferred on to New Zealand or returned to the UK. Replacement for the early Darts are Jit Luen-bodied Volvo B6BLEs. The body styling is illustrated on 1360, HV7267. *Ken MacKenzie*

901-950

Volvo Olympian YN3RV18Z4   Alexander RH   B53/38D   1996-97

901	GU8600	911	GV6994	921	GW2858	931	GZ6225	941	GZ9904
902	GV397	912	GW4298	922	GW3268	932	GZ6061	942	GZ9408
903	GV1124	913	GW3415	923	GX6793	933	GZ4643	943	GZ9708
904	GV226	914	GV8261	924	GX8298	934	GZ5771	944	HA3556
905	GV317	915	GV7869	925	GX6728	935	GZ6498	945	HA4190
906	GW3682	916	GW3343	926	GZ2353	936	GZ5231	946	HA8541
907	GU9984	917	GW2544	927	GZ690	937	GZ5683	947	HA3808
908	GV6014	918	GW3432	928	GZ1921	938	GZ8685	948	HA2922
909	GV6276	919	GW3787	929	GZ5804	939	GZ9279	949	HA2514
910	GV5780	920	GW4016	930	GZ4632	940	GZ8681	950	HA4312

951-1000

Volvo Olympian   Alexander RH   B53/38D   1997-98

951	HP7153	961	HR2697	971	HR6960	981	HS6505	991	HT817
952	HP7780	962	HR3712	972	HR6591	982	HS6560	992	HT641
953	HP7753	963	HR8259	973	HS5344	983	HT1574	993	HT6228
954	HP7176	964	HR2817	974	HR6577	984	HS6860	994	HT6478
955	HP8095	965	HR3878	975	HS5207	985	HS8397	995	HT4344
956	HP6885	966	HR6854	976	HS6205	986	HT1366	996	HT4030
957	HP7626	967	HR6533	977	HS6140	987	HT4739	997	HT3818
958	HP7685	968	HR8359	978	HS5817	988	HT1937	998	HT3126
959	HR2908	969	HR8463	979	HS7280	989	HT1648	999	HT5860
960	HR2784	970	HR8002	980	HS8067	990	HT1123	1000	HT6493

1001-1040

Volvo Olympian   Alexander RH   B53/38D   1998

1001	HT3827	1009	HT4659	1017	HT9551	1025	HV7671	1033	HW1311
1002	HT6374	1010	HT9714	1018	HT9479	1026	HV7257	1034	HW3695
1003	HT5882	1011	HT9893	1019	HT9681	1027	HV6743	1035	HW3061
1004	HT4489	1012	HT8643	1020	HT8973	1028	HV8123	1036	HW4031
1005	HT4676	1013	HT9707	1021	HV8472	1029	HV7448	1037	HW8373
1006	HT5740	1014	HT9318	1022	HW1646	1030	HV6947	1038	HW8104
1007	HT5957	1015	HU3986	1023	HV8093	1031	HW977	1039	HW8193
1008	HU418	1016	HU4328	1024	HV6596	1032	HW1045	1040	HW7897

MAN have supplied vehicles for all the Stagecoach operations and while those for the New Zealand and British fleets are bodied by local coachbuilders, those on Honk Kong are the popular integral model NL262 built to right-hand drive. Representing the eighty now in use in Hong Kong is 1525, HT9511, seen heading for North Point. *Ken MacKenzie*

1041	HP9730	Volvo Olympian	Alexander RH	B53/39D	1997	China Motor Bus, 2001
1042	HR1121	Volvo Olympian	Alexander RH	B53/39D	1997	China Motor Bus, 2001
1266	EP2969	Volvo B10M-60	Van Hool Alizée	C49FT	1990	

1271-1275 Volvo B10M-60 — Van Hool Alizée — C49FT — 1992

1271	FB9806	1272	FC9565	1273	FC9356	1274	FD207	1275	FC8623

1276	HH1319	Volvo B10M-62	Xian Silver	C47DT	1997
1277	HH2450	Volvo B10M-62	Xian Silver	C47DT	1997

1302-1311 Volvo B6LE — Plaxton Pointer — NC41F* — 1996 — *1302/3 are NC31F

1302	GT7186	1306	GU8201	1308	GU9787	1310	GV5985	1311	GV425
1303	GT7587	1307	GU7005	1309	GV265				

1332-1361 Volvo B6LE — Jit Luen — NC34D — 1998

1332	HU4227	1338	HU5293	1344	HV4841	1350	HV5220	1357	HV5716
1333	HU9997	1339	HU4792	1345	HV5285	1351	HV9997	1358	HV4766
1334	HU4294	1340	HU6050	1346	HV4669	1352	HV6780	1359	HV6653
1335	HU4796	1341	HU6030	1347	HV4509	1353	HV8346	1360	HV7267
1336	HU3286	1342	HV6320	1348	HV5667	1354	HV8135	1361	HV7805
1337	HU2986	1343	HV5003	1349	HV6358	1356	HV6835		

1501-1560 MAN NL262/R — MAN — N31D — 1998

1501	HP6440	1513	HU266	1525	HT9511	1537	HV6508	1549	HV165
1502	HT8914	1514	HU1016	1526	HU1574	1538	HU8264	1550	HU4928
1503	HT8509	1515	HT9507	1527	HT8514	1539	HU5465	1551	HU4619
1504	HT9100	1516	HT8960	1528	HU5428	1540	HU6012	1552	HU8327
1505	HT9095	1517	HU609	1529	HT9142	1541	HU5697	1553	HU9891
1506	HT9806	1518	HU798	1530	HU1304	1542	HU9824	1554	HU5441
1507	HT8615	1519	HU265	1531	HT8707	1543	HV7871	1555	HU8151
1508	HT9373	1520	HU5793	1532	HT9125	1544	HV371	1556	HU5156
1509	HT9534	1521	HU4821	1533	HU4558	1545	HU7461	1557	HU8506
1510	HU493	1522	HU3157	1534	HU7221	1546	HU6297	1558	HU9443
1511	HT8562	1523	HU685	1535	HU3159	1547	HU5040	1559	HU5706
1512	HU2412	1524	HU1632	1536	HU7425	1548	HU9297	1560	HU4891

1561-1580   MAN NL262/R   MAN   N31D   2000

1561	JL8180	1565	JL7509	1569	JL8007	1573	JL6596	1577	JL7600
1562	JM1746	1566	JM764	1570	JM1872	1574	JL8491	1578	JM3964
1563	JL8297	1567	JL7352	1571	JM1951	1575	JM1334	1579	JM4418
1564	JL7265	1568	JL6936	1572	JL8120	1576	JM4266	1580	JM4430

2100	HM1086	Dennis Trident 3-axle	Duple Metsec	CN53/25D	1997

2101-2111   Dennis Trident 3-axle   Alexander ALX500   CN51/21D   1998

2101	HR2174	2104	HN7737	2106	HN4867	2108	HR287	2110	HP4451
2102	HN3697	2105	HN9651	2107	HN8465	2109	HN7602	2111	HP2678
2103	HN5545								

2112-2161   Dennis Trident 3-axle   Duple Metsec   CN53/25D   1998

2112	HS6637	2122	HS7876	2132	HT6221	2142	HU293	2152	HT9327
2113	HS8204	2123	HU6912	2133	HT5320	2143	HT8976	2153	HT9364
2114	HS7147	2124	HT3115	2134	HT5018	2144	HT9935	2154	HU1416
2115	HT2588	2125	HT3877	2135	HT6278	2145	HT9266	2155	HT9303
2116	HS7792	2126	HT3633	2136	HT9646	2146	HU290	2156	HU1057
2117	HS8472	2127	HT4452	2137	HU261	2147	HT9187	2157	HT9589
2118	HS6714	2128	HT6310	2138	HT9127	2148	HT9500	2158	HU4937
2119	HS7791	2129	HT4830	2139	HU356	2149	HU269	2159	HU7617
2120	HS7326	2130	HT6075	2140	HT9542	2150	HU2507	2160	HU6305
2121	HS8500	2131	HT5826	2141	HT9961	2151	HT9721	2161	HV7107

2200	HN1822	Dennis Trident 3-axle	Alexander ALX500	CN57/35D	1998
2201	HN4366	Dennis Trident 3-axle	Duple Metsec	N57/34D	1998

2202-2231   Dennis Trident 3-axle   Duple Metsec   CN55/29D   1998-2000

2202	HV8262	2208	HW849	2214	JM8115	2220	HX4541	2226	HZ1054
2203	HV6654	2209	HW3621	2215	HW6956	2221	HY2758	2227	HZ2031
2204	HV6874	2210	HW6791	2216	HW6835	2222	HX4605	2228	HZ3898
2205	HV7903	2211	HW3550	2217	HX5301	2223	HY5381	2229	HZ3467
2206	HW4172	2212	HW8068	2218	HY4120	2224	HY5113	2230	HZ4270
2207	HV7644	2213	HW8037	2219	HX6499	2225	HY6005	2231	JD107

2232-2261   Dennis Trident 3-axle   Duple Metsec   CN55/35F   1998-99

2232	HV7244	2238	HV7100	2244	HV7488	2250	HW5290	2256	HW2231
2233	HV7880	2239	HW5088	2245	HV6689	2251	HW5108	2257	HW1450
2234	HV7471	2240	HW5399	2246	HW4900	2252	HW3181	2258	HW3686
2235	HV7692	2241	HV6640	2247	HV6518	2253	HX6255	2259	HX5754
2236	HW1198	2242	HW2377	2248	HV7177	2254	HW1120	2260	HW2791
2237	HV6915	2243	HV7299	2249	HW674	2255	HW1568	2261	HW5383

2262-2301   Dennis Trident 3-axle   Duple Metsec   N59/28D   1999

2262	HZ2973	2270	HZ4238	2278	HZ7152	2286	HJA220	2294	HZ8881
2263	HZ7381	2271	HZ7457	2279	HZ3357	2287	JB3698	2295	HZ8980
2264	HZ8144	2272	HZ8014	2280	HZ9371	2288	HZ2879	2296	JA499
2265	HZ6968	2273	HZ7895	2281	HZ4048	2289	HZ3766	2297	JB2934
2266	HZ3418	2274	HZ6993	2282	HZ9534	2290	HZ8573	2298	JB2927
2267	HZ7065	2275	HZ3619	2283	HZ3575	2291	HZ8722	2299	JB3675
2268	HZ7336	2276	HZ7266	2284	HZ3656	2292	HZ9308	2300	JB7459
2269	HZ6585	2277	HZ8499	2285	HZ8789	2293	JA449	2301	JB7500

2500	HN1013	MAN 24.350 HOLN -R	Volgren CR221LD	N59/36D	1998
2700	JB5571	Dennis Trident 3-axle	Duple Metsec	C47/31F	1999
2800	KJ1502	Scania K94UB	Volgren CR223LD	N59/32F	2001

3101-3130   Flxible   Flxible   B40D   1997

3101	A Z0638	3107	A Z0642	3113	A Z0653	3119	A Z0651	3125	A Z0655
3102	A Z0647	3108	A Z0666	3114	A Z0664	3120	A Z0648	3126	A Z0665
3103	A Z0645	3109	A Z0640	3115	A Z0658	3121	A Z0663	3127	A Z0661
3104	A Z0646	3110	A Z0637	3116	A Z0650	3122	A Z0662	3128	A Z0656
3105	A Z0643	3111	A Z0660	3117	A Z0652	3123	A Z0641	3129	A Z0644
3106	A Z0649	3112	A Z0657	3118	A Z0654	3124	A Z0659	3130	A Z0639

The double-deck low-floor needs of Citybus have so far been met by the 3-axle version of the Dennis Trident. Bodywork for the type has been provided by Transbus' Alexander and Duple Metsec divisions. While many of the new buses are allocated to bus routes their main impact has been on the Cityflyer services that connect to the new airport which lies on Lantau island. Illustrating Cityflyer livery is 2151, HT9721. *Keith Grimes*

3301-3318

		King Long			Golden Dragon		B38D	1998	
3301	A 65901	3305	A 65916	3309	A 65909	3313	A 65913	3316	A 65900
3302	A 65902	3306	A 65917	3310	A 65910	3314	A 65914	3317	A 65906
3303	A 65903	3307	A 65907	3311	A 65911	3315	A 65915	3318	A 65905
3304	A 65904	3308	A 65908	3312	A 65912				

Ancillary vehicles

19	ET3822	Leyland Olympian ONTL11/2R	Eastern Coach Works	TV	1984	Leyland demonstrator, 1990
36	CN2611	Leyland Victory Mk2 ser2	Alexander	TV	1982	New Lantao Bus, 1993
T1	DD8288	Dennis Dragon DDA 1810	Duple Metsec	TV	1990	New World First Bus, 2000
T2	DS8288	Dennis Dragon DDA 1810	Duple Metsec	TV	1990	New World First Bus, 2000
T3	GG8288	Dennis Dragon DDA 1810	Duple Metsec	TV	1990	New World First Bus, 2000

Previous UK Registrations:

DN584	CUB58Y	DN4435	CUB57Y	FK5095	J248WWK
DN680	CUB56Y	EZ8347	703DYE		
DN779	CUB49Y	EB1030	ADD50Y		
DN1648	CUB62Y	ES4007	ALD873B		
DN3750	CUB59Y	ET3822	B770GSC	HK1931	288CLT

Previous HK Registrations:

FU1528	FS8222		GU1089	GL8001
GS3278	GM8878		HR7642	EW3999

Depots: Aldrich Bay; Fo Tan; Ap Lei Chau Island; Siu Ho Wan; Tong Yan San. Tsuen Outstations: Ocean Park.
Operations Many of 300-314 are owned by, and in the livery of China Light & Power (CL&P).

Coach USA

The acquisition of Coach USA was completed on 26th July 1999 with regulatory approval confirmed on 7th September. Operating in 35 US States and Canada, Coach USA is the largest provider of charter, tour and sightseeing services in North America, with some 6500 coaches and 3000 taxicabs with an average fleet age of less than five years.

New vehicles included almost 100 of the Van Hool T2145 delivered during 1999 along with twenty Prevost H345. Around a hundred Thompson International school buses are operated by the Wisconsin Coach Lines. The oldest vehicle from the special event buses is a 1947 Chevrolet that operates with Powder River while Gray Line San Francisco operate seven Leyland double-decks and Shortline of Mahwah in New Jersey run a fleet of thirty Bristol VRs, with new double-deck buses from the UK expected shortly.

In addition to the coaches and minibuses Coach USA operate the traditional American Trolley through Kerrville Bus Company, Lenzner Coach Lines and several others designs aimed at the tourist market.

In Canada, the fleetname used is Coach Canada where a maple-leaf is used in place of the start within the large 'C'. During the editor's visit to Toronto the new styling was much in evidence on coaches of Trentway.

The operators that form Coach USA are:

ACT TRAVEL, 5275 Raleigh LaGrange, Memphis. TN38134
ACE EXPRESS Inc, 14000 West 44th Ave, Golden. CO80403.
ADVENTURE TRAILS/CAPE TRANSIT/LEISURE LINES SOUTH, 711 New Rd, Pleasantville. NJ08232.
AIRPORT BUS OF BAKERSFIELD, Bakersfield. CA
ALL WEST COACH LINES Inc, 7701 Wilburway, Sacramento. CA95828.
AMERICOACH TOURS LTD/GRAY LINE OF MEMPHIS, 5275 Raleigh LaGrange,Memphis.TN38134.
AMERICA CHARTERS, 3636 Glenn Ave, Winston Salem. NC27105.
AMERICA CHARTERS, 408 Center St, Jacksonville. NC28546.
AMERICA CHARTERS, 1251 W.cRAIGHEAD Road, Charlotte. NC28206.
AMERICAN COACH LINES/GRAY LINE ATLANTA, 705 Lively Ave, Norcross. GA30091.
ANTELOPE VALLEY BUS INC, 660 W.Avenue L, Lancaster. CA93534.
ARROW LINE INC, 19 George Street, East Hartford. CT06460.
ARROW LINE INC, 312 Woodmont Rd, Milford. CT06460.
ARROW LINE INC, 30, Fargo Rd, Waterford. CT06320.
ARROW STAGE LINES INC, 4001 South 34th Street, Phoenix. AZ85040.
ATLANTA AIRPORT SHUTTLE, 359,Whitehall St SW, Atlanta, GA30303.
AUSTIN AMERICAN YELLOW CAB COMPANY, 10315 McCalla Place, Austin. TX78750.
BONANZA BUS LINES, One Bonanza Way, Providence, RI02904.
CAMJO INC,CLEARWATER/ST PETERSBURG YELLOW CAB, 2045,Lawson Rd, Clearwater,FL33763.
CALIFORNIA CHARTER,3333 E 69TH St,Long Beach, CA90805.
CENTRAL CHARTERS & TOURS INC, PO BOX 6467, Wheeling, WV26003.
CHICAGO TROLLEY, 1709 S.Prairie Ave, Chicago, IL60619.
COACH USA-HOUSTON DIVISION, 950, McCarty Dr, Houston, TX77029.
COACH USA BENTONVILLE,One Airport Blvd, Bentonville, AR72764.
COACH USA CHICAGO(Downtown Operations) 4400 S, Racine Ave, Chicago, IL60609.
COACH USA CHICAGO(O'Hare)2700 Mount Prospect Rd, Des Plaines, IL60018.
COACH USA Corporate, One Riversway Suite 500, Houston, TX77056.
COACH USA INDIANAPOLIS, 3801 W,Morris St, Indianapolis, IN46241.
COACH USA JACKSON, 231-B North Parkway, Jackson, TN38305.
COACH USA LITTLE ROCK,2401 West Dixon, Little Rock, AR72206.
COACH USA ORLANDO,4950 L.B.McLeod Rd, Orlando, FL32811.
COACH USA SOUTH FLORIDA, 11077 North West 36th Ave, Miami, FL33167.
COMMODORE TOURS Inc, 709 Rivervale Rd, River Vale, NJ07675.

Pictured in New York in the fall of 2002, open-top Trident 71322 displays the Metsec body which also carries Alexander badges. The type now dominate the New York sightseeing service as well as those in other major cities. *Bill Potter*

COMMUNITY COACH,315 Howe Ave, Paramus, NJ07652.
COUNTRY ROAD TOURS, 416 Hewes Ave,Clarksburg, WV26301.
El EXPRESO ,812 Delano St,Houston, TX77003.
EXPRESS SHUTTLE USA,950,McCarty Dr, Houston, TX77029.
FLORIDA CRUISE CONNECTION,31,Sarasota Center Blvd, Sarasota, FL34240.
FUN TIME TOURS, 5875 Agnes St, Corpus Christi, TX78406.
GADABOUT TOURS Inc,44015 State Route 14, Columbia, OH44408.
GATOR CITY TAXI, 5320 Springfield, Jacksonville, FL32208.
GOLDEN ISLE COACHES, 3501 W.Beaver Street, Jacksonville,FL32254.
GOODALL'S/GRAY LINE SAN DIEGO,1775 Hamock St, San Diego,CA92110.
GRAY LINE DALLAS-FORT Worth, 710 E.Davis St, Grand Prairie, TX75050.
GRAY LINE SAN ANTONIO-AUSTIN, 217 Alama Plaza Suite B,San Antonio,TX78206.
GRAY LINE OF ALBUQUERQUE, 8401 Jefferson NE-A, Albuquerque, NM87113.
GRAY LINE OF FORT LAUDERDALE,1800 NW 23RD Ave, Fort Lauderdale, FL33311.
GRAY LINE OF LAS VEGAS,953 E.Sahara, Suite E1B, Las Vegas,NV89104.
GRAY LINE OF SALT LAKE CITY,553 West 100 South, Salt Lake City,UT84101.
GRAY LINE OF SANFRANCISCO, 350 8th Street,SanFrancisco,CA94103.
GREATER HOUSTON TRANSPORTATION COMPANY, Taxis Fiesta,1406 Hayes St Houston, TX77009.
GROSVENOR Bus lines Inc, 2300 Kasch Park Rd, Everett, WA98204.
INTERNATIONAL EXPRESS CORP/EXPRESS SHUTLE, 3920 Nicollet Ave South, South Minneapolis,MN55409.
K-T SERVICES,Elko West Exit,PO Box 429 Elko, NV89801.
K-T SERVICES,4020 E.Lone Mountain Rd, Las Vegas, NV89031.
KERRVILLE BUS COMPANY, 1915 Barton Dr, Shreveport, LA71101.
KERRVILLE BUS COMPANY, 958 Birdsong Rd,Lafayette, LA70507.
KERRVILLE BUS COMPANY, 1430 East Houston, San Antonio,TX78202.
MAIN LINE, 184 Main St, South Portland,ME04106.
METRO TAXI OF DENVER INC, 5909 East 38th Ave, Denver CO80207,
METRO TRANSPORTATION SERVICES,11077 North West 36th Ave, Miami,FL33167.
METROPOLITAN TRANSPORTATION SERVICES INC, 522 Lucust,Kansas City,MO64106.
MIDNIGHT SUN TOURS, 511 East Coast St,Lake Worth, FL33460,
MINI-COACH OF BOSTON, 333 Third St,Chelsea, MA02150.
MOUNTAINEER COACH INC, 260 Industrial Park Rd, Beaver, WV25813.
OLYMPIA TRAILS, 200 Relocated Baywayn Ave, Elizabeth, NJ07202.
PACIFIC COAST SIGHTSEEING/GRAY LINE OF ANAHEIM,2001, S.Manchester,Anaheim,CA92802.
PALM BEACH TRANSPORTATION/EXPRESS SHUTTLE USA,1700,N.Florida Mango Rd,West Palm Beach,FL33409.
PARK TOURS CHARTER & TOUR SERVICES,4401,Camden Ave,Parkersburg,WV26101.
PAWTUXET VALLEY BUS LINES,76 Industrial Lane,West Warwick,RI02893.
POWDER RIVER TRANSPORTATION,POBOX218, Gillette,WY82717.
ROSS TOURS INC,980,Motsie Rd,Suite A,Biloxi,MS39532.

Touring New England and at rest in Quechee is this tri-axle Prevost coach 3380. While the main scheme is that of the Coach USA, the Southern Coach Company names are still promoted. *Bill Potter*

SHORT LINE,17 Franklin Turnpike, Mahwah, NJ07430.
SOUTHERN COACH COMPANY,1300 E.Pettigrew St, Durham, NC27701.
SURBURBAN TRANSIT CORPORATION,750 Somerset St, New Brunswick, NJ08901.
TIPPETT TRAVEL & TOURS dba Marie's Charter Bus,3095 s.Military Trial, Lake Worth. FL33463.
TUCKER TRANSPORTATION COMPANY Yellow Cab,1000 W.Leonard St, Pensacola, FL32501
UNITED TRANSPORTATION,4950 L.B. McLEOD Rd, Orlando, FL32811.
VALEN TRANSPORTATION, 2025 S.Manchester, Anaheim, CA92802.
VAN GALDER BUS COMPANY,715, S.Pearl St, Janesville, WI53545.
VAUGHT CHARTERS,8012 Mosson Rd, Fort Worth, TX76119.
WISCONSIN COACH LINES, 1520, Arcadian Ave, Waukesha, WI53186.
YELLOW CAB COMPANY,1314 Valley St, Colorado Springs, CO80915.
YELLOW CAB COMPANY, 3801 W.Morris St, PO BOX 421009, Indianapolis , IN46242.

COACH COMPANIES IN CANADA

AUTOCAR CONNAISSEUR/GRAY LINE De MONTREAL, 1140, Wellington, Montreal, PQ H3C 1V8.
CENTURY AIRLINE SERVICE, 791 Webber AVE,POBOX 1017,PETERBOROUGH,ON K9J 7A5.
ERIE COACH LINES, 15 TOWERLINE, PLACE LONDON, ON N6E 2T3.
TRENTWAY WAGER, 791, WEBBER AVE, PO BOX 1017 PETERBOROUGH ON K9J 7A5.

Index to UK Vehicles

Reg	No.	Depot	Reg	No.	Depot	Reg	No.	Depot
B108WUV	11108	Wales & West	B918TVR	15018	Manchester	C462SSO	14462	East Scotland
B109ETX	48003	Wales & West	B919TVR	15019	Manchester	C463SSO	14463	East Scotland
R110SJA	13110	Manchester	B920TVR	15020	Manchester	C466SSO	14466	West Scotland
B112WUV	11112	Wales & West	B960ODU	14933	South Midlands	C467SSO	14467	East Scotland
B114SJA	13114	Manchester	BFW136W	29859	East Midlands	C468SSO	14468	East Scotland
B116WUV	11116	East Scotland	BHO441V	26773	East Midlands	C469SSO	14469	East Scotland
B117TVU	13117	North West	BJV103L	15514	East Midlands	C470SSO	14470	East Scotland
B117WUV	11117	East	BMS222	59922	East Scotland	C472SSO	14472	East
B118TVU	13118	Manchester	BSJ895T	25795	West Scotland	C508UNV	48012	East
B119TVU	13119	Manchester	BSJ917T	25797	West Scotland	C544RAO	29544	North East
B119WUV	11119	East Scotland	BSK744	52067	East Scotland	C601LFT	14601	West Scotland
B121TVU	13121	Manchester	BSK756	52193	East Scotland	C602LFT	14602	West Scotland
B121WUV	11121	South East	BVP772V	25472	South Midlands	C603LFT	14603	West Scotland
B122TVU	13122	Manchester	C105DWR	52072	North West	C604LFT	14604	West Scotland
B122WUV	11122	East Scotland	C112CHM	14367	North East	C605LFT	14605	North East
B124TVU	13124	Manchester	C114CHM	14364	North East	C608LFT	14608	West Scotland
B124WUV	11124	South East	C115CHM	14365	South Midlands	C609LFT	14609	Wales & West
B125TVU	13125	Manchester	C119CHM	14369	South Midlands	C610LFT	14610	Wales & West
B125WUV	11125	South East	C120CHM	14370	South East	C611LFT	14611	North East
B126WNB	13126	Manchester	C121CHM	14371	South Midlands	C612LFT	14612	West Scotland
B132WNB	13132	Manchester	C122CHM	14472	South East	C613LFT	14613	Manchester
B133WNB	13133	Manchester	C156YBA	13156	Manchester	C614LFT	14614	North East
B135WNB	13135	Manchester	C158YBA	13158	Manchester	C615LFT	14615	North East
B137WNB	13137	Manchester	C164YBA	13159	Manchester	C616LFT	14616	West Scotland
B138WNB	13138	Manchester	C165YBA	13165	Manchester	C617LFT	14617	North East
B143WNB	13143	Manchester	C166YBA	13166	Manchester	C618LFT	14618	North East
B145WNB	13145	Manchester	C167BNX	48008	South East	C619LFT	14619	West Scotland
B146XNA	13146	Manchester	C167YBA	13167	Manchester	C621LFT	14621	North East
B147XNA	13147	Manchester	C168BNX	48009	South East	C622LFT	14622	West Scotland
B149XNA	13149	Manchester	C169YBA	13169	Manchester	C623LFT	14623	West Scotland
B150XNA	13151	Manchester	C170ECK	14170	North West	C624LFT	14624	Wales & West
B153XNA	13153	Manchester	C170YBA	13170	Manchester	C625LFT	14625	West Scotland
B154XNA	13154	Manchester	C172YBA	13172	Manchester	C626LFT	14626	West Scotland
B155XNA	13155	Manchester	C173YBA	13173	Manchester	C627LFT	14627	West Scotland
B177FFS	15277	East Scotland	C174ECK	14174	North West	C628LFT	14628	West Scotland
B179FFS	15279	East Scotland	C174YBA	13174	Manchester	C629LFT	14629	West Scotland
B180FFS	15280	East Scotland	C175ECK	14175	North West	C630LFT	14630	North East
B181FFS	15281	East Scotland	C175YBA	13175	Manchester	C631LFT	14631	Manchester
B182FFS	15282	East Scotland	C176ECK	14176	North West	C632LFT	14632	North East
B183FFS	15283	East Scotland	C176YBA	13176	Manchester	C633LFT	14633	North East
B184FFS	15284	East Scotland	C177ECK	14177	North West	C634LFT	14634	North East
B185FFS	15285	East Scotland	C178YBA	13178	Manchester	C635LFT	14635	North East
B186FFS	15286	East Scotland	C179ECK	14179	North West	C636LFT	14636	North East
B348LSO	14448	East Scotland	C179YBA	13179	Manchester	C637LFT	14637	North East
B350LSO	14450	East Scotland	C181YBA	13181	Manchester	C638LFT	14638	West Scotland
B351LSO	14451	East Scotland	C184YBA	13184	Manchester	C639LFT	14639	North East
B352LSO	14452	East Scotland	C185YBA	13185	Manchester	C640LFT	14640	West Scotland
B354LSO	14454	West Scotland	C191YBA	13191	Manchester	C641LFT	14641	Wales & West
B355LSO	14455	East Scotland	C193YBA	13193	Manchester	C642LFT	14642	North East
B356LSO	14456	East Scotland	C195YBA	13195	Manchester	C643LFT	14643	North East
B357LSO	14457	East Scotland	C196YBA	13196	Manchester	C644LFT	14644	North East
B358LSO	14458	East Scotland	C197YBA	13197	Manchester	C645LFT	14645	North East
B360LSO	14460	East Scotland	C198YBA	13198	Manchester	C646LFT	14646	North East
B461FCS	48005	West Scotland	C199YBA	13199	Manchester	C647LFT	14647	West Scotland
B625DWF	25825	East Midlands	C205CBU	13205	Manchester	C648LFT	14648	North East
B626DWF	25826	East Midlands	C207CBU	13207	Manchester	C649LFT	14649	North East
B627DWF	25827	East Midlands	C208CBU	13208	Manchester	C650LFT	14650	Wales & West
B628DWF	25828	East Midlands	C210CBU	13210	Manchester	C651LFT	14651	North East
B629DWF	25829	East Midlands	C212CBU	13212	Manchester	C652LFT	14652	North East
B630DWF	25830	East Midlands	C213CBU	13213	North West	C653LFT	14653	West Scotland
B631DWF	25831	East Midlands	C214CBU	13214	Manchester	C654LFT	14654	West Scotland
B632DWF	25832	East Midlands	C215CBU	13215	Manchester	C655LFT	14655	North East
B633DWF	25833	East Midlands	C216CBU	13216	Manchester	C656LFT	14656	West Scotland
B866JVK	48006	North East	C219WAJ	15059	North East	C657LFT	14657	West Scotland
B892UAS	14216	North West	C220WAJ	15060	North East	C658LFT	14658	North East
B893UAS	14217	North West	C221CBU	13221	Manchester	C659LFT	14659	Wales & West
B895UAS	14219	North West	C221WAJ	15061	North East	C661LFT	14661	North East
B896UAS	14220	North West	C222WAJ	15062	North East	C662LFT	14662	West Scotland
B899UAS	14223	North West	C224CBU	13224	Manchester	C663LFT	14663	West Scotland
B900WRN	25800	North West	C226ENE	13226	Manchester	C664LFT	14664	North East
B902TVR	15002	East Midlands	C230ENE	13230	Manchester	C665LFT	14665	North East
B903TVR	15003	East Midlands	C234ENE	13234	Manchester	C787USG	15287	East Scotland
B904TVR	15004	East Midlands	C236EVU	13236	Manchester	C788USG	15288	East Scotland
B905TVR	15005	Manchester	C249UNV	48010	East	C789USG	15289	East Scotland
B907TVR	15007	East Midlands	C255FRJ	13255	Manchester	C790USG	15290	East Scotland
B908TVR	15008	East Midlands	C307KER	48011	East	C791USG	15291	East Scotland
B909TVR	15009	East Midlands	C326HWJ	14326	East Midlands	C792USG	15292	East Scotland
B910ODU	14930	South Midlands	C327HWJ	14327	East Midlands	C793USG	15293	East Scotland
B910TVU	15010	Manchester	C329HWJ	14329	East Midlands	C794USG	15294	East Scotland
B911ODU	14931	South Midlands	C330DND	52004	East Scotland	C795USG	15295	East Scotland
B911TVR	15011	Manchester	C331HWJ	14331	North East	C796USG	15296	East Scotland
B912ODU	14932	South Midlands	C332HWJ	14332	East Midlands	C797USG	15297	East Scotland
B912TVR	15012	Manchester	C333HWJ	14333	North East	C798USG	15298	East Scotland
B913TVR	15013	Manchester	C334HWJ	14334	North East	C799USG	15299	East Scotland
B914TVR	15014	Manchester	C335HWJ	14335	East Midlands	C800HCS	14412	West Scotland
B915TVR	15015	Manchester	C336HWJ	14336	East Midlands	C800USG	15270	East Scotland
B916JVK	48007	North East	C382SAO	14473	North West	C801USG	15271	East Scotland
B916TVR	15016	Manchester	C383SAO	14474	North West	C802USG	15272	East Scotland
B917TVR	15017	Manchester	C461SSO	14461	East Scotland	C803USG	15273	East Scotland

Reg	No.	Region	Reg	No.	Region	Reg	No.	Region
C804USG	15274	East Scotland	D692ENV	48043	East	EJR108W	15808	North East
C805USG	15275	East Scotland	D765ENV	48044	South Midlands	EJR110W	15810	North East
C806USG	15276	East Scotland	D780ENV	48045	East	EJR111W	15811	North East
C807USG	15269	East Scotland	D891DWP	48046	Wales & West	EJR118W	15818	North East
C918AHN	48013	North East	D918KPT	48047	North East	EJV32Y	27032	Wales & West
C962XVC	14935	South Midlands	D932TWE	48048	East Midlands	EJV34Y	27034	Wales & West
C963XVC	14936	South Midlands	D933TWE	48049	East Midlands	EKA215Y	59015	North West
C964XVC	14937	South Midlands	D935TJO	48050	South Midlands	EKA220Y	59020	North West
CD7045	19945	South East	D935TWE	48051	East Midlands	ESU435	52177	East Scotland
CKC624X	59024	North West	D953TWE	48052	East Midlands	ETC310W	25710	South East
CKC626X	59026	North West	DBV100W	14100	North West	EWS746W	15761	South East
CSU920	52232	East Scotland	DBV134Y	14134	North West	EWS748W	15762	South East
CSU921	52233	East Scotland	DBV24W	15724	North West	EWS751W	15763	South East
CSU922	52234	East Scotland	DGS625	39925	East Scotland	EWY74Y	14279	East Scotland
CSU923	52235	East Scotland	DSV943	52306	East Scotland	EWY75Y	14280	East Scotland
CSU978	52218	South West	DWF24V	25714	East Midlands	EYE236V	10236	West Scotland
CSU992	52219	London	E32RNV	48061	East	EYE244V	10244	South East
CUB72Y	14278	North West	E36RRP	48062	East	EYE246V	10246	West Scotland
CUL179V	10179	North West	E47HFE	47999	East Midlands	F41XCS	14520	North East
CUL180V	10180	South East	E61JFV	20401	South Midlands	F75TFU	15075	East Midlands
CUL190V	10190	South East	E62JFV	20402	South Midlands	F76TFU	15076	East Midlands
CUL197V	10197	West Scotland	E63JFV	20403	Wales & West	F77TFU	15077	East Midlands
CUL208V	10208	West Scotland	E64JFV	20404	Wales & West	F78TFU	15078	East Midlands
CUL209V	10209	West Scotland	E65JFV	20405	Wales & West	F101HVK	29101	North East
CUV272C	12272	London	E66JFV	20406	Wales & West	F102HVK	29102	North East
CUV286C	12286	London	E90YWB	40990	East Midlands	F103HVK	29103	North East
CUV300C	12300	London	E91YWB	40991	East Midlands	F104HVK	29104	North East
CUV303C	12303	London	E94YWB	40994	East Midlands	F105HVK	29105	North East
CUV311C	12311	London	E95YWB	40995	East Midlands	F106HVK	29106	North East
D34PAX	48028	Wales & West	E98YWB	40998	East Midlands	F107HVK	29107	North East
D56SNE	48055	Manchester	E131ORP	52061	North West	F108HVK	29108	North East
D123FYM	14373	South Midlands	E132ORP	52062	North West	F109HVK	29109	North East
D124FYM	14374	South Midlands	E132SAT	15052	North East	F110HVK	29110	North East
D125FYM	14375	South Midlands	E133ORP	52063	North West	F110NES	14000	East
D126FYM	14376	South East	E134ORP	52064	North West	F111HVK	29111	North East
D127FYM	14377	South Midlands	E140SAT	15041	North East	F112HVK	29112	North East
D128FYM	14378	South Midlands	E250AKU	48056	East Midlands	F113HVK	29113	North East
D129FYM	14379	North East	E260CVR	48057	Manchester	F114HVK	29114	North East
D130FYM	14380	North East	E269CVR	48058	Manchester	F115HVK	29115	North East
D131FYM	14381	South Midlands	E293PDC	48059	Manchester	F116HVK	29116	North East
D132FYM	14382	South Midlands	E301FSO	48060	East Scotland	F117HVK	29117	North East
D134FYM	14384	South East	E306BWL	40204	North East	F118HVK	29118	North East
D136FYM	14386	South Midlands	E316HLO	41981	Wales & West	F119HVK	29119	North East
D137FYM	14387	South Midlands	E432AFT	40840	North East	F120HVK	29120	North East
D142FYM	14392	South Midlands	E500LFL	14500	Wales & West	F121HVK	29121	North East
D155HHN	48020	North East	E501LFL	14501	Wales & West	F122HVK	29122	North East
D157HHN	48022	North East	E502LFL	14502	Wales & West	F123HVK	29123	North East
D216HHN	48021	North East	E510PVV	40211	Manchester	F124HVK	29124	North East
D235MEA	48023	South East	E664UNE	52014	East Scotland	F125HVK	29125	North East
D240SNC	48024	East Midlands	E685FTM	48063	South Midlands	F135SPX	27035	North West
D241MEA	48025	South East	E709MFV	29545	North East	F135URP	52065	North West
D260JVR	13260	Manchester	E800ERR	48064	South East	F136SPX	27036	North West
D268JVR	13268	Manchester	E864RCS	15247	West Scotland	F137SPX	27037	North West
D269JVR	13269	Manchester	E865ECS	15248	East Scotland	F142BKH	15042	North East
D272JVR	13272	Manchester	E866RCS	15249	West Scotland	F143BKH	15043	North East
D277JVR	13277	Manchester	E867RCS	15250	East Scotland	F144BKH	15044	North East
D298YTY	48026	North East	E875GRG	48065	North East	F146BKH	15046	North East
D305YTY	48027	North East	E901KYR	14901	North East	F147BKH	15047	North East
D375DCK	48029	North West	E905KYR	14905	North East	F148BKH	15048	North East
D379XRS	14479	East	E906KYR	14906	North East	F149BKH	15049	North East
D380XRS	14480	North West	E907KYR	14907	North East	F149XCS	14522	West Scotland
D381XRS	14481	North West	E908KYR	14908	North East	F150BKH	15050	North East
D382XRS	14482	East	E909KSG	15259	East Scotland	F151BKH	15051	North East
D383XRS	14483	East	E909KYR	14909	North East	F187LSA	48072	East Scotland
D384XAO	14475	North West	E910KSG	15260	East Scotland	F201FHH	14239	Manchester
D384XRS	14484	East	E910KYR	14910	North East	F202FHH	14240	Manchester
D385XRS	14485	East Scotland	E911KYR	14911	North East	F251JRM	29541	North East
D386XRS	14486	East Scotland	E912KYR	14912	North East	F252JRM	29542	North East
D387XRS	14487	East Scotland	E914KYR	14914	North East	F253KAO	29543	North East
D388XRS	14488	East Scotland	E915KYR	14915	North East	F282DRJ	13282	Manchester
D389XRS	14489	East Scotland	E917KYR	14917	North East	F283DRJ	13283	Manchester
D39FBD	48030	South Midlands	E918KYR	14918	North East	F285DRJ	13285	Manchester
D402VKK	48031	South East	E919KYR	14919	North East	F289DRJ	13289	Manchester
D406VKK	48032	South East	E920HCD	48071	South East	F291DRJ	13291	Manchester
D41SNE	48070	Manchester	E920KYR	14920	North East	F294DRJ	13294	Manchester
D431SNC	48033	Manchester	E921KYR	14921	North East	F295DRJ	13295	Manchester
D443GAV	48034	East	E922KYR	14922	North East	F296DRJ	13296	North West
D452UGB	48035	West Scotland	E923KYR	14923	North East	F297DRJ	13297	North West
D467SNC	48036	South Midlands	E924KYR	14924	North East	F298DRJ	13298	Manchester
D474SNC	48037	Manchester	E925KYR	14925	North East	F300DRJ	13300	Manchester
D475SNC	48038	Manchester	E927KYR	14927	North East	F301DRJ	13301	Manchester
D513XAO	48039	North West	E927PBE	25821	East Midlands	F301MYJ	15201	South East
D548MVR	52006	East Scotland	E928PBE	25822	East Midlands	F302MYJ	15202	South East
D551MVR	52009	East Scotland	E929PBE	25823	East Midlands	F303MYJ	15203	South East
D553MVR	52011	East Scotland	E930PBE	25824	East Midlands	F304DRJ	13304	Manchester
D560RCK	41998	East	E968CVM	48069	Manchester	F304MYJ	15204	South East
D595GAV	48040	East	EDS50A	12060	West Scotland	F305MYJ	15205	South East
D601GAV	48041	East	EFU935Y	25775	East Midlands	F306MYJ	15206	South East
D676GCD	48042	South East	EGB53T	25753	North West	F307MYJ	15207	South East

The 2003 Stagecoach Bus Handbook

Reg	No.	Area	Reg	No.	Area	Reg	No.	Area
F308MYJ	15208	South East	F916JRG	28916	North East	G615CEF	29615	North East
F309MYJ	15209	South East	F917JRG	28917	North East	G616CEF	29616	North East
F310MYJ	15210	East Scotland	F918JRG	28918	North East	G617CEF	29617	North East
F311MYJ	15211	East Scotland	F919JRG	28919	North East	G618CEF	29618	North East
F312MYJ	15212	East Scotland	F020JRG	28920	North East	G619CEF	29619	North East
F344ECK	48074	North West	FAO427V	15727	North West	G620CEF	29620	North East
F392DHL	40205	Wales & West	FES831W	59931	East Scotland	G639EVV	14039	East
F409KOD	40989	Manchester	FSU739	52309	East Scotland	G640EVV	14040	East
F481DMS	48076	East Scotland	G31TGW	32331	Wales & West	G641EVV	14041	East
F506NJE	14506	East	G33TGW	32333	South West	G642EVV	14042	East
F507NJE	14507	East	G38TGW	32338	Wales & West	G643EVV	14043	East
F508NJE	14508	East	G39TGW	32339	Wales & West	G644EVV	14044	East
F509NJE	14509	East	G40TGW	32340	Wales & West	G645EVV	14045	East
F510NJE	14510	East	G49TGW	32349	East Scotland	G646EVV	14046	East
F511NJE	14511	East	G67PFR	20407	Wales & West	G647EVV	14047	East
F512NJE	14512	East	G68PFR	20408	Wales & West	G648EVV	14048	East
F513NJE	14513	East	G79VFW	15079	East Midlands	G649EVV	14049	East
F514NJE	14514	East	G80VFW	15080	East Midlands	G665PHH	40675	North West
F515NJE	14515	South Midlands	G81VFW	15081	East Midlands	G675XTN	48078	North East
F516NJE	14516	South Midlands	G86VNX	32982	Wales & West	G684KNW	26010	London
F517NJE	14517	South Midlands	G101AAD	14271	Wales & West	G701TCD	14981	South East
F524WSJ	14521	West Scotland	G102AAD	14272	Wales & West	G702TCD	14982	South East
F601MSL	14951	South East	G103AAD	14273	Wales & West	G703TCD	14983	South East
F601UVN	29601	North East	G104AAD	14274	Wales & West	G704TCD	14984	South East
F602MSL	14952	South East	G105AAD	14275	Wales & West	G705TCD	14975	South East
F602UVN	29602	North East	G108CEH	28938	North East	G706TCD	14976	South East
F603MSL	14953	South East	G113SKX	28927	North East	G707TCD	14977	South East
F603UVN	29603	North East	G180JHG	14180	North East	G708TCD	14978	South East
F604MSL	14954	South East	G181JHG	14181	North East	G709TCD	14979	South East
F604UVN	29604	North East	G181PAO	40181	North East	G710TCD	14980	South East
F605MSL	14955	South East	G182JHG	14182	North East	G736XTN	48079	North East
F605UVN	29605	North East	G183JHG	14183	North East	G806YTA	48080	South West
F606MSL	14956	South East	G184JHG	14184	North East	G807RTS	14957	South East
F606UVN	29606	North East	G185JHG	14185	North East	G808RTS	14958	South East
F607UVN	29607	North East	G185PAO	40185	North East	G809RTS	14959	South East
F608UVN	29608	North East	G186JHG	14186	North East	G818YTA	48081	South West
F609UVN	29609	North East	G187JHG	14187	North West	G821KWF	41932	East Midlands
F610UVN	29610	North East	G188JHG	14188	North East	G847LNP	48082	South West
F620MSL	14020	East	G189JHG	14189	North East	G921TCU	28921	North East
F621MSL	14021	East	G192PAO	40192	North West	G922TCU	28922	North East
F622MSL	14022	East	G194PAO	40194	East Scotland	G923TCU	28923	North East
F623MSL	14023	East	G195PAO	40195	East Scotland	G924TCU	28924	North East
F624MSL	14024	East	G197PAO	40197	East Scotland	G925TCU	28925	North East
F625MSL	14025	East	G198PAO	40198	East Scotland	G926TCU	28926	North East
F626MSL	14026	East	G203PAO	40203	East Scotland	G976ARV	40806	North East
F627MSL	14027	East	G210SSL	14960	South East	GAZ4381	47900	East
F628MSL	14028	East	G211SSL	14961	South East	GAZ4382	47901	East
F629MSL	14029	East	G212SSL	14962	East Scotland	GCS58V	25758	West Scotland
F630MSL	14030	East	G213SSL	14963	East Scotland	GCS61V	25761	West Scotland
F631MSL	14031	East	G214SSL	14964	East Scotland	GCS69V	25769	West Scotland
F632MSL	14032	East	G251TSL	40251	North East	GJ02LVT	48201	North East
F633MSL	14033	East	G263TSL	40263	North West	GJ02LVU	48202	North East
F634MSP	14034	East	G264TSL	40264	North West	GRS643E	59943	East Scotland
F635YRP	14035	East	G265TSL	40265	North West	GSO1V	14471	East Scotland
F636YRP	14036	East	G266TSL	40266	North West	GSO6V	14476	East
F637YRP	14037	East	G267TSL	40267	North West	GSO7V	14477	East
F638YRP	14038	East	G268TSL	40268	North West	GSO8V	14478	East Midlands
F701BAT	28701	South West	G269TSL	40269	North East	GSU341	52030	East Scotland
F702BAT	28702	South West	G270TSL	40270	East Scotland	GSU839T	25739	East Scotland
F703BAT	28703	North East	G277TSL	40277	North East	GSU859T	25759	North West
F704BAT	28704	South West	G280TSL	40280	North East	GSU950	52169	East Scotland
F705BAT	28705	South West	G281TSL	40281	North East	GX51PUJ	22009	South East
F706CAG	28706	South West	G282TSL	40282	North East	GYE252W	10252	West Scotland
F781KKP	15311	South East	G283TSL	40283	North East	GYE254W	10254	North West
F782KKP	15312	South East	G286TSL	40286	North East	GYE273W	10273	West Scotland
F803FAO	14243	North West	G313BJO	48077	South Midlands	GYE281W	10281	North West
F804FAO	14244	North West	G337KKW	14337	East Scotland	H71MOB	32347	East Scotland
F805FAO	14245	North West	G338KKW	14338	East Scotland	H71XKH	39851	North East
F806FAO	14246	North West	G339KKW	14339	North East	H79MOB	32348	East Scotland
F807FAO	14247	North West	G340KKW	14340	East Midlands	H112SAO	14252	North West
F808FAO	14248	North West	G341KKW	14341	North West	H113SAO	14253	North West
F809FAO	14249	North West	G342KKW	14342	East Midlands	H114SAO	14254	North West
F810FAO	14250	North West	G343KKW	14343	East Midlands	H115SAO	14255	North West
F811FAO	14251	North West	G344FFX	52073	East Scotland	H116SAO	14256	North West
F901JRG	28901	North East	G386PNV	52075	North West	H117SAO	14257	North West
F902JRG	28902	North East	G387PNV	52076	West Scotland	H118SAO	14258	North West
F903JRG	28903	North East	G520LWU	52077	North West	H119SAO	14259	North West
F904JRG	28904	North East	G525LWU	52078	East Midlands	H126ACU	29126	North East
F905JRG	28905	North East	G531LWU	52082	East Scotland	H127ACU	29127	North East
F906JRG	28906	North East	G532LWU	52083	East Scotland	H131GVM	15031	Manchester
F907JRG	28907	North East	G566PRM	40666	North West	H132GVM	15032	Manchester
F908JRG	28908	North East	G567PRM	40667	North West	H133GVM	15033	Manchester
F909JRG	28909	North East	G570PRM	40670	North West	H134GVM	15034	Manchester
F910JRG	28910	North East	G571PRM	40671	North West	H135GVM	15035	Manchester
F911JRG	28911	North East	G578PRM	40678	North East	H136GVM	15036	Manchester
F912JRG	28912	North East	G611CEF	29611	North East	H137GVM	15037	Manchester
F913JRG	28913	North East	G612CEF	29612	North East	H138GVM	15038	Manchester
F914JRG	28914	North East	G613CEF	29613	North East	H139GVM	15039	Manchester
F915JRG	28915	North East	G614CEF	29614	North East	H140GVM	15040	Manchester

Reg	No	Region	Reg	No	Region	Reg	No	Region
H146MOB	32346	East Scotland	H819CBP	14819	South East	J353XET	14353	East Midlands
H149CVU	52086	West Scotland	H838GLD	41083	East	J372BNW	47910	North East
H151MOB	32341	East Scotland	H839GLD	41984	East	J374BNW	47912	North East
H153MOB	32343	East Scotland	HDV639E	59939	East Scotland	J401LKO	26001	London
H154MOB	32344	East Scotland	HGM335E	19935	East Scotland	J402LKO	26002	London
H162NON	32342	East Scotland	HIL6075	48083	Wales & West	J403LKO	26003	London
H181EGU	52091	East Midlands	HIL8410	48053	Wales & West	J407PRW	41507	East Scotland
H182EGU	52092	London	HSK760	52130	East Scotland	J408PRW	41508	Wales & West
H191WFR	14191	North East	HSV194	52227	East Scotland	J409PRW	41509	East Scotland
H192WFR	14192	North East	HSV195	52071	Wales & West	J410PRW	41510	South Midlands
H193WFR	14193	North West	HSV196	52059	Wales & West	J411PRW	41511	East Scotland
H194WFR	14194	North East	IIL1321	52051	East Midlands	J412PRW	41512	East Scotland
H195WFR	14195	North West	IIL3507	52070	North West	J413PRW	41513	East Scotland
H196WFR	14196	North West	J24MCW	20424	North West	J414PRW	41514	Wales & West
H197WFR	14197	North West	J25MCW	20425	North West	J415PRW	41515	South Midlands
H257THL	40999	East Midlands	J92DJV	15092	East Midlands	J416PRW	41516	Wales & West
H344SWA	14344	East Midlands	J93DJV	15093	East Midlands	J417PRW	41517	East Scotland
H345SWA	14345	East Midlands	J94DJV	15094	East Midlands	J418PRW	41518	South Midlands
H346SWA	14346	East Midlands	J120AAO	14260	North West	J454JRH	32999	Wales & West
H347SWA	14347	East Midlands	J120AHH	52098	North West	J456FSR	52095	East Midlands
H348SWA	14348	East Midlands	J120XHH	14490	East Scotland	J501FPS	32801	East Scotland
H401MRW	41501	Wales & West	J121AAO	14261	North West	J501GCD	32501	South East
H403MRW	41503	Wales & West	J121AHH	52099	North West	J502FPS	32802	East Scotland
H404MRW	41504	South Midlands	J121XHH	14491	East Scotland	J502GCD	32502	South East
H406MRW	41506	South Midlands	J122AAO	14262	North West	J503FPS	32803	East Scotland
H407GAV	52089	East	J122XHH	14492	East Scotland	J503GCD	32503	South East
H421BNL	15301	North East	J123XHH	14263	North West	J504FPS	32804	East Scotland
H422BNL	15302	North East	J124XHH	14264	North West	J504GCD	32504	South East
H423BNL	15303	North East	J125XHH	14265	North West	J505FPS	32805	East Scotland
H424BNL	15304	North East	J126XHH	14266	North West	J505GCD	32505	South East
H425BNL	15305	North East	J127XHH	14267	North West	J506FPS	32806	East Scotland
H426BNL	15306	North East	J132HMT	15332	South East	J506GCD	32506	South East
H427BNL	15307	North East	J133HMT	15333	South East	J507FPS	32807	East Scotland
H428BNL	15308	North East	J134HMT	15334	South East	J507GCD	32507	South East
H428EFT	28928	North East	J135HMT	15335	South East	J508FPS	32808	East Scotland
H429BNL	15309	North East	J136HMT	15336	South East	J508GCD	32508	South East
H429EFT	28929	North East	J137HMT	15337	South East	J509FPS	32809	East Scotland
H430BNL	15310	North East	J138HMT	15338	South East	J509GCD	32509	South East
H430EFT	28930	North East	J139HMT	15339	South East	J510FPS	32810	East Scotland
H431EFT	28931	North East	J140HMT	15340	South East	J510GCD	32510	South East
H432EFT	28932	North East	J141HMT	15341	South East	J511FPS	32811	East Scotland
H433EFT	28933	North East	J142HMT	15342	South East	J511GCD	32511	South East
H434EFT	28934	North East	J143HMT	15343	South East	J512FPS	32812	East Scotland
H435EFT	28935	North East	J144HMT	15344	South East	J512GCD	32512	South East
H436EFT	28936	North East	J145HMT	15345	South East	J513GCD	32513	South East
H437EFT	28937	North East	J196YSS	14496	East Scotland	J514GCD	32514	South East
H463GVM	15313	Manchester	J197YSS	14497	East Scotland	J515GCD	32515	South East
H464GVM	15314	Manchester	J198HFR	14198	North West	J516GCD	32516	South East
H465GVM	15315	Manchester	J198YSS	14498	East Scotland	J517GCD	32517	South East
H466GVM	15316	Manchester	J199HFR	14199	North West	J518GCD	32518	South East
H467GVM	15317	Manchester	J199YSS	14499	East Scotland	J519GCD	32519	South East
H473CEG	14523	East	J201HFR	14201	North West	J520GCD	32520	South East
H474CEG	14524	East	J202HFR	14202	North West	J521GCD	32521	South East
H475CEG	14525	East	J203HFR	14203	North West	J522GCD	32522	South East
H484BEE	15084	East Midlands	J204HFR	14204	North West	J523GCD	32523	South East
H485BEE	15085	East Midlands	J205HFR	14205	North West	J524GCD	32524	South East
H495MRW	41505	South Midlands	J206HFR	14206	North West	J526GCD	32526	South East
H617ACK	20417	North West	J207HFR	14207	North West	J527GCD	32527	South East
H618ACK	20418	North West	J208HFR	14208	North West	J528GCD	32528	South East
H619ACK	20419	North West	J209HFR	14209	North West	J529GCD	32529	South East
H620ACK	20420	Wales & West	J210HFR	14210	North West	J530GCD	32530	South East
H621ACK	20421	Wales & West	J213AET	41713	North East	J531GCD	32531	South East
H622ACK	20422	North West	J214AET	41714	North East	J532GCD	32532	South East
H623ACK	20423	North West	J215AET	41715	East Midlands	J533GCD	32533	South East
H654VVV	14054	East	J216AET	41716	North East	J534GCD	32534	South East
H667BNL	14667	North East	J217AET	41717	East Midlands	J535GCD	32535	South East
H668BNL	14668	North East	J218AET	41718	East Midlands	J536GCD	32536	South East
H669BNL	14669	North East	J219AET	41719	East Midlands	J537GCD	32537	South East
H670BNL	14670	North East	J230XKY	15330	South East	J538GCD	32538	South East
H671BNL	14671	North East	J231XKY	15331	South East	J539GCD	32539	South East
H672BNL	14672	North East	J301BRM	32401	West Scotland	J541GCD	32541	South East
H673BNL	14673	North East	J302BRM	32402	West Scotland	J542GCD	32542	South East
H674BNL	14674	North East	J303BRM	32403	West Scotland	J543GCD	32543	South East
H675BNL	14675	North East	J304BRM	32404	West Scotland	J544GCD	32544	South East
H676BNL	14676	North East	J304UKG	41304	East Scotland	J545GCD	32545	South East
H801BKK	14801	South East	J305BRM	32405	West Scotland	J546GCD	32546	South East
H802BKK	14802	South East	J305UKG	41305	Wales & West	J547GCD	32547	South East
H803BKK	14803	South East	J306BRM	32406	West Scotland	J548GCD	32548	South East
H804BKK	14804	South East	J306UKG	41306	Wales & West	J549GCD	32549	South East
H805BKK	14805	South East	J307BRM	32407	West Scotland	J550GCD	32550	South East
H806BKK	14806	South East	J307UKG	41307	Wales & West	J551GCD	32551	South East
H807BKK	14807	South East	J308BRM	32408	West Scotland	J552GCD	32552	South East
H808BKK	14808	South East	J309BRM	32409	West Scotland	J620GCR	14493	East
H809BKK	14809	South East	J310BRM	32400	West Scotland	J621GCR	14494	East
H810BKK	14810	South East	J349XET	14349	East Midlands	J622GCR	14495	East
H815CBP	14815	South East	J350XET	14350	East Midlands	J623GCR	14973	South East
H816CBP	14816	South East	J351XET	14351	East Midlands	J624GCR	14974	South East
H817CBP	14817	South East	J352XET	14352	East Midlands	J701KCU	32701	North East
H818CBP	14818	South East				J701YRM	32581	South East

J702CWT	52106	North West	K91BNY	32991	Wales & West	K310YKG	41310	Wales & West
J702KCU	32702	North East	K92BNY	32992	Wales & West	K311YKG	41311	Wales & West
J702YRM	32582	South East	K93BNY	32993	Wales & West	K312YKG	41312	Wales & West
J703YRM	32583	South East	K94AAX	32994	Wales & West	K313YKG	41313	Wales & West
J711CYG	26011	London	K95AAX	32995	Wales & West	K314YKG	41314	Wales & West
J712CYG	26012	London	K96AAX	32996	Wales & West	K315YKG	41315	Wales & West
J713DAP	26013	London	K97XNY	32997	Wales & West	K317YKG	41317	Wales & West
J714CYG	26014	London	K98XNY	32998	Wales & West	K320YKG	40593	East Scotland
J715DAP	26015	London	K101JWJ	16471	East Midlands	K321YKG	40594	East Scotland
J716CYG	26016	London	K101XHG	32101	East Scotland	K322YKG	41322	Wales & West
J717CYG	26017	London	K102JWJ	16472	East Midlands	K323YKG	41323	Wales & West
J718CYG	26018	London	K102XHG	32102	East Scotland	K324YKG	41324	Wales & West
J719CYG	26019	London	K103JWJ	16473	East Midlands	K325YKG	41325	Wales & West
J720CYG	26020	London	K103XHG	32103	East Scotland	K350ANV	40350	East
J720GAP	14970	South East	K104JWJ	16474	East Midlands	K351ANV	40351	East
J721CYG	26021	London	K104XHG	32104	East Scotland	K352ANV	40352	East
J721GAP	14971	South East	K105JWJ	16475	East Midlands	K353ANV	40353	East
J722CYG	26022	London	K105XHG	32105	East Scotland	K354ANV	40354	East
J722GAP	14972	South East	K106JWJ	16476	East Midlands	K354DWJ	14354	East Midlands
J723CYG	26023	London	K106XHG	32106	East Scotland	K355ANV	40355	East
J724CYG	26024	London	K107JWJ	16477	East Midlands	K355DWJ	14355	East Midlands
J725CYG	26025	London	K107XHG	32107	South East	K356ANV	40356	East
J726CYG	26026	London	K108XHG	32108	South East	K356DWJ	14356	East Midlands
J727CYG	26027	London	K109SRH	32147	East Midlands	K357ANV	40357	East
J728CYG	26028	London	K109XHG	32109	South East	K357DWJ	14357	East Midlands
J729CYG	26029	London	K110SRH	32148	East Midlands	K358ANV	40358	East
J801WFS	14701	East Scotland	K110XHG	32110	East Scotland	K358DWJ	14358	East Midlands
J802WFS	14702	East Scotland	K112SRH	32112	North East	K359ANV	40359	East
J803WFS	14703	East Scotland	K112XHG	40412	North West	K359DWJ	14359	East Midlands
J804WFS	14704	East Scotland	K113SRH	32113	East Midlands	K360DWJ	14360	East Midlands
J805WFS	14705	East Scotland	K113XHG	40413	North West	K361DWJ	14361	East Midlands
J806WFS	14706	East Scotland	K114SRH	32114	East Midlands	K362DWJ	14362	East Midlands
J807WFS	14707	East Scotland	K114XHG	40414	North West	K363DWJ	14363	East Midlands
J808WFS	14708	East	K115SRH	32115	East Midlands	K391KVA	47981	East
J811NKK	14811	South East	K116SRH	32116	East Midlands	K392KVA	47982	East
J812NKK	14812	South East	K116XHG	40416	North West	K402EDT	32990	Wales & West
J813NKK	14813	South East	K117SRH	32117	North East	K420ARW	41520	East Scotland
J814NKK	14814	South East	K117XHG	40417	North West	K421ARW	41521	South Midlands
J822HMC	15322	South West	K118SRH	32118	East Midlands	K423ARW	41523	South Midlands
J823HMC	15323	South West	K118XHG	40418	North West	K425ARW	41525	South Midlands
J824HMC	15324	South West	K120SRH	32120	West Scotland	K485FFS	40085	North East
J825HMC	15325	South West	K120XHG	40420	North West	K486FFS	40086	East Scotland
J826HMC	15326	South West	K121SRH	32121	North East	K487FFS	40087	East Scotland
J827HMC	15327	South West	K121XHG	40421	North West	K488FFS	40088	East Scotland
J828HMC	15328	South West	K122SRH	32122	East Scotland	K489FFS	40089	East Scotland
J829HMC	15329	South West	K123SRH	32123	North East	K490TFS	40090	East Scotland
J901UKV	29621	North East	K124SRH	32124	North East	K491TFS	40091	East Scotland
JAH552D	19952	East	K124XHG	40424	North West	K492FFS	40092	North East
JAH553D	19953	East	K125SRH	32125	North East	K493FFS	40093	North East
JDZ2359	32269	Wales & West	K126SRH	32126	Wales & West	K494FFS	40094	North East
JDZ2360	32260	South West	K127SRH	32127	North East	K508ESS	14408	East Scotland
JDZ2361	32261	South West	K128DAO	14268	North West	K510ESS	14410	East Scotland
JDZ2362	32262	South West	K128SRH	32128	North East	K511ESS	14411	East Scotland
JDZ2363	32263	South West	K129DAO	14229	North West	K515ESS	14415	East Scotland
JDZ2364	32264	South West	K129SRH	32129	North East	K518ESS	14418	East Scotland
JDZ2365	32265	South West	K130DAO	14230	North West	K553NHC	32553	South East
JDZ2371	32271	South West	K130SRH	32130	Wales & West	K554NHC	32554	South East
JFR2W	14102	North West	K131DAO	14231	North West	K556NHC	32556	South East
JHU899X	14282	Wales & West	K132DAO	14232	North West	K557NHC	32557	South East
JHU912X	14284	Wales & West	K132SRH	32132	Wales & West	K558NHC	32558	South East
JJD392D	12392	London	K133DAO	14233	North West	K559NHC	32559	South East
JJD399D	12399	London	K133SRH	32133	North East	K561NHC	32561	South East
JJD402D	12402	London	K134DAO	14234	North West	K562NHC	32562	South East
JJD415D	12415	London	K134SRH	32134	North East	K563NHC	32563	South East
JJD429D	12429	London	K135DAO	14235	North West	K564NHC	32564	South East
JJD435D	12435	London	K150DNV	52120	East	K565NHC	32565	South East
JJD437D	12437	London	K151DNV	52121	East	K566NHC	32566	South East
JJD444D	12444	London	K152DNV	52122	East	K567NHC	32567	South East
JJD445D	12445	London	K153DNV	52123	East	K568NHC	32568	South East
JJD450D	12450	London	K154DNV	52124	East	K569NHC	32569	South East
JJD451D	12451	London	K163FYG	47920	North East	K570NHC	32570	South East
JJD456D	12456	London	K171CAV	46383	South West	K571DFS	52141	North East
JJD462D	12462	London	K173CAV	46385	South West	K571LTS	20171	East Scotland
JJD470D	12470	London	K184YDW	47924	Wales & West	K571NHC	32571	South East
JJD481D	12481	London	K185YDW	47925	Wales & West	K572DFS	52142	East Scotland
JJD488D	12488	London	K186YDW	47926	Wales & West	K572LTS	20172	East Scotland
JJD493D	12493	London	K187YDW	47927	Wales & West	K572NHC	32572	South East
JJD495D	12495	London	K205OHS	40527	Wales & West	K573DFS	52143	North East
JJD496D	12496	London	K206OHS	40528	Wales & West	K573LTS	20173	East Scotland
JJD497D	12497	London	K211SRH	32111	East Midlands	K573NHC	32573	South East
JJD527D	12527	London	K235NHC	14985	South East	K574DFS	52144	West Scotland
JJD541D	12541	London	K236NHC	14986	South East	K574LTS	20174	East Scotland
JJD550D	12550	London	K237NHC	14987	South East	K574NHC	32574	South East
JJD565D	12565	London	K238NHC	14988	South East	K575DFS	52145	East Midlands
JJD581D	12581	London	K239NHC	14989	South East	K575LTS	20175	East Scotland
JJD592D	12592	London	K240NHC	14990	South East	K575NHC	32575	South East
JOU160P	15760	South East	K306ARW	40106	South Midlands	K576DFS	52146	North East
JPU817	52057	North West	K308YKG	41308	Wales & West	K576LTS	20176	East Scotland
JWV251W	15751	South East	K309YKG	41309	Wales & West	K576NHC	32576	South East

Reg	No	Region	Reg	No	Region	Reg	No	Region
K577DFS	52147	North East	K709DAO	20709	North West	K762DAO	20762	North West
K577LTS	20177	East Scotland	K709PCN	32709	North East	K763DAO	20763	North West
K577NHC	32577	South East	K710ASC	14710	East	K764DAO	20764	North West
K578LTS	20178	East Scotland	K710DAO	20710	North West	K765DAO	20765	North West
K578NHC	32578	South East	K710PCN	32710	North East	K766DAO	20766	North West
K579NHC	32579	South East	K711DAO	20711	North West	K767DAO	20767	North West
K580NHC	32580	South East	K711PCN	32711	North East	K768DAO	20768	North West
K584ODY	32584	South East	K711UTT	46335	South West	K769DAO	20769	North West
K585ODY	32585	South East	K712DAO	20712	North West	K770DAO	20770	North West
K586ODY	32586	South East	K712PCN	32712	North East	K771DAO	20771	North West
K587ODY	32587	South East	K713ASC	14713	East	K772DAO	20772	North West
K588ODY	32588	South East	K713DAO	20713	North West	K773DAO	20773	North West
K601ESH	32201	East Scotland	K713PCN	32713	North East	K774DAO	20774	North West
K602ESH	32202	East Scotland	K714DAO	20714	North West	K775DAO	20775	North West
K603ESH	32203	East Scotland	K714PCN	32714	North East	K776DAO	20776	North West
K604ESH	32204	East Scotland	K715ASC	14715	South East	K777DAO	20777	North West
K605ESH	32205	East Scotland	K715DAO	20715	North West	K778DAO	20778	North West
K610UFR	40810	North West	K715PCN	32715	North East	K779DAO	20779	North West
K611UFR	40811	North West	K716ASC	14716	South East	K780DAO	20780	North West
K612UFR	40812	North West	K716DAO	20716	North West	K781DAO	20781	North West
K613UFR	40813	North West	K717ASC	14717	South East	K783DAO	20783	North West
K614UFR	40814	North West	K717DAO	20717	North West	K784DAO	20784	North West
K615UFR	40815	North West	K717PCN	32717	North East	K785DAO	20785	North West
K616UFR	40816	North West	K718ASC	14718	East Scotland	K786DAO	20786	North West
K617UFR	40817	North East	K718DAO	20718	North West	K787DAO	20787	North West
K618UFR	40818	North West	K718PCN	32718	North East	K788DAO	20788	North West
K619UFR	40819	North West	K718UTT	46390	South West	K789DAO	20659	South East
K620UFR	40820	North West	K719ASC	14719	East Scotland	K790DAO	20660	South East
K622UFR	40822	North West	K719DAO	20719	North West	K791DAO	20661	South East
K622YVN	29622	North East	K719UTT	46339	South West	K801OMW	41801	East Scotland
K623UFR	40823	North West	K720ASC	14720	East Scotland	K802OMW	41802	East Midlands
K623YVN	29623	North East	K720DAO	20720	North West	K806WFJ	46362	South West
K624UFR	40824	North West	K720PCN	32720	North East	K816WFJ	46363	South West
K624YVN	29624	North East	K721ASC	14721	East Scotland	K821TKP	14821	South East
K625UFR	40825	North West	K721DAO	20721	North West	K821WFJ	46356	South West
K625YVN	29625	North East	K721PCN	32721	North East	K822TKP	14822	South East
K626UFR	40826	North West	K722ASC	14722	East Scotland	K823TKP	14823	South East
K626YVN	29626	North East	K722DAO	20722	North West	K824TKP	14824	South East
K627UFR	40827	North East	K722PCN	32722	North East	K824WFJ	46354	South West
K627YVN	29627	North East	K723ASC	14723	East Scotland	K825TKP	14825	South East
K628UFR	40828	North East	K723DAO	20723	North West	K846LMK	15346	South East
K628YVN	29628	North East	K723PNL	32723	North East	K847LMK	15347	South East
K629YVN	29629	North East	K724ASC	14724	East Scotland	K848LMK	15348	South East
K630HWX	26030	London	K724DAO	20724	North West	K849LMK	15349	South East
K630YVN	29630	North East	K724PNL	32724	North East	K850LMK	15350	South East
K631HWX	26031	London	K725ASC	14725	East Scotland	K851LMK	15351	South East
K632HWX	26032	London	K725DAO	20725	North West	K852LMK	15352	South East
K633HWX	26033	London	K725PNL	32725	North East	K853LMK	15353	South East
K634HWX	26034	London	K725UTT	46344	South West	K854LMK	15354	South East
K635HWX	26035	London	K726DAO	20726	North West	K855LMK	15355	South East
K655NHC	32555	South East	K726PNL	32726	North East	K856LMK	15356	South East
K655UNH	14055	East	K727DAO	20727	North West	K857LMK	15357	South East
K656UNH	14056	East	K727PNL	32727	North East	K858LMK	15358	South East
K657UNH	14057	East	K728DAO	20728	North West	K859LMK	15359	South East
K658UNH	14058	East	K728PNL	32728	North East	K860LMK	15360	South East
K659UNH	14059	East	K729DAO	20729	North West	K861LMK	15361	South East
K660NHC	32560	South East	K730DAO	20730	North West	K862LMK	15362	South East
K660UNH	14060	East	K731DAO	20731	North West	K863LMK	15363	South East
K661UNH	14061	East	K731UTT	46348	South West	K864LMK	15364	South East
K662UNH	14062	East	K732DAO	20732	North West	K865LMK	15365	South East
K663UNH	14063	East	K733DAO	20733	North West	K866LMK	15366	South East
K664UNH	14064	East	K734DAO	20734	North West	K867LMK	15367	South East
K665UNH	14065	East	K735DAO	20735	North West	K868LMK	15368	South East
K667UNH	14067	East	K736DAO	20736	North West	K869LMK	15369	South East
K668UNH	14068	East	K737DAO	20737	North West	K870LMK	15370	South East
K669UNH	14069	East	K738DAO	20738	North West	K871GHH	40034	North West
K670UNH	14070	East	K739DAO	20739	North West	K871LMK	15371	South East
K699ERM	20699	North West	K741DAO	20741	North West	K872GHH	40035	North West
K700DAO	20700	North West	K742DAO	20742	North West	K873GHH	40036	North West
K701DAO	20701	North West	K743DAO	20743	North West	K874GHH	40037	North West
K701NDO	27701	East Midlands	K744DAO	20744	North West	K875GHH	40038	North West
K702DAO	20702	North West	K745DAO	20745	North West	K875ODY	40875	North West
K702NDO	27702	East Midlands	K746DAO	20746	North West	K876GHH	40039	North West
K702UTT	46334	South West	K748DAO	20748	North West	K876ODY	40876	North West
K703DAO	20703	North West	K749DAO	20749	North West	K877GHH	40040	North West
K703NDO	27703	East Midlands	K750DAO	20750	North West	K877ODY	40877	North West
K703PCN	32703	North East	K751DAO	20751	North West	K878GHH	40081	North West
K704ERM	20704	North West	K752DAO	20752	North West	K878ODY	40878	North West
K704NDO	27704	East Midlands	K753DAO	20753	North West	K921OWV	32221	South East
K704PCN	32704	South Midlands	K754DAO	20754	North West	K922OWV	32222	South East
K705DAO	20705	North West	K755DAO	20755	North West	K923OWV	32223	South East
K705PCN	32705	South Midlands	K756DAO	20756	North West	K926VDV	46352	South West
K706DAO	20706	North West	K757DAO	20757	North West	K927VDV	46353	South West
K706PCN	32706	South Midlands	K758DAO	20758	North West	K964HUB	47964	East
K707DAO	20707	North West	K758FYG	52116	East Scotland	K971HUB	47971	East
K707PCN	32707	East	K759DAO	20759	North West	K972HUB	47972	East
K708DAO	20708	North West	K759FYG	52117	East Scotland	K973HUB	47973	East
K708PCN	32708	East	K760DAO	20760	North West	K974HUB	47974	East
K709ASC	14709	East	K761DAO	20761	North West	KRM431W	15731	North West

Reg	Fleet	Operator	Reg	Fleet	Operator	Reg	Fleet	Operator
KRM435W	15735	North West	L161JNH	52161	East	L308YDU	40108	South Midlands
KSU461	52644	East Midlands	L162JNH	52162	East	L309PSC	20309	East Scotland
KSU462	52645	East Midlands	L188DDW	47928	Wales & West	L310PSC	20310	East Scotland
KX51CRU	47001	South Midlands	L188SDY	40888	North West	L310YDU	40110	South Midlands
KX51CRV	47002	South Midlands	L193FDV	46065	South West	L312YDU	40112	South East
KX51CRZ	47003	South Midlands	L194FDV	46366	South West	L313YDU	40113	South East
KX51CSF	47004	South Midlands	L195FDV	46367	South West	L314YDU	40114	South East
KX51CSO	47005	South Midlands	L197FDV	46368	South West	L315JSA	40585	East Scotland
KX51CSU	47006	South Midlands	L201FDV	46369	South West	L315YDU	40115	South East
KX51CSV	47007	South Midlands	L201YAG	27201	North West	L316JSA	40586	East Scotland
KX51CSY	47008	South Midlands	L202YAG	27202	North West	L316YDU	40116	South East
KX51CSZ	47009	South Midlands	L203FDV	46370	South West	L317YDU	40117	South East
KX51CTE	47010	South Midlands	L203YAG	27203	North West	L318BOD	46388	South West
KX51CTF	47011	South Midlands	L204FDV	46371	South West	L318YDU	40118	South East
KX51CTK	47012	South Midlands	L204YAG	27204	North West	L319YDU	40119	South East
KX51CTO	47013	South Midlands	L205YAG	27205	North West	L320YDU	40120	South East
KX51CTU	47014	South Midlands	L206YAG	27206	North West	L321YDU	40121	South East
KX51CTV	47015	South Midlands	L207YAG	27207	North West	L322YDU	40122	South East
KYN285X	10285	North West	L208FDV	46372	South West	L323YDU	40123	South East
KYV311X	10311	North West	L208PSB	32382	West Scotland	L324YDU	40124	South East
KYV334X	10334	North West	L208YAG	27208	North West	L325YDU	40125	South East
KYV340X	10340	North West	L209FDV	46373	South West	L326CHB	41326	Wales & West
KYV348X	10348	South East	L209YAG	27209	North West	L326YKV	40126	South Midlands
KYV410X	10410	West Scotland	L210FDV	46374	South West	L327YKV	40127	South Midlands
KYV444X	10444	South East	L210YAG	27210	North West	L328YKV	40128	South Midlands
KYV462X	10462	South East	L211FDV	46375	South West	L329CHB	41329	Wales & West
KYV469X	10469	South East	L211YAG	27211	North West	L329YKV	40129	South East
KYV473X	10473	South East	L212FDV	46376	South West	L330CHB	41330	Wales & West
KYV492X	10492	Wales & West	L214FDV	46377	South West	L330YKV	40130	South East
KYV511X	10511	South East	L237CCW	30237	North West	L331CHB	41331	Wales & West
KYV512X	10512	South East	L238CCW	30238	North East	L334FWO	40534	East Scotland
KYV542X	10542	Wales & West	L239CCW	30239	North East	L335FWO	40535	East Scotland
L26JSA	16198	East Scotland	L240CCW	30240	Wales & West	L336FWO	40536	East Scotland
L27JSA	16199	East Scotland	L241CCK	30241	North West	L337FWO	40537	Wales & West
L31HHN	21031	North East	L241SDY	16241	South East	L338FWO	40538	Wales & West
L32HHN	21032	North East	L242CCK	30242	North East	L338KCK	20438	South East
L33HHN	21033	North East	L242SDY	16242	South East	L339FWO	40539	Wales & West
L34HHN	21034	North East	L243CCK	30243	North East	L339KCK	20439	East Midlands
L35HHN	21035	North East	L243SDY	16243	North West	L340FWO	40540	East Scotland
L36HHN	21036	North East	L244CCK	30244	North West	L340KCK	20440	East Midlands
L37HHN	21037	North East	L244SDY	16244	North West	L341FWO	40541	Wales & West
L79CWO	30729	Wales & West	L245CCK	30245	North East	L341KCK	20441	East Midlands
L82CWO	30732	Wales & West	L245SDY	16245	North West	L342FWO	40542	East Scotland
L83CWO	32983	Wales & West	L246CCK	30246	North East	L342KCK	20442	East Midlands
L84CWO	32984	Wales & West	L246SDY	16246	South East	L343FWO	40543	Wales & West
L85CWO	32985	Wales & West	L247CCK	30247	North West	L343KCK	20443	East Midlands
L86CWO	32986	Wales & West	L247SDY	16247	South East	L344KCK	20444	East Midlands
L87CWO	32987	Wales & West	L248CCK	30248	Wales & West	L345KCK	20445	South East
L89CWO	32989	Wales & West	L248SDY	16248	East Scotland	L346KCK	20446	South East
L100JLB	16610	East Scotland	L249CCK	30249	North East	L347KCK	20447	South East
L101GHN	30101	North East	L249SDY	16249	East Scotland	L360JBD	40360	East
L101JSA	16201	East Scotland	L250CCK	30250	North East	L361JBD	40361	East
L102GHN	30102	North East	L250SDY	16250	East Scotland	L362JBD	40362	East
L102JSA	16202	East Scotland	L251CCK	30251	Wales & West	L363JBD	40363	East
L103GHN	30103	North East	L252CCK	30252	North West	L364JBD	40364	East
L108LHL	16478	East Midlands	L253CCK	30253	Wales & West	L365JBD	40365	East
L109LHL	16479	East Midlands	L254CCK	30254	North West	L366JBD	40366	East
L119DRN	40419	North West	L255CCK	30255	North West	L367JBD	40367	East
L122DRN	40422	North West	L256CCK	30256	North West	L368JBD	40368	East
L123DRN	40423	North West	L267CCK	30267	East Scotland	L369JBD	40369	East
L125DRN	40425	North West	L268CCK	30268	East Scotland	L370JBD	40370	East
L125NAO	52195	North West	L269CCK	30269	East Scotland	L371JBD	40371	East
L126DRN	40426	North West	L270EHB	32988	Wales & West	L372JBD	40372	East
L126NAO	52196	North West	L270LHH	30270	North West	L373JBD	40373	East
L127DRN	40427	North West	L271LHH	30271	North West	L374JBD	40374	East
L127NAO	52197	South East	L272LHH	30272	North West	L375JBD	40375	East
L128DRN	40428	North West	L273LHH	30273	North West	L376JBD	40376	East
L137VRH	32137	West Scotland	L274LHH	30274	North West	L377JBD	40377	East
L138VRH	32138	West Scotland	L275JAO	30275	North West	L378JBD	40378	East
L139VRH	32139	South West	L276JAO	30276	North West	L379JBD	40379	East
L140VRH	32140	South West	L277JAO	30277	North West	L380JBD	40380	East
L141VRH	32141	South West	L278JAO	30278	North West	L381NBD	40381	East
L143BFV	59143	North West	L279JAO	30279	North East	L382NBD	40382	East
L145VRH	32145	West Scotland	L281JAO	30281	North West	L383NBD	40383	East
L146VRH	32146	West Scotland	L282JAO	30282	North West	L392LNA	15198	Manchester
L152BFV	59152	North West	L283JAO	30283	North West	L401JBD	30401	East
L154BFV	59154	North West	L28JSA	16200	East Scotland	L402JBD	30402	East
L155JNH	52155	East	L301JSA	40101	West Scotland	L403JBD	30403	East
L156JNH	52156	East	L301PSC	20301	East Scotland	L404JBD	30404	East
L156LBW	52021	East	L302JSA	40102	East Scotland	L405JBD	30405	East
L157JNH	52157	East	L302PSC	20302	East Scotland	L406JBD	30406	East
L157LBW	52022	London	L303JSA	40103	East Scotland	L407JBD	30407	East
L158JNH	52158	East	L303PSC	20303	East Scotland	L408JBD	30408	East
L158LBW	52023	London	L304PSC	20304	East Scotland	L409JBD	30409	East
L159JNH	52159	East	L305PSC	20305	East Scotland	L410JBD	30410	East
L159LBW	52024	East	L306PSC	20306	East Scotland	L411JBD	30411	East
L160CCW	59160	North West	L307PSC	20307	East Scotland	L412JBD	30412	East
L160JNH	52160	East	L307SKV	40107	South Midlands	L413JBD	30413	East
L161CCW	59161	North West	L308PSC	20308	East Scotland	L414JBD	30414	East

The 2003 Stagecoach Bus Handbook

Reg	No	Area	Reg	No	Area	Reg	No	Area
L414SFL	32960	Wales & West	L634BFV	40834	North West	L730VNL	32730	North East
L415JBD	30415	East	L634TDY	20634	South East	L731LWA	40777	East Midlands
L416JBD	30416	East	L635BFV	40835	North West	L731VNL	32731	North East
L417JBD	30417	East	L635TDY	20635	South East	L732LWA	40778	East Midlands
L418JBD	30418	East	L636BFV	40836	North West	L732VNL	32732	North East
L419JBD	30419	East	L637LDT	52207	East Midlands	L733LWA	40779	East Midlands
L420JBD	30420	East	L638LDT	52208	East Midlands	L733VNL	32733	North East
L421JBD	30421	East	L639LDT	52209	East Midlands	L734LWA	40780	East Midlands
L422MVV	30422	East	L640LDT	52210	East Midlands	L734VNL	32734	North East
L423MVV	30429	East Scotland	L641LDT	52211	East Midlands	L735LWA	40781	East Midlands
L423XVV	30423	East	L642LDT	52212	East Midlands	L735VNL	32735	North East
L424MVV	30430	East Scotland	L643LDT	52213	East Midlands	L736LWA	40736	East Midlands
L424TJK	20604	South East	L651HKS	30651	East Scotland	L736VNL	32736	North East
L424XVV	30424	East	L652HKS	30652	East Scotland	L737LWA	40737	East Midlands
L425MVV	30431	East Scotland	L653HKS	30653	East Scotland	L737VNL	32737	North East
L425TJK	20605	South East	L654HKS	30654	East Scotland	L738LWA	40738	East Midlands
L425XVV	30425	East	L655HKS	30655	East Scotland	L738VNL	32738	North East
L426MVV	30426	East Scotland	L656HKS	30656	East Scotland	L739LWA	40739	East Midlands
L426TJK	20606	South East	L657HKS	30657	East Scotland	L739VNL	32739	North East
L427MVV	30427	East Scotland	L658HKS	30658	East Scotland	L740LWA	40740	East Midlands
L427TJK	20607	South East	L659HKS	30659	East Scotland	L740VNL	32740	North East
L428MVV	30428	East Scotland	L660HKS	30660	Wales & West	L741LWA	40741	East Midlands
L435LWA	30435	East Midlands	L661MSF	30661	Wales & West	L741VNL	32741	North East
L436LWA	30436	East Midlands	L662MSF	30662	North West	L742LWA	40742	East Midlands
L437LWA	30437	East Midlands	L663MSF	30663	Wales & West	L742VNL	32742	North East
L438LWA	30438	East Midlands	L664MSF	30664	Wales & West	L743LWA	40743	East Midlands
L439LWA	30439	East Midlands	L665MSF	30665	North West	L743VNL	32743	North East
L440LWA	30440	East Midlands	L667MSF	30667	Wales & West	L744LWA	40744	East Midlands
L441LWA	30441	East Midlands	L668MSF	30668	North West	L744VNL	32744	North East
L442LWA	30442	East Midlands	L669MSF	30669	Wales & West	L745LWA	40745	East Midlands
L443LWA	30443	East Midlands	L671HNV	16671	East	L745VNL	32745	North East
L445LWA	30445	East Midlands	L672HNV	16672	East	L746LWA	40746	East Midlands
L446LWA	30446	East Midlands	L673HNV	16673	East	L746VNL	32746	North East
L447LWA	30447	East Midlands	L674HNV	16674	East	L748LWA	40748	East Midlands
L448LWA	30448	East Midlands	L675HNV	16675	East	L748VNL	32748	North East
L449LWA	30449	East Midlands	L676HNV	16676	East	L749LWA	40749	East Midlands
L450LWA	30450	East Midlands	L677HNV	16677	East	L749VNL	32749	North East
L451LWA	30451	East Midlands	L678HNV	16678	East	L750LWA	40750	East Midlands
L451YAC	30551	East	L679HNV	16679	East	L750VNL	32750	North East
L452LWA	30452	East Midlands	L680HNV	16680	East	L751LHL	40751	East Midlands
L452YAC	30552	East	L681HNV	16681	East	L751VNL	32751	North East
L453LHL	30453	East Midlands	L682HNV	16682	East	L752VNL	32752	North East
L453YAC	30553	East	L683HNV	16683	East	L753VNL	32753	North East
L454YAC	30554	East	L684HNV	16684	East	L754VNL	32754	East
L455YAC	30555	East	L685CDD	40685	South West	L755VNL	32755	East
L456YAC	30556	East	L685JBD	16685	East	L756VNL	32756	East
L550JFS	41950	East Scotland	L686CDD	40686	South West	L757VNL	32757	East
L577NSB	40529	West Scotland	L687CDD	40687	South West	L758VNL	32758	East
L578HSG	52178	East Scotland	L688CDD	40688	South West	L759VNL	32759	North East
L579HSG	52179	East	L689CDD	40689	South West	L760ARG	32760	North East
L580HSG	52180	Wales & West	L690CDD	40690	South West	L761ARG	32761	North East
L580JSA	52170	East Scotland	L691CDD	40691	South West	L762ARG	32762	North East
L581HSG	52181	Wales & West	L692CDD	40692	South West	L763ARG	32763	North East
L582HSG	52182	Wales & West	L693CDD	40693	South West	L764ARG	32764	North East
L582JSA	52172	East	L694CDD	40694	South West	L765ARG	32765	North East
L583HSG	52183	East Scotland	L695CDD	40695	South West	L803XDG	41803	Wales & West
L584HSG	52184	East Scotland	L696CDD	40696	South West	L804XDG	41804	Wales & West
L585HSG	52185	East Scotland	L701FWO	30701	Wales & West	L805XDG	41805	Wales & West
L586HSG	52186	Wales & West	L702FWO	30702	Wales & West	L806XDG	41806	Wales & West
L587HSG	52187	East	L703FWO	30703	Wales & West	L826BKK	14826	South East
L588HSG	52188	East Scotland	L704FWO	30704	Wales & West	L827BKK	14827	South East
L589HSG	52189	East	L705FWO	30705	Wales & West	L828BKK	14828	South East
L590HSG	52190	East	L705HFU	27705	East Midlands	L829BKK	14829	South East
L601VCD	20601	South East	L706FWO	30706	Wales & West	L830BKK	14830	South East
L602VCD	20602	South East	L706HFU	27706	East Midlands	L831CDG	30831	Wales & West
L603VCD	20603	South East	L707FWO	30707	Wales & West	L832CDG	30832	Wales & West
L608TDY	20608	South East	L707HFU	27707	East Midlands	L833CDG	30833	Wales & West
L609TDY	20609	South East	L708FWO	30708	Wales & West	L834CDG	30834	Wales & West
L616TDY	20616	South East	L708HFU	27708	East Midlands	L835CDG	30835	Wales & West
L617TDY	20617	South East	L709FWO	30709	Wales & West	L836CDG	30836	Wales & West
L619TDY	20619	South East	L709HFU	27709	East Midlands	L837CDG	30837	East
L620TDY	20620	South East	L709JUD	32009	South East	L838CDG	30838	East
L621TDY	20621	South East	L710FWO	30710	Wales & West	L839CDG	30839	Wales & West
L622TDY	20622	South East	L710JUD	32010	South East	L840CDG	30840	Wales & West
L623TDY	20623	South East	L711FWO	30711	Wales & West	L841CDG	30841	Wales & West
L624TDY	20624	South East	L711JUD	32011	South East	L842CDG	30842	Wales & West
L625TDY	20625	South East	L712FWO	30712	Wales & West	L881SDY	40881	North West
L626TDY	20626	South East	L712JUD	32012	South East	L882LFS	40082	West Scotland
L627TDY	20627	South East	L713JUD	32013	South East	L882SDY	40882	North West
L628TDY	20628	South East	L714JUD	32014	South West	L883SDY	40883	North West
L629TDY	20629	South East	L715JUD	32015	South West	L884SDY	40884	North West
L630BFV	40830	North West	L716JUD	32016	South West	L885SDY	40885	North West
L630TDY	20630	South East	L717JUD	32017	South West	L886SDY	40886	North West
L631BFV	40831	North West	L718JUD	32018	South West	L887SDY	40887	North West
L631TDY	20631	South East	L719JUD	32019	London	L914UGA	40531	Wales & West
L632BFV	40832	North West	L720JUD	32020	South West	L927UGA	40532	Wales & West
L632TDY	20632	South East	L721JUD	32021	South West	L928UGA	40533	Wales & West
L633BFV	40833	North West	L722JUD	32022	South West	L929CTT	46300	South West
L633TDY	20633	South East	L729VNL	32729	North East	L930CTT	46301	South West

Reg	No	Depot	Reg	No	Depot	Reg	No	Depot
L931CTT	46302	South West	LV52HJZ	34348	London	LX51FHL	34325	London
L932CTT	46303	South West	LV52HKA	34349	London	LX51FHN	17394	London
L933CTT	46304	South West	LV52HKB	34350	London	LX51FHO	17396	London
L934CTT	46305	South West	LV52HKC	34351	London	LX51FHP	17399	London
L935CTT	46306	South West	LV52HKD	34352	London	LX51FHS	17403	London
L936CTT	46307	South West	LV52HKE	34353	London	LX51FHT	17405	London
L937CTT	46308	South West	LV52HKF	34354	London	LX51FHU	17408	London
L938CTT	46309	South West	LV52HKG	34355	London	LX51FHV	17410	London
L939CTT	46310	South West	LV52HKH	34356	London	LX51FHW	17411	London
L940CTT	46311	South West	LV52HKJ	34357	London	LX51FHY	17412	London
L941CTT	46312	South West	LV52HKK	34358	London	LX51FHZ	17413	London
L942CTT	46313	South West	LV52HKL	34359	London	LX51FJA	17414	London
L942RJN	27212	North West	LV52HKM	34360	London	LX51FJC	17415	London
L943CTT	46314	South West	LV52HKN	34361	London	LX51FJD	17416	London
L945EOD	46389	South West	LV52HKO	34362	London	LX51FJE	17417	London
L947EOD	46391	South West	LV52HKP	34363	London	LX51FJF	17418	London
L948EOD	46392	South West	LV52HKT	34364	London	LX51FJJ	17419	London
L949EOD	46393	South West	LV52HKU	34365	London	LX51FJK	17420	London
L950EOD	46386	South West	LV52USF	17561	London	LX51FJN	17421	London
LAT505V	15905	North East	LV52VFW	23001	London	LX51FJO	17422	London
LAT514V	15914	North East	LV52VFX	23002	London	LX51FJP	17423	London
LCU112	19912	North East	LV52VFY	23003	London	LX51FJV	17424	London
LDS201A	12107	East Scotland	LV52VFZ	23004	London	LX51FJY	17425	London
LFF875	12156	London	LV52VGA	23005	London	LX51FJZ	17426	London
LRV992	19992	South West	LV52VGC	23006	London	LX51FKA	17427	London
LSK545	52029	East Scotland	LV52VGD	23007	London	LX51FKB	17428	London
LV52HDO	17562	London	LV52VGE	23008	London	LX51FKD	17430	London
LV52HDU	17563	London	LV52VGF	23009	London	LX51FKE	17431	London
LV52HDX	17564	London	LV52VGG	23010	London	LX51FKF	17432	London
LV52HDY	17565	London	LV52VGJ	23011	London	LX51FKG	17433	London
LV52HDZ	17566	London	LV52VGK	23012	London	LX51FKJ	17435	London
LV52HEJ	17567	London	LV52VGL	23013	London	LX51FKL	17439	London
LV52HEU	17568	London	LV52VGM	23014	London	LX51FKO	17444	London
LV52HFA	17569	London	LV52VGN	23015	London	LX51FKR	17451	London
LV52HFB	17570	London	LV52VGO	23016	London	LX51FKT	17457	London
LV52HFC	17571	London	LV52VGP	23017	London	LX51FKU	17459	London
LV52HFD	17572	London	LV52VGR	23018	London	LX51FKW	17461	London
LV52HFE	17573	London	LV52VGT	23019	London	LX51FKZ	17463	London
LV52HFF	17574	London	LV52VGU	23020	London	LX51FLB	17465	London
LV52HFH	17575	London	LV52VGX	23021	London	LX51FLC	17466	London
LV52HFJ	17576	London	LV52VGY	23022	London	LX51FLD	17467	London
LV52HFK	17577	London	LV52VGZ	23023	London	LX51FLE	17468	London
LV52HFL	17578	London	LV52VHA	23024	London	LX51FLF	17469	London
LV52HFM	17579	London	LV52VHB	23025	London	LX51FLG	17471	London
LV52HFN	17580	London	LV52VHC	23026	London	LX51FLH	17472	London
LV52HFO	17581	London	LV52VHD	23027	London	LX51FLJ	17473	London
LV52HFP	17582	London	LV52VHE	23028	London	LX51FLK	17474	London
LV52HFR	17583	London	LV52VHF	23029	London	LX51FLL	17475	London
LV52HFS	17584	London	LV52VHG	23030	London	LX51FLM	17476	London
LV52HFT	17585	London	LV52VHH	23031	London	LX51FLN	17477	London
LV52HFU	17586	London	LV52VHJ	23032	London	LX51FLP	17478	London
LV52HFW	17587	London	LV52VHK	23033	London	LX51FLR	17479	London
LV52HFX	17588	London	LV52VHL	23034	London	LX51FLV	17480	London
LV52HFY	17589	London	LV52VHM	23035	London	LX51FLW	17481	London
LV52HFZ	17590	London	LWS33Y	14285	Wales & West	LX51FLZ	17482	London
LV52HGA	17591	London	LWS34Y	14286	Wales & West	LX51FMA	17483	London
LV52HGC	34366	London	LWS35Y	14287	Wales & West	LX51FMC	17484	London
LV52HGD	34367	London	LWS36Y	14288	Wales & West	LX51FMD	17485	London
LV52HGE	34368	London	LWS37Y	14289	Wales & West	LX51FME	17486	London
LV52HGF	34369	London	LWS38Y	14290	Wales & West	LX51FMF	17487	London
LV52HGG	34370	London	LWS39Y	14291	Wales & West	LX51FMG	17488	London
LV52HGJ	34371	London	LWS40Y	14292	Wales & West	LX51FMJ	17489	London
LV52HGK	34372	London	LWS41Y	14293	Wales & West	LX51FMK	17490	London
LV52HGL	34373	London	LX51FFO	34341	London	LX51FML	17491	London
LV52HGM	34374	London	LX51FFW	34290	London	LX51FMM	17492	London
LV52HGN	34375	London	LX51FGA	34303	London	LX51FMO	17493	London
LV52HHA	17592	London	LX51FGD	34306	London	LX51FMP	17494	London
LV52HHB	17593	London	LX51FGE	34305	London	LX51FMU	17495	London
LV52HHC	17594	London	LX51FGF	34304	London	LX51FMV	17496	London
LV52HHD	17595	London	LX51FGG	34307	London	LX51FMY	17497	London
LV52HHE	17596	London	LX51FGJ	34311	London	LX51FMZ	17498	London
LV52HHF	17597	London	LX51FGK	34309	London	LX51FNA	17499	London
LV52HHG	17598	London	LX51FGM	34308	London	LX51FNC	17500	London
LV52HHJ	17599	London	LX51FGN	34312	London	LX51FND	17501	London
LV52HHK	17600	London	LX51FGO	34313	London	LX51FNE	17502	London
LV52HHL	17601	London	LX51FGP	34314	London	LX51FNF	17503	London
LV52HHM	17602	London	LX51FGU	34315	London	LX51FNG	17504	London
LV52HHN	17603	London	LX51FGV	34310	London	LX51FNH	17505	London
LV52HHO	17604	London	LX51FGZ	34316	London	LX51FNJ	17506	London
LV52HHP	17605	London	LX51FHA	34319	London	LX51FNK	17507	London
LV52HHR	17606	London	LX51FHB	34318	London	LX51FNL	17508	London
LV52HHS	17607	London	LX51FHC	34320	London	LX51FNM	17509	London
LV52HHT	17608	London	LX51FHD	34321	London	LX51FNN	17510	London
LV52HHU	17609	London	LX51FHE	34322	London	LX51FNO	17511	London
LV52HHW	17610	London	LX51FHF	34323	London	LX51FNP	17512	London
LV52HHX	17611	London	LX51FHG	34317	London	LX51FNR	17513	London
LV52HHY	17731	London	LX51FHH	34326	London	LX51FNS	17514	London
LV52HHZ	17732	London	LX51FHJ	34327	London	LX51FNT	17515	London
LV52HJA	17733	London	LX51FHK	34324	London	LX51FNU	17516	London

174

Reg	No.	Region	Reg	No.	Region	Reg	No.	Region
LX51FNV	17517	London	M87WBW	32087	North East	M309DGP	16409	South West
LX51FNW	17518	London	M89WBW	32089	North East	M310DGP	16410	South West
LX51FNY	17519	London	M91WBW	32091	South East	M311DGP	16411	South West
LX51FNZ	17520	London	M92WBW	32092	South East	M311YSC	20311	South East
LX51FOA	17521	London	M93WBW	32093	South East	M312DGP	16412	South West
LX51FOC	17522	London	M94WBW	32094	South East	M312YSC	20312	South East
LX51FOD	17523	London	M95WBW	32095	South East	M313DGP	16413	South West
LX51FOF	17524	London	M96WBW	32096	South East	M313YSC	20313	South East
LX51FOH	17525	London	M97WBW	32097	South East	M314DGP	16414	South West
LX51FOJ	17526	London	M98WBW	32098	South East	M314PKS	20314	East Scotland
LX51FOK	17527	London	M100AAB	28955	West Scotland	M315DGP	16415	South West
LX51FOM	17528	London	M101WBW	32088	South East	M315PKS	20315	East Scotland
LX51FON	17529	London	M102WBW	32090	South East	M316DGP	16416	South West
LX51FOP	17530	London	M103WBW	32099	South West	M317DGP	16417	South West
LX51FOT	17531	London	M103XBW	52026	West Scotland	M317RSO	40587	East Scotland
LX51FOU	17532	London	M104PVN	30104	North East	M318DGP	16418	South West
LX51FOV	17533	London	M105CCD	59105	South West	M318RSO	40588	East Scotland
LX51FPA	17534	London	M105PVN	30105	North East	M319DGP	16419	South West
LX51FPC	17387	London	M106CCD	59106	South West	M319RSO	40589	East Scotland
LX51FPD	17390	London	M106PVN	30106	North East	M320DGP	16420	South West
LX51FPE	34278	London	M107PVN	30107	North East	M320RSO	40590	East Scotland
LX51FPF	17383	London	M108CCD	59108	South West	M321RSO	40591	East Scotland
LX51FPJ	34300	London	M108PVN	30108	North East	M331LHP	40131	South East
LY02OAA	17535	London	M151FGB	21051	West Scotland	M332DRP	40132	East
LY02OAB	17536	London	M160CCD	52260	West Scotland	M332LHP	40132	South East
LY02OAC	17537	London	M161CCD	52261	West Scotland	M334DRP	40334	East
LY02OAD	17538	London	M162CCD	52262	West Scotland	M334LHP	40134	South Midlands
LY02OAE	17539	London	M163CCD	52263	West Scotland	M335DRP	40335	East
LY02OAG	17540	London	M164CCD	52264	West Scotland	M335LHP	40135	South Midlands
LY02OAN	17541	London	M164SCK	52267	North West	M336DRP	40336	East
LY02OAO	17542	London	M165CCD	52265	West Scotland	M336LHP	40136	South Midlands
LY02OAP	17543	London	M165SCK	52268	North West	M337DRP	40337	East
LY02OAS	17544	London	M166CCD	52266	West Scotland	M337LHP	40137	South Midlands
LY02OAU	17545	London	M191HTT	46332	South West	M338DRP	40338	East
LY02OAV	17546	London	M192HTT	46326	South West	M338LHP	40138	South Midlands
LY02OAW	17547	London	M193HTT	46328	South West	M339DRP	40339	East
LY02OAX	17548	London	M194HTT	46331	South West	M339LHP	40139	South Midlands
LY02OAZ	17549	London	M201DRG	27301	East Midlands	M340DRP	40340	East
LY02OBB	17550	London	M201LHP	20201	South Midlands	M340LHP	40140	South Midlands
LY02OBC	17551	London	M202DRG	27302	East Midlands	M341DRP	40341	East
LY02OBD	17552	London	M202LHP	20202	South Midlands	M341LHP	40141	South Midlands
LY02OBE	17553	London	M203DRG	27303	East Midlands	M342DRP	40342	East
LY02OBF	17554	London	M203LHP	20203	South Midlands	M342LHP	40142	South Midlands
LY02OBG	17555	London	M204DRG	27304	East Midlands	M343DRP	40343	East
LY02OBH	17556	London	M204LHP	20204	South Midlands	M343LHP	40143	South Midlands
LY02OBJ	17557	London	M205LHP	20205	South Midlands	M343NOD	30343	South West
LY02OBK	17558	London	M209LHP	20209	South Midlands	M344DRP	40344	East
LY02OBL	17559	London	M210LHP	20210	South Midlands	M344JBO	40544	Wales & West
LY02OBM	17560	London	M223SVN	16823	North East	M344LHP	40144	Wales & West
M38PVN	21038	North East	M224SVN	16824	North East	M345DRP	40345	East
M39PVN	21039	North East	M225SVN	16825	North East	M345JBO	40545	South West
M40PVN	21040	North East	M226SVN	16826	North East	M345LHP	40145	Wales & West
M41PVN	21041	North East	M226UTM	40226	South West	M346DRP	40346	East
M42PVN	21042	North East	M227SVN	16827	North East	M346JBO	40546	Wales & West
M59VJO	32066	North East	M227UTM	40227	South West	M346KWK	40146	South Midlands
M61VJO	32041	South East	M228UTM	40228	South West	M347DRP	40347	East
M62VJO	32070	South East	M229UTM	40229	South West	M347JBO	40547	Wales & West
M63VJO	32077	South East	M230TBV	20430	North West	M348DRP	40348	East
M64HHB	32964	Wales & West	M230UTM	40230	South West	M348JBO	40548	Wales & West
M64VJO	32080	North East	M231UTM	40231	South West	M349DRP	40349	East
M65HHB	32965	Wales & West	M232UTM	40232	South West	M349JBO	40549	Wales & West
M65VJO	32065	South East	M233UTM	40233	South West	M350JBO	40550	Wales & West
M67HHB	32967	Wales & West	M234UTM	40234	South West	M351JBO	40551	Wales & West
M67VJO	32067	North East	M235TBV	20435	North West	M352JBO	40552	Wales & West
M68HHB	32968	Wales & West	M235UTM	40235	South West	M353JBO	40553	Wales & West
M68VJO	32068	North East	M236TBV	20436	North West	M354JBO	40554	Wales & West
M69HHB	32969	Wales & West	M236UTM	40236	South West	M355JBO	40555	Wales & West
M69VJO	32069	North East	M237UTM	40237	South West	M356JBO	40556	Wales & West
M71HHB	30721	Wales & West	M238UTM	40238	South West	M357JBO	40557	Wales & West
M71VJO	32071	North East	M239UTM	40239	South West	M358JBO	40558	Wales & West
M73HHB	30723	Wales & West	M240UTM	40240	South West	M359JBO	40559	Wales & West
M73VJO	32073	North East	M241UTM	40241	South West	M360JBO	40560	South West
M74HHB	30724	North West	M242UTM	40242	South West	M361LAX	40561	Wales & West
M74VJO	32074	South East	M243UTM	40243	South West	M362LAX	40562	Wales & West
M75HHB	30725	Wales & West	M244UTM	40244	South West	M363LAX	40563	Wales & West
M75VJO	32075	South East	M245UTM	40245	South West	M364LAX	40564	Wales & West
M76HHB	30726	North West	M246UTM	40246	South West	M365LAX	40565	Wales & West
M76VJO	32076	South East	M247UTM	40247	South West	M366LAX	40566	Wales & West
M78HHB	30728	Wales & West	M248UTM	40248	South West	M367LAX	40567	Wales & West
M78VJO	32078	South East	M249UTM	40249	South West	M368LAX	40568	Wales & West
M79VJO	32079	South Midlands	M250UTM	40250	South West	M369LAX	40569	Wales & West
M81WBW	32081	North East	M301DGP	16401	South West	M370LAX	40570	Wales & West
M82WBW	32082	North East	M302DGP	16402	South West	M371LAX	40571	Wales & West
M83WBW	32083	North East	M303DGP	16403	South West	M379TJA	15197	Manchester
M84WBW	32084	South Midlands	M304DGP	16404	South West	M387KVR	32794	North East
M85DEW	32936	Wales & West	M305DGP	16405	South West	M395KVR	40985	West Scotland
M85WBW	32085	Wales & West	M306DGP	16406	South West	M396KVR	40986	West Scotland
M86DEW	32937	Wales & West	M307DGP	16407	South West	M397KVR	40987	West Scotland
M86WBW	32086	Wales & West	M308DGP	16408	South West	M401SPY	20291	North East

M402SPY	20292	North East	M592OSO	20192	East Scotland	M682TDB	15182	Manchester
M403SPY	20293	North East	M593OSO	20193	East Scotland	M683TDB	15183	Manchester
M404BFG	52214	East Scotland	M594OSO	20194	East Scotland	M684TDB	15184	Manchester
M404SPY	20294	North East	M595OCO	20195	East Scotland	M685TDB	15185	Manchester
M405BFG	52215	Wales & West	M596OSO	20196	East Scotland	M686TDB	15186	Manchester
M405SPY	20295	North East	M597OSO	20197	East Scotland	M687TDB	15187	Manchester
M406BFG	52216	North West	M597SSB	32795	North East	M688TDB	15188	Manchester
M406SPY	20296	North East	M598OSO	20198	South East	M689TDB	15189	Manchester
M407SPY	20297	North East	M601VHE	20491	East Midlands	M690TDB	15190	Manchester
M408SPY	20298	North East	M602VHE	20492	East Midlands	M691TDB	15191	Manchester
M409SPY	20299	North East	M603VHE	20493	East Midlands	M692TDB	15192	Manchester
M410BFG	52220	Wales & West	M604VHE	20494	East Midlands	M693TDB	15193	Manchester
M410SPY	20300	North East	M605VHE	20495	East Midlands	M694TDB	15194	Manchester
M411RRN	20411	East Midlands	M606VHE	20496	East Midlands	M695TDB	15195	Manchester
M412RRN	20412	East Midlands	M607VHE	20497	East Midlands	M696TDB	15196	Manchester
M413RRN	20413	East Midlands	M608WET	20498	East Midlands	M697EDD	40697	South West
M414RRN	20414	East Midlands	M609WET	20499	East Midlands	M698EDD	40698	South West
M451VCW	20451	North West	M610APN	20610	South East	M699CDD	40699	South West
M452VCW	20452	North West	M611APN	20611	South East	M699TDB	15199	Manchester
M454VCW	20454	North West	M612APN	20612	South East	M701EDD	40701	South West
M454VHE	30454	North West	M613APN	20613	South East	M702EDD	40702	South West
M455VCW	20455	North West	M614APN	20614	South East	M703JDG	40703	South West
M455VHE	30455	North West	M615APN	20615	South East	M704JDG	40704	South West
M456VCW	20456	North West	M622HDV	46330	South West	M705JDG	40705	South West
M456VHE	30456	North West	M623HDV	46322	South West	M706JDG	40706	South West
M457VCW	20457	North West	M624HDV	46321	South West	M707JDG	40707	South West
M457VHE	30457	North West	M625HDV	46323	South West	M707KRH	20267	North East
M458VCW	20458	North West	M625KKG	32970	Wales & West	M708JDG	40708	Wales & West
M458VHE	30458	North West	M626HDV	46325	South West	M708KRH	20268	North East
M459VCW	20459	North West	M627HDV	46329	South West	M709JDG	40709	Wales & West
M459VHE	30459	North West	M628HDV	46324	South West	M709KRH	20269	North East
M460VCW	20460	South East	M629HDV	46320	South West	M710JDG	40710	Wales & West
M460VHE	30460	North West	M630HDV	46327	South West	M710KRH	20270	North East
M461VCW	20461	South East	M634FJF	41634	Manchester	M711FMR	40711	Wales & West
M461VHE	30461	North West	M636BCD	20636	South East	M711KRH	20271	North East
M462VCW	20462	South East	M636HDV	46318	South West	M712FMR	40712	Wales & West
M462VHE	30462	North West	M637BCD	20637	South East	M712KRH	20272	North East
M463VCW	20465	North West	M637HDV	46317	South West	M713FMR	40713	Wales & West
M466ASW	20583	West Scotland	M638BCD	20638	South East	M713KRH	20273	North East
M467ASW	20594	West Scotland	M638HDV	46315	South West	M714FMR	40714	Wales & West
M468ASW	20512	West Scotland	M639BCD	20639	South East	M714KRH	20274	North East
M469ASW	20509	West Scotland	M639HDV	46319	South West	M715FMR	40715	Wales & West
M470ASW	20570	West Scotland	M640HDV	46316	South West	M715KRH	20275	North East
M471ASW	20571	West Scotland	M641HDV	46333	South West	M716KRH	20276	North East
M472ASW	20572	West Scotland	M648FYS	40098	West Scotland	M717KRH	20277	North East
M473ASW	20573	West Scotland	M649FYS	40099	West Scotland	M718BCS	30318	West Scotland
M474ASW	20574	West Scotland	M650BCD	20650	South East	M718KRH	20278	North East
M475ASW	20575	West Scotland	M650FYS	40100	West Scotland	M719BCS	30319	West Scotland
M476ASW	20576	West Scotland	M651BCD	20651	South East	M720BCS	30320	West Scotland
M477ASW	20577	West Scotland	M651FYS	40066	West Scotland	M721BCS	30321	West Scotland
M478ASW	20578	West Scotland	M652BCD	20652	South East	M722BCS	30322	West Scotland
M479ASW	20579	West Scotland	M652FYS	40069	West Scotland	M723BCS	30323	West Scotland
M480ASW	20565	West Scotland	M653FYS	40053	West Scotland	M724BCS	30324	West Scotland
M481ASW	20510	West Scotland	M654FYS	40054	West Scotland	M725BCS	30325	West Scotland
M482ASW	20569	West Scotland	M655FYS	40055	West Scotland	M726BCS	30326	West Scotland
M483ASW	20511	West Scotland	M656FYS	40056	West Scotland	M727BCS	30327	West Scotland
M484ASW	20581	West Scotland	M657FYS	40057	West Scotland	M732BSJ	30332	West Scotland
M485ASW	20508	West Scotland	M658FYS	40058	West Scotland	M733BSJ	30333	North West
M486ASW	20566	West Scotland	M659FYS	40059	West Scotland	M734BSJ	30334	North West
M487ASW	20567	West Scotland	M660FYS	40060	West Scotland	M735BSJ	30335	West Scotland
M488ASW	20505	West Scotland	M661FYS	40061	West Scotland	M736BSJ	30336	West Scotland
M489ASW	20568	West Scotland	M662ECD	20662	South East	M737BSJ	30337	West Scotland
M490ASW	16846	West Scotland	M662FYS	40062	West Scotland	M738BSJ	30338	West Scotland
M491ASW	16847	West Scotland	M663ECD	20663	South East	M739BSJ	30339	West Scotland
M492ASW	16848	West Scotland	M663FYS	40063	West Scotland	M740BSJ	30340	West Scotland
M510FWV	30800	South East	M664ECD	20664	South East	M741BSJ	30341	West Scotland
M511FWV	30801	South East	M664FYS	40064	West Scotland	M741PRS	30301	North West
M536RSO	52236	East Scotland	M665ECD	20665	South East	M742PRS	30302	North West
M537RSO	52237	East Scotland	M665FYS	40065	West Scotland	M743PRS	30303	North West
M538RSO	52238	East Scotland	M667ECD	20667	South East	M744PRS	30304	North West
M539RSO	52239	East Scotland	M667FYS	40067	West Scotland	M745PRS	30305	North West
M540RSO	52240	East Scotland	M668ECD	20668	South East	M746PRS	30306	North West
M541RSO	52241	East Scotland	M668FYS	40068	West Scotland	M748PRS	30308	North West
M542RSO	52242	East Scotland	M669ECD	20669	South East	M749PRS	30309	North West
M543RSO	52243	East Scotland	M670ECD	20670	South East	M750LAX	20350	Wales & West
M543SPY	20243	North East	M670SSX	30670	East Scotland	M750PRS	30310	North West
M544SPY	20244	North East	M671SSX	30671	East Scotland	M751LAX	20351	Wales & West
M545SPY	20245	North East	M672SSX	30672	East Scotland	M752LAX	20352	Wales & West
M546SPY	20246	North East	M673SSX	30673	West Scotland	M753LAX	20353	Wales & West
M547SPY	20247	North East	M674SSX	30674	West Scotland	M754LAX	20354	Wales & West
M548SPY	20248	North East	M675SSX	30675	West Scotland	M755LAX	20355	Wales & West
M549SPY	20249	North East	M676SSX	30676	West Scotland	M756LAX	20356	Wales & West
M550SPY	20250	North East	M677SSX	30677	West Scotland	M757LAX	20357	Wales & West
M551SPY	20251	North East	M678SSX	30678	West Scotland	M758LAX	20358	Wales & West
M552SPY	20252	North East	M679SSX	30679	East Scotland	M759LAX	20359	Wales & West
M562JTG	32966	Wales & West	M680SSX	30680	East Scotland	M760LAX	20360	Wales & West
M589OSO	20189	South East	M680TDB	15180	Manchester	M761LAX	20361	Wales & West
M590OSO	20190	South East	M681SSX	30681	East Scotland	M762LAX	20362	Wales & West
M591OSO	20191	East Scotland	M681TDB	15181	Manchester	M763LAX	20363	Wales & West

The 2003 Stagecoach Bus Handbook　　　　　　　　　　　　　　　　**176**

M764LAX	20364	Wales & West	M977WWR	47977	East	N136AET	16486	East Midlands
M765RAX	20365	Wales & West	M978WWR	47978	East	N137AET	16487	East Midlands
M766DRG	32766	North East	MBE613R	15513	East Midlands	N138AET	16488	East Midlands
M766RAX	20366	Wales & West	MFN41R	15741	South East	N139AET	16489	East Midlands
M767DRG	32767	North East	MFN946F	19946	South East	N140AET	16490	East Midlands
M767RAX	20367	Wales & West	MHS4P	14464	Wales & West	N141AET	16491	East Midlands
M768DRG	32768	North East	MHS5P	14465	Wales & West	N142AET	16492	East Midlands
M768RAX	20368	Wales & West	MIL4693	52084	West Scotland	N142XSA	52282	West Scotland
M769DRG	32769	North East	MK02EFU	17715	Manchester	N143AET	16493	East Midlands
M769RAX	20369	Wales & West	MK02EFV	17716	Manchester	N143XSA	52283	West Scotland
M770DRG	32770	North East	MK02EFW	17717	Manchester	N144AET	16494	East Midlands
M770RAX	20370	Wales & West	MK02EFX	17718	Manchester	N144XSA	52284	West Scotland
M770TFS	40070	East Scotland	MK02EFY	17719	Manchester	N145XSA	52285	West Scotland
M771DRG	32771	East	MK02EFZ	17720	Manchester	N148XSA	52288	West Scotland
M771TFS	40071	East Scotland	MK02EGC	17721	Manchester	N149XSA	52289	West Scotland
M772BCS	30312	West Scotland	MK02EGD	17722	Wales & West	N150XSA	52290	West Scotland
M772TFS	40072	East Scotland	MK02EGE	17723	Manchester	N151MTG	41151	Wales & West
M773BCS	30313	West Scotland	MK02EGF	17724	Manchester	N151XSA	52291	East Scotland
M773TFS	40073	East Scotland	MK02EGJ	17725	Manchester	N152MTG	41152	Wales & West
M774TFS	40074	East Scotland	MK02EGU	17726	Manchester	N152XSA	52292	East Scotland
M775TFS	40075	East Scotland	MK02EGV	17727	Manchester	N153MTG	41153	Wales & West
M776TFS	40076	East Scotland	MK02EGX	17728	Wales & West	N153XSA	52293	East Scotland
M778TFS	40078	East Scotland	MK02EGY	17729	Wales & West	N154MTG	41154	Wales & West
M779TFS	40079	East Scotland	MK02EGZ	17730	Manchester	N154XSA	52294	East Scotland
M780TFS	40080	East Scotland	MK02EHC	17710	Manchester	N155MTG	41155	Wales & West
M784PRS	20584	West Scotland	MK02EHD	17711	Manchester	N156MTG	41156	Wales & West
M785PRS	20585	West Scotland	ML02KCO	17703	Manchester	N157MTG	41157	Wales & West
M786PRS	20586	West Scotland	ML02KCU	17706	Manchester	N158MTG	41158	Wales & West
M787PRS	20587	West Scotland	ML02KCV	17709	Manchester	N159MTG	41159	Wales & West
M788PRS	20588	West Scotland	ML02KNO	17704	Manchester	N160MTG	41160	Wales & West
M789PRS	20589	West Scotland	ML02RWJ	17712	Manchester	N182CMJ	46378	South West
M790PRS	20590	West Scotland	ML02RWK	17713	Manchester	N183CMJ	46379	South West
M791PRS	20591	West Scotland	ML02RWN	17714	Manchester	N188GFR	46398	South West
M792PRS	20592	West Scotland	ML02RWO	17701	Manchester	N189GFR	46396	South West
M793PRS	20593	West Scotland	ML02RWU	17702	Manchester	N190GFR	46381	South West
M808JTY	52269	East Midlands	ML02RWV	17705	Manchester	N191LPN	40891	South East
M808WWR	47988	East	ML02RWW	17707	Manchester	N192LPN	40892	South East
M809WWR	47989	East	ML02RWY	17708	Manchester	N193LPN	40893	South East
M810WWR	47990	East	MSU463	52038	East Scotland	N194LFV	40394	North East
M817KRH	16817	North East	MSU466	51076	West Scotland	N194LPN	40894	South East
M818KRH	16818	North East	MWG623X	25423	East Midlands	N195LFV	40395	North East
M819KRH	16819	North East	N47EJO	32047	South East	N195LPN	40895	South East
M843EMW	30843	Wales & West	N48EJO	32048	Manchester	N196LFV	40396	North East
M844EMW	30844	Wales & West	N51KBW	32051	South Midlands	N196LPN	40896	South East
M845EMW	30845	Wales & West	N52KBW	32052	South Midlands	N197LFV	40397	North East
M846HDF	30846	North West	N53KBW	32053	South Midlands	N197LPN	40897	South East
M847HDF	30847	Wales & West	N54KBW	32054	South Midlands	N198LFV	40398	North East
M847PRS	30307	North East	N56KBW	32056	South Midlands	N198LPN	40898	South East
M866LNY	41150	West Scotland	N57KBW	32057	South Midlands	N199LFV	40399	North East
M869ASW	20506	West Scotland	N58KBW	32058	South Midlands	N199LPN	40899	South East
M870ASW	20580	West Scotland	N59KBW	32059	South Midlands	N201LFV	40401	North East
M871ASW	20507	West Scotland	N61KBW	32061	South Midlands	N201LPN	40901	South East
M872ASW	20582	West Scotland	N62MTG	32962	Wales & West	N201LTN	20101	North East
M889ECD	40889	South East	N63KBW	32063	South Midlands	N201UHH	40001	North East
M890ECD	40890	South East	N63MTG	32963	Wales & West	N202LFV	40402	North East
M901DRG	21001	North East	N64KBW	32064	South Midlands	N202LPN	40902	South East
M902DRG	21002	North East	N91RVK	52281	Wales & West	N202LTN	20102	North East
M911WJK	52271	East Scotland	N95ALS	40095	East Scotland	N202UHH	40002	North East
M913WJK	52273	Wales & West	N96ALS	40096	East Scotland	N203LPN	40903	South East
M914WJK	52274	Wales & West	N97ALS	40097	East Scotland	N203LTN	20103	North East
M915WJK	52275	Wales & West	N116YHH	40016	North West	N203UHH	40003	North West
M916WJK	52276	Wales & West	N117YHH	40017	North West	N204LPN	40904	South East
M917WJK	52277	Wales & West	N118YHH	40018	North West	N204LTN	20104	North East
M918WJK	52278	Wales & West	N119YHH	40019	North West	N204UHH	40004	North West
M942TSX	52259	East Midlands	N120YHH	40020	North West	N205LTN	20105	North East
M943TSX	52257	East Midlands	N121YHH	40021	North West	N205UHH	40005	North West
M944TSX	52258	East Scotland	N122YHH	40022	North West	N206LTN	20106	North East
M945TSX	52245	East Scotland	N123YHH	40023	North West	N206TDU	20206	South Midlands
M946TSX	52246	East Scotland	N124YHH	40024	North West	N206UHH	40006	North West
M947TSX	52247	East Scotland	N125YHH	40025	North West	N207LTN	20107	East Scotland
M948TSX	52248	East Scotland	N126YRM	40026	North West	N207TDU	20207	South Midlands
M949EGE	32380	West Scotland	N127YRM	40027	North West	N207UHH	40007	North West
M949TSX	52249	East Scotland	N128VAO	52328	North West	N208LTN	20108	East Scotland
M950EGE	32381	West Scotland	N128YRM	40028	North West	N208TDU	20208	South Midlands
M950JBO	59130	South West	N129VAO	52329	North West	N208UHH	40008	North West
M950TSX	52250	East Scotland	N129YRM	40029	North West	N209LTN	20109	East Scotland
M951DRG	28951	North East	N130AET	16480	East Midlands	N209UHH	40009	North West
M951TSX	52251	East Scotland	N130VAO	52330	North West	N210LTN	20110	West Scotland
M952DRG	28952	North East	N130YRM	40030	North West	N210UHH	40010	North West
M952TSX	52252	East Scotland	N131AET	16481	East Midlands	N211LTN	20111	East Scotland
M953DRG	28953	North East	N131VAO	52331	North West	N211TDU	20211	South Midlands
M953TSX	52253	East Scotland	N131YRM	40031	North West	N211UHH	40011	North West
M954DRG	28954	North East	N132AET	16482	East Midlands	N212LTN	20112	East Scotland
M954TSX	52254	East Scotland	N132VAO	52332	North West	N212TDU	20212	South Midlands
M955TSX	52255	East Scotland	N132YRM	40032	North West	N212UHH	40012	North West
M956TSX	52256	East Scotland	N133AET	16483	East Midlands	N213LTN	20113	East Scotland
M959VWY	47979	East	N133YRM	40033	North West	N213TDU	20213	South Midlands
M975WWR	47975	East	N134AET	16484	East Midlands	N213UHH	40013	North West
M976WWR	47976	East	N135AET	16485	East Midlands	N214LTN	20114	West Scotland

Reg	No	Area	Reg	No	Area	Reg	No	Area
N214TDU	20214	South Midlands	N329HGK	16429	East Scotland	N368AVV	40168	South Midlands
N214UHH	40014	North West	N329NPN	16329	North West	N368LPN	16368	South East
N215LTN	20115	North East	N329VMS	20329	East Scotland	N369AVV	40169	South Midlands
N215TDU	20215	South Midlands	N329XRP	40329	North West	N369LPN	16369	South East
N215UHH	40015	North West	N330HGK	16430	East Scotland	N370AVV	40170	South Midlands
N216LTN	20116	North East	N330NPN	16330	North West	N370LPN	16370	South East
N216TDU	20216	South Midlands	N331NPN	16331	North West	N371AVV	40171	South Midlands
N217LTN	20117	North East	N332NPN	16332	North West	N371LPN	16371	South East
N247XSA	52287	West Scotland	N334NPN	16334	North West	N372AVV	40172	South Midlands
N301AMC	32301	North East	N335NPN	16335	North West	N372LPN	16372	South East
N301XRP	40301	East	N336NPN	16336	North West	N372PNY	40572	Wales & West
N302AMC	32302	North East	N337NPN	16337	North West	N373LPN	16373	South East
N302XRP	40302	East	N338HGK	16438	South Midlands	N373PNY	40573	Wales & West
N303AMC	32303	North East	N338NPN	16338	North West	N374LPN	16374	South East
N303XRP	40303	East	N339HGK	16439	South Midlands	N374PNY	40574	Wales & West
N304AMC	32304	East Scotland	N339NPN	16339	North West	N375LPN	16375	South East
N304XRP	40304	East	N340HGK	16440	South Midlands	N375PNY	40575	Wales & West
N305AMC	32305	North East	N340NPN	16340	North West	N376LPN	16376	South East
N305XRP	40305	East	N341HGK	16441	Wales & West	N376PNY	40576	Wales & West
N306AMC	32306	East Scotland	N341KKH	40791	North East	N377LPN	16377	South East
N306XRP	40306	East	N341MPN	16341	South East	N377PNY	40577	Wales & West
N307AMC	32307	East Scotland	N342HGK	16442	Wales & West	N378LPN	16378	South East
N307XRP	40307	East	N342KKH	40792	North East	N378PNY	40578	Wales & West
N308AMC	32308	East Scotland	N342MPN	16342	South East	N379LPN	16379	South East
N308XRP	40308	East	N343HGK	16443	Wales & West	N379PNY	40579	Wales & West
N309AMC	32309	South East	N343KKH	40793	North East	N380LPN	16380	South East
N309XRP	40309	East	N343MPN	16343	South East	N380PNY	40580	Wales & West
N310AMC	32310	South East	N344HGK	16444	Wales & West	N381LPN	16381	South East
N310XRP	40310	East	N344KKH	40794	North East	N381PNY	40581	Wales & West
N311AMC	32311	South East	N344MPN	16344	South East	N382LPN	16382	South East
N311XRP	40311	East	N345HGK	16445	Wales & West	N382PNY	40582	Wales & West
N312AMC	32312	South East	N345KKH	40795	North East	N383LPN	16383	South East
N312XRP	40312	East	N345MPN	16345	South East	N383PNY	40583	Wales & West
N313AMC	32313	Wales & West	N346HGK	16446	Wales & West	N384LPN	16384	South East
N313XRP	40313	East	N346KKH	40796	North East	N384PNY	40584	Wales & West
N314AMC	32314	South East	N346MPN	16346	South East	N385LPN	16385	South East
N314XRP	40314	East	N347AVV	40147	South Midlands	N386LPN	16386	South East
N315AMC	32315	South East	N347HGK	16447	Wales & West	N387LPN	16387	South East
N315XRP	40315	East	N347KKH	40797	North East	N388LPN	16388	South East
N316AMC	32316	South East	N347MPN	16347	South East	N389LPN	16389	South East
N316VMS	20316	East Scotland	N348AVV	40148	South Midlands	N390LPN	16390	South East
N316XRP	40316	East	N348HGK	16448	South West	N391LPN	16391	South East
N317AMC	32317	Wales & West	N348KKH	40798	North East	N392LPN	16392	South East
N317VMS	20317	East Scotland	N348MPN	16348	South East	N393LPN	16393	South East
N317XRP	40317	East	N349AVV	40149	South Midlands	N394LPN	16394	South East
N318AMC	32318	Wales & West	N349HGK	16449	Wales & West	N395LPN	16395	South East
N318VMS	20318	East Scotland	N349KKH	40799	North East	N396LPN	16396	South East
N318XRP	40318	East	N349MPN	16349	South East	N397LPN	16397	South East
N319AMC	32319	Wales & West	N350AVV	40150	South Midlands	N398LPN	16398	South East
N319VMS	20319	East Scotland	N350HGK	16450	Wales & West	N399LPN	16399	South East
N319XRP	40319	East	N350KKH	40800	North East	N401LDF	20681	Wales & West
N320AMC	32320	Wales & West	N350MPN	16350	South East	N401WVR	41401	Wales & West
N320VMS	20320	East Scotland	N350YFL	32650	East	N402LDF	20682	Wales & West
N320XRP	40320	East	N351HGK	16451	Wales & West	N402WVR	41402	Wales & West
N321AMC	32321	South East	N351MPN	16351	South East	N403LDF	20683	Wales & West
N321HGK	16421	East Scotland	N351YFL	32651	East	N403WVR	41403	Wales & West
N321VMS	20321	East Scotland	N352AVV	40152	South Midlands	N404LDF	20684	Wales & West
N321XRP	40321	East	N352LPN	16352	South East	N404WVR	41404	Wales & West
N322AMC	32322	South East	N352YFL	32652	East	N405LDF	20685	Wales & West
N322HGK	16422	East Scotland	N353AVV	40153	South Midlands	N405WVR	41405	Wales & West
N322VMS	20322	East Scotland	N353MPN	16353	South East	N406LDF	20686	Wales & West
N322XRP	40322	East	N354AVV	40154	South Midlands	N406WVR	41406	Wales & West
N323AMC	32323	South East	N354MPN	16354	South East	N407LDF	20687	Wales & West
N323HGK	16423	East Scotland	N355AVV	40155	South Midlands	N407WVR	41407	Wales & West
N323VMS	20323	East Scotland	N355MPN	16355	South East	N408LDF	20688	Wales & West
N323XRP	40323	East	N356AVV	40156	South Midlands	N408WVR	41408	Wales & West
N324AMC	32324	South East	N356MPN	16356	South East	N409LDF	20689	Wales & West
N324HGK	16424	East Scotland	N357AVV	40157	South Midlands	N409WVR	41409	Wales & West
N324VMS	20324	East Scotland	N357MPN	16357	South East	N410MBW	32410	South West
N324XRP	40324	East	N358AVV	40158	South Midlands	N410WVR	41410	Wales & West
N325AMC	32325	South East	N358MPN	16358	South East	N411MBW	32411	Wales & West
N325HGK	16425	East Scotland	N359AVV	40159	South Midlands	N411WVR	41411	Wales & West
N325NPN	16325	North West	N359MPN	16359	South East	N412MBW	32412	South East
N325VMS	20325	East Scotland	N360AVV	40160	South Midlands	N412WVR	41412	Wales & West
N325XRP	40325	East	N360LPN	16360	South East	N413MBW	32413	South East
N326AMC	32326	South East	N361AVV	40161	South Midlands	N413WVR	41413	Wales & West
N326HGK	16426	East Scotland	N361LPN	16361	South East	N414MBW	32414	South East
N326NPN	16326	North West	N362AVV	40162	South Midlands	N414WVR	41414	Wales & West
N326VMS	20326	East Scotland	N362LPN	16362	South East	N415MBW	32415	East Midlands
N326XRP	40326	East	N363AVV	40163	South Midlands	N415WVR	41415	Wales & West
N327AMC	32327	South East	N363LPN	16363	South East	N416MBW	32416	East Midlands
N327HGK	16427	East Scotland	N364AVV	40164	South East	N416WVR	41416	Wales & West
N327NPN	16327	North West	N364LPN	16364	South East	N417MBW	32417	East Midlands
N327VMS	20327	East Scotland	N365AVV	40165	South Midlands	N417WVR	41417	Wales & West
N327XRP	40327	North West	N365LPN	16365	South East	N418MBW	32418	East Midlands
N328HGK	16428	East Scotland	N366AVV	40166	South Midlands	N418WVR	41418	Wales & West
N328NPN	16328	North West	N366LPN	16366	South East	N419MBW	32419	East Midlands
N328VMS	20328	East Scotland	N367AVV	40167	South Midlands	N419UWN	46274	Wales & West
N328XRP	40328	North West	N367LPN	16367	South East	N419WVR	41419	Wales & West

Reg	No	Location	Reg	No	Location	Reg	No	Location
N420MRW	32420	East Midlands	N493RVK	40493	North East	N639VSS	40639	West Scotland
N420WVR	41420	Wales & West	N494RVK	40494	North East	N640LPN	20640	South East
N421MBW	32421	East Midlands	N495RVK	40495	North East	N640VSS	40640	East Scotland
N421PWV	30141	South East	N496RVK	40496	North East	N641LPN	20641	South East
N421WVR	41421	Wales & West	N497RVK	40497	North East	N641VSS	40641	North West
N422MBW	32422	East Midlands	N498RVK	40498	North East	N642LPN	20642	South East
N422PWV	30142	South East	N499RVK	40499	North East	N642VSS	40642	North East
N422WVR	41422	Wales & West	N501RVK	40501	North East	N643LPN	20643	South East
N423MBW	32423	East Midlands	N506BJA	40506	South West	N643VSS	40643	Wales & West
N423WVR	41423	Wales & West	N507BJA	40507	South West	N644LPN	20644	South East
N424MBW	32424	East Midlands	N508BJA	40508	South West	N644VSS	40644	Wales & West
N424WVR	41424	Wales & West	N509BJA	40509	South West	N645LPN	20645	South East
N425MBW	32425	East Midlands	N510BJA	40510	South West	N645VSS	40645	North West
N425WVR	41425	Wales & West	N511BJA	40511	South West	N646VSS	40646	North West
N426MBW	32426	East Midlands	N512BJA	40512	South West	N647VSS	40647	North West
N426WVR	41426	Wales & West	N513BJA	40513	South West	N648VSS	40648	North West
N427MBW	32427	East Midlands	N514BJA	40514	South West	N649VSS	40649	North West
N427WVR	41427	Wales & West	N515BJA	40515	South West	N650VSS	40650	North West
N428WVR	41428	Wales & West	N516BJA	40516	South West	N651VSS	40651	North West
N429WVR	41429	Wales & West	N517BJA	40517	South West	N652VSS	40652	North West
N430WVR	41430	Wales & West	N518BJA	40518	South West	N653VSS	40653	South Midlands
N445XVA	52295	West Scotland	N518XER	16598	South Midlands	N654VSS	40654	South Midlands
N446TOS	40530	West Scotland	N519BJA	40519	North West	N655VSS	40655	South East
N446XVA	52296	West Scotland	N519XER	16599	South Midlands	N656VSS	40656	South East
N447XVA	52297	North West	N520BJA	40520	North West	N657VSS	40657	South Midlands
N448XVA	52298	Wales & West	N520XER	16600	South Midlands	N658VSS	40658	South Midlands
N449XVA	52299	Wales & West	N550MTG	23950	Wales & West	N659VSS	40659	South Midlands
N450XVA	52300	Wales & West	N551MTG	23951	Wales & West	N660VSS	40660	Manchester
N451PAP	32451	South East	N551VDC	20261	North East	N661VSS	40661	South East
N451XVA	52301	Wales & West	N552VDC	20262	North East	N662VSS	40662	South East
N452PAP	32452	South East	N553VDC	20263	North East	N663VSS	40663	Manchester
N452VOD	40452	North West	N582XSA	52312	East Scotland	N664VSS	40664	Manchester
N452VOD	52302	South Midlands	N583XSA	52313	East Scotland	N665VSS	40665	Manchester
N453PAP	32453	South East	N584XSA	52314	East Scotland	N701LTN	16701	North East
N454PAP	32454	South East	N599DWY	32599	South West	N702LTN	16702	North East
N455PAP	32455	South East	N601KGF	32601	South East	N703LTN	16703	North East
N455VOD	40455	North West	N601VSS	40601	West Scotland	N704LTN	16704	North East
N456PAP	32456	South East	N602KGF	32602	South East	N705LTN	16705	North East
N457PAP	32457	South East	N602VSS	40602	West Scotland	N706LTN	16706	North East
N458PAP	32458	South East	N603KGF	32603	South East	N707LTN	16707	North East
N459PAP	32459	South East	N603VSS	40603	West Scotland	N708LTN	16708	North East
N460PAP	32460	South East	N604KGF	32604	South East	N709LTN	16709	North East
N461PAP	32461	South East	N604VSS	40604	West Scotland	N710LTN	16710	North East
N461RVK	40461	North East	N605KGF	32605	South East	N711LTN	16711	North East
N461VOD	40441	North West	N605VSS	40605	West Scotland	N712LTN	16712	North East
N462PAP	32462	South East	N606KGF	32606	West Scotland	N713LTN	16713	North East
N462RVK	40462	North East	N606VSS	40606	West Scotland	N714LTN	16714	North East
N462VOD	40442	North West	N607KGF	32607	South East	N715LTN	16715	North East
N463HRN	46382	South East	N607VSS	40607	West Scotland	N716KAM	40716	Wales & West
N463PAP	32463	South East	N608KGF	32608	South East	N716LTN	16716	North East
N463RVK	40463	North East	N608VSS	40608	South East	N717KAM	40717	Wales & West
N463VOD	40443	North West	N609KGF	32609	South Midlands	N717LTN	16717	North East
N464HRN	46399	South East	N609VSS	40609	West Scotland	N718LTN	16718	North East
N464PAP	32464	South East	N610KGF	32610	South Midlands	N719LTN	16719	North East
N464RVK	40464	North East	N610VSS	40610	West Scotland	N719RDD	40719	Wales & West
N465PAP	32465	South East	N611LGC	32611	South Midlands	N720LTN	16720	North East
N465RVK	40465	North East	N611VSS	40611	West Scotland	N720RDD	40720	Wales & West
N465VOD	40445	North West	N612LGC	32612	South Midlands	N721LTN	16721	North East
N466PAP	32466	South East	N612VSS	40612	West Scotland	N721RDD	40721	Wales & West
N466RVK	40466	North East	N613LGC	32613	South Midlands	N722LTN	16722	North East
N466VOD	40446	North West	N613VSS	40613	North West	N722RDD	40722	Wales & West
N467PAP	32467	South East	N614LGC	32614	South Midlands	N723LTN	16723	North East
N467RVK	40467	North East	N614VSS	40614	North West	N723RDD	40723	Wales & West
N467VOD	40447	North West	N615VSS	40615	North West	N724LTN	16724	North East
N468RVK	40468	North East	N616VSS	40616	North West	N724RDD	40724	Wales & West
N469RVK	40469	North East	N617VSS	40617	North West	N725LTN	16725	North East
N470RVK	40470	North East	N618USS	52308	South Midlands	N725RDD	40725	Wales & West
N471RVK	40471	North East	N618VSS	40618	Wales & West	N726LTN	16726	North East
N472RVK	40472	North East	N619VSS	40619	North West	N726RDD	40726	Wales & West
N473RVK	40473	North East	N620VSS	40620	North East	N727LTN	16727	North East
N474RVK	40474	North East	N621VSS	40621	West Scotland	N727RDD	40727	Wales & West
N475RVK	40475	North East	N622VSS	40622	West Scotland	N728LTN	16728	North East
N476RVK	40476	North East	N623VSS	40623	West Scotland	N728RDD	40728	Wales & West
N477RVK	40477	North East	N624VSS	40624	West Scotland	N729LTN	16729	North East
N478RVK	40478	North East	N625VSS	40625	West Scotland	N729RDD	40729	Wales & West
N479RVK	40479	North East	N626VSS	40626	West Scotland	N730LTN	16730	North East
N480RVK	40480	North East	N627VSS	40627	West Scotland	N730RDD	40730	Wales & West
N481RVK	40481	North East	N628VSS	40628	West Scotland	N731LTN	16731	North East
N482RVK	40482	North East	N629VSS	40629	West Scotland	N731RDD	40731	Wales & West
N483RVK	40483	North East	N62KBW	32062	South Midlands	N732LTN	16732	North East
N484RVK	40484	North East	N630VSS	40630	West Scotland	N732RDD	40732	Wales & West
N485RVK	40485	North East	N631VSS	40631	West Scotland	N732XDV	32432	South West
N486RVK	40486	North East	N632VSS	40632	West Scotland	N733LTN	16733	North East
N487RVK	40487	North East	N633VSS	40633	West Scotland	N733RDD	40733	Wales & West
N488RVK	40488	North East	N634VSS	40634	West Scotland	N733XDV	32433	South West
N489RVK	40489	North East	N635VSS	40635	West Scotland	N734LTN	16734	North East
N490RVK	40490	North East	N636VSS	40636	East Scotland	N734RDD	40734	Wales & West
N491RVK	40491	North East	N637VSS	40637	East Scotland	N734XDV	32434	South West
N492RVK	40492	North East	N638VSS	40638	West Scotland			

Reg	No	Area	Reg	No	Area	Reg	No	Area
N735LTN	16735	North East	N866VHH	16866	West Scotland	NDZ3016	32216	East Scotland
N735RDD	40735	Wales & West	N879AVV	40429	Manchester	NDZ3017	33027	South East
N735XDV	32435	South West	N880AVV	40430	Manchester	NDZ3018	33028	South East
N736LTN	16736	North East	N881AVV	40431	Manchester	NDZ3019	33025	South East
N736XDV	32436	South West	N882AVV	40432	Manchester	NDZ3020	34014	South East
N737LTN	16737	North East	N883AVV	40433	Manchester	NDZ3021	22191	South East
N737XDV	32437	South West	N884AVV	40434	Manchester	NDZ3022	22192	South East
N738LTN	16738	North East	N885AVV	40435	North West	NDZ3023	22194	South East
N738XDV	32438	South West	N901PFC	27901	South Midlands	NDZ3024	32224	West Scotland
N739LTN	16739	North East	N902PFC	27902	South Midlands	NDZ3025	32225	West Scotland
N739XDV	32439	South West	N903PFC	27903	South Midlands	NDZ3026	32226	West Scotland
N740LTN	16740	North East	N905NAP	40905	South East	NDZ3133	32233	Wales & West
N740XDV	32440	South West	N906NAP	40906	South East	NDZ3134	32234	Wales & West
N741XDV	32441	South West	N907NAP	40907	South East	NDZ3135	32235	Wales & West
N742XDV	32442	South West	N908NAP	40908	South East	NDZ3136	32236	Wales & West
N743XDV	32443	South West	N909NAP	40909	South East	NDZ3137	32237	Wales & West
N744XDV	32444	South West	N910NAP	40910	South East	NDZ3138	32238	Wales & West
N746YVR	40838	Manchester	N911NAP	40911	South East	NDZ3139	32239	Wales & West
N748YVR	40839	Manchester	N912NAP	40912	South East	NDZ3140	32240	Wales & West
N752CKU	40752	East Midlands	N913NAP	40913	South East	NDZ3141	32241	Wales & West
N753CKU	40753	East Midlands	N914NAP	40914	South East	NDZ3142	32242	Wales & West
N754CKU	40754	East Midlands	N915NAP	40915	South East	NDZ3143	32243	Wales & West
N755CKU	40755	East Midlands	N916NAP	40916	South East	NDZ3144	32244	Wales & West
N756CKU	40756	East Midlands	N917NAP	40917	South East	NDZ3145	32245	Wales & West
N757CKU	40757	East Midlands	N918NAP	40918	South East	NDZ3146	32246	East Scotland
N758CKU	40758	East Midlands	N920NAP	40920	South East	NDZ3147	32247	South East
N759CKU	40759	East Midlands	N921NAP	40921	South East	NDZ3148	32248	Wales & West
N760CKU	40760	East Midlands	N922NAP	40922	South East	NDZ3149	32249	Wales & West
N761CKU	40761	East Midlands	N923NAP	40923	South East	NDZ3150	32250	Wales & West
N762EWG	40762	East Midlands	N924NAP	40924	South East	NDZ3151	32251	South West
N763EWG	40763	East Midlands	N925NAP	40925	South East	NDZ3152	32252	South West
N764EWG	40764	East Midlands	N926NAP	40926	South East	NDZ3153	32253	South West
N765EWG	40765	East Midlands	N927NAP	40927	South East	NDZ3154	32254	Wales & West
N766EWG	40766	East Midlands	N928NAP	40928	South East	NDZ3155	32255	Wales & West
N767EWG	40767	East Midlands	N929NAP	40929	South East	NDZ3156	32256	Wales & West
N768EWG	40768	East Midlands	N930NAP	40930	South East	NDZ3157	32257	Wales & West
N769EWG	40769	East Midlands	N931NAP	40931	South East	NDZ3158	32258	Wales & West
N770EWG	40770	East Midlands	N932NAP	40932	South East	NDZ3159	32259	Wales & West
N771EWG	40771	East Midlands	N933NAP	40933	South East	NFX667	32716	South East
N772EWG	40772	East Midlands	N934NAP	40934	South East	NHL302X	14302	East Midlands
N772RVK	32772	East	N935NAP	40935	South East	NHL303X	14303	North East
N773EWG	40773	East Midlands	N936NAP	40936	South East	NIB4138	11114	East Scotland
N773RVK	32773	North East	N937NAP	40937	South East	NIB5232	11100	North West
N774EWG	40774	East Midlands	N938NAP	40938	South East	NIB5233	11093	East Scotland
N774RVK	32774	East	N939NAP	40939	South East	NIB5455	11106	East Scotland
N775EWG	40775	East Midlands	N940NAP	40940	South East	NIL9313	39853	Manchester
N775RVK	32775	East	N941NAP	40941	South East	NML607E	12607	London
N776EWG	40776	East Midlands	N942NAP	40942	South East	NML610E	12610	London
N776RVK	32776	East	N943NAP	40943	South East	NML616E	12616	London
N778RVK	32777	North East	N944NAP	40944	South East	NML624E	12624	London
N779RVK	32778	North East	N945NAP	40945	South East	NML639E	12639	London
N780RVK	32779	North East	N946NAP	40946	South East	NML641E	12641	London
N789VRM	20789	North West	N947NAP	40947	South East	NML642E	12642	London
N790VRM	20790	North West	N948NAP	40948	South East	NML657E	12657	London
N801DNE	20801	South West	N949NAP	40949	South East	NOE602R	25402	South Midlands
N802DNE	20802	South West	N950NAP	40950	South East	NOE605R	25405	South Midlands
N803DNE	20803	South Midlands	N951NAP	40951	South East	NSU132	52175	East Scotland
N804DNE	20804	South Midlands	N952NAP	40952	South East	NSU133	52027	East Scotland
N805DNE	20805	South Midlands	N953NAP	40953	South East	NTC132Y	14294	Wales & West
N806DNE	20806	Wales & West	N954NAP	40954	South East	NUF276	52194	East Scotland
N807DNE	20807	Wales & West	N955NAP	40955	South East	NUW555Y	10555	East Scotland
N808DNE	20808	South Midlands	N956NAP	40956	South East	NUW556Y	10556	East
N809DNE	20809	South Midlands	N957NAP	40957	South East	NUW558Y	10558	East Scotland
N810DNE	20810	Wales & West	N958NAP	40958	South East	NUW559Y	10559	East
N811DNE	20811	Wales & West	N959NAP	40959	South East	NUW560Y	10560	East Scotland
N812DNE	20812	South Midlands	N960NAP	40960	South East	NUW562Y	10562	East
N813DNE	20813	South Midlands	N961NAP	40961	South East	NUW565Y	10565	East
N814DNE	20814	South Midlands	N962NAP	40962	South East	NUW566Y	10566	East Scotland
N815DNE	20815	Wales & West	N963NAP	40963	South East	NUW569Y	10569	East
N816DNE	20816	South Midlands	N964NAP	40964	South East	NUW571Y	10571	East Scotland
N817DNE	20817	Wales & West	N965NAP	40965	South East	NUW572Y	10572	East Scotland
N818DNE	20818	Wales & West	N966NAP	40966	South East	NUW574Y	10574	East Scotland
N849VHH	16849	West Scotland	N967NAP	40967	South East	NUW576Y	10576	East
N850VHH	16850	West Scotland	N968NAP	40968	South East	NUW577Y	10577	East Scotland
N851VHH	16851	West Scotland	N969NAP	40969	South East	NUW582Y	10582	East Scotland
N852VHH	16852	West Scotland	N970NAP	40970	South East	NUW584Y	10584	East
N853VHH	16853	West Scotland	N971NAP	40971	South East	NUW585Y	10585	South West
N854VHH	16854	West Scotland	N972NAP	40972	South East	NUW586Y	10586	East Scotland
N855VHH	16855	West Scotland	N973NAP	40973	South East	NUW587Y	10587	East Scotland
N856VHH	16856	West Scotland	N974NAP	40974	South East	NUW588Y	10588	East
N857VHH	16857	West Scotland	N975NAP	40975	South East	NUW589Y	10589	Wales & West
N858VHH	16858	West Scotland	N976NAP	40976	South East	NUW590Y	10590	East
N859VHH	16859	West Scotland	N977NAP	40977	South East	NUW591Y	10591	East Scotland
N860VHH	16860	West Scotland	N978NAP	40978	South West	NUW592Y	10592	Wales & West
N861VHH	16861	West Scotland	N979NAP	40979	South West	NUW593Y	10593	East Scotland
N862VHH	16862	West Scotland	N980NAP	40980	South West	NUW596Y	10596	South East
N863VHH	16863	West Scotland	N981NAP	40981	South West	NUW601Y	10601	East Scotland
N864VHH	16864	West Scotland	N982NAP	40982	South West	NUW602Y	10602	Wales & West
N865VHH	16865	West Scotland	NDZ3015	32215	East Scotland	NUW605Y	10605	East Scotland

Reg	No	Region	Reg	No	Region	Reg	No	Region
NUW606Y	10606	Wales & West	P120XCN	20120	North East	P266VPN	16266	South East
NUW615Y	10615	East Scotland	P121XCN	20121	North East	P267VPN	16267	South East
NUW619Y	10619	Wales & West	P122XCN	20122	North East	P268VPN	16268	South East
NUW621Y	10621	Wales & West	P123XCN	20123	North East	P269VPN	16269	South East
NUW622Y	10622	East Scotland	P124XCN	20124	North East	P270VPN	16640	North West
NUW623Y	10623	East Scotland	P125XCN	20125	North East	P271VPN	16641	North West
NUW626Y	10626	East Scotland	P126XCN	20126	North East	P272VPN	16642	North West
NUW634Y	10634	North East	P127XCN	20127	North West	P273VPN	16643	North West
NUW643Y	10643	North East	P128XCN	20128	North West	P274VPN	16644	North West
NUW645Y	10645	South East	P129XCN	20129	North West	P275VPN	16645	North West
NUW646Y	10646	Wales & West	P130XCN	20130	North West	P276VPN	16276	South East
NUW647Y	10647	South East	P131XCN	20131	North West	P277VPN	16277	South East
NUW648Y	10648	North East	P132XCN	20132	North West	P278VPN	16278	South East
NUW649Y	10649	North East	P133XCN	20133	North West	P279VPN	16279	South East
NUW651Y	10651	North East	P134XCN	20134	North West	P281VPN	16281	South East
NUW654Y	10654	East Scotland	P135XCN	20135	North East	P281XYS	52396	Wales & West
NUW659Y	10659	North East	P145KWJ	16495	East Midlands	P282VPN	16282	South East
NUW660Y	10660	South West	P146KWJ	16496	East Midlands	P283VPN	16283	South East
NUW662Y	10662	Wales & West	P148ASA	52348	West Scotland	P284VPN	16284	South East
NUW664Y	10664	North East	P148KWJ	16498	East Midlands	P285VPN	16285	South East
NUW665Y	10665	Wales & West	P149ASA	52349	West Scotland	P286VPN	16286	South East
NUW666Y	10666	North East	P149KWJ	16499	East Midlands	P287VPN	16287	South East
NUW668Y	10668	North East	P150ASA	52350	West Scotland	P288VPN	16288	South East
NUW670Y	10670	South East	P150KWJ	16500	East Midlands	P289VPN	16289	South East
NUW673Y	10673	North East	P151ASA	52351	East Midlands	P290VPN	16290	South East
NUW675Y	10675	North East	P151KWJ	16455	East Midlands	P299AYJ	33029	South East
OCU822R	15522	East Midlands	P152ASA	52352	East Scotland	P301AYJ	33031	South East
OFV16X	14116	North West	P152KWJ	16497	East Midlands	P302AYJ	33032	South East
OFV17X	14117	North West	P153ASA	52353	East Scotland	P315EFL	20695	North East
OHV684Y	10684	North West	P153KWJ	16453	East Midlands	P316EFL	20696	North East
OHV686Y	10686	Wales & West	P154ASA	52354	East Scotland	P317EFL	20697	Wales & West
OHV699Y	10699	Wales & West	P154KWJ	16454	East Midlands	P318EFL	20698	Wales & West
OHV700Y	10700	West Scotland	P156ASA	52356	East Scotland	P319EFL	20694	Wales & West
OHV702Y	10702	Wales & West	P156KWJ	16456	East Midlands	P320EFL	31320	South Midlands
OHV719Y	10719	Wales & West	P157ASA	52357	East Midlands	P321EFL	31319	South Midlands
OHV728Y	10728	North West	P157KWJ	16457	East Midlands	P321JND	31321	South Midlands
OHV729Y	10729	North West	P158ASA	52358	West Scotland	P322EFL	33322	East
OHV738Y	10738	North West	P158KWJ	16458	East Midlands	P322JND	31322	South Midlands
OHV751Y	10751	East Scotland	P159KAK	16459	East Midlands	P323EFL	33323	East
OHV762Y	10762	West Scotland	P160ASA	52360	West Scotland	P323JND	31323	South Midlands
OHV789Y	10789	East Scotland	P160KAK	16460	East Midlands	P324EFL	33324	East
OHV791Y	10791	East Scotland	P161TDW	41161	Wales & West	P324JND	31324	South Midlands
OHV801Y	10801	East Scotland	P162TDW	41162	Wales & West	P325JND	31325	South Midlands
OHV802Y	10802	East Scotland	P163TNY	41163	Wales & West	P326JND	31326	South Midlands
OHV809Y	10809	North West	P164TNY	41164	Wales & West	P327JND	31327	South Midlands
OIW5804	52001	North West	P165TNY	41165	Wales & West	P328JND	31328	South Midlands
OIW7025	25475	West Scotland	P166TNY	41166	Wales & West	P329JND	31329	South Midlands
OJL823Y	59076	East Midlands	P167TNY	41167	Wales & West	P330AYJ	33030	South East
OSK784	52093	Wales & West	P168TNY	52368	East	P330JND	31330	South Midlands
OU51WLK	22942	South Midlands	P168TNY	41168	Wales & West	P331JND	31331	South Midlands
OU51WLL	22943	South Midlands	P169KBD	52369	East	P332JND	31332	South Midlands
OU51WLN	22944	South Midlands	P169TNY	41169	Wales & West	P334JND	31334	South Midlands
OV51AMO	22948	South Midlands	P170KBD	52370	East	P341ASO	40041	East Scotland
OV51KAE	22945	South Midlands	P170TNY	41170	Wales & West	P342ASO	40042	East Scotland
OV51KAJ	22946	South Midlands	P171KBD	52371	East	P343ASO	40043	East Scotland
OV51KAK	22947	South Midlands	P171TNY	41171	Wales & West	P343AYJ	33033	South East
P21HMF	34001	East Midlands	P172KBD	52372	East	P344ASO	40044	East Scotland
P23HMF	34003	East Midlands	P173KBD	52373	East	P345ASO	40045	East Scotland
P24HMF	34004	East Midlands	P178PRH	52378	North East	P346ASO	40046	East Scotland
P25HMF	34005	East Midlands	P179PRH	52379	North East	P347ASO	40047	East Scotland
P26HMF	34006	East Midlands	P180PRH	52380	East Scotland	P348ASO	40048	East Scotland
P27HMF	34007	East Midlands	P181PRH	52381	North East	P349ASO	40049	East Scotland
P28HMF	34008	East Midlands	P217HBD	20217	South Midlands	P350ASO	40050	East Scotland
P29HMF	34009	East Midlands	P218HBD	20218	South Midlands	P350JND	31350	South Midlands
P31HMF	34002	East Midlands	P219HBD	20219	South Midlands	P351ASO	40051	East Scotland
P54XBO	33554	Wales & West	P220HBD	20220	South Midlands	P351JND	31351	South Midlands
P56XBO	33556	Wales & West	P224VCK	16624	North West	P351NKH	40801	East Midlands
P57XBO	33557	Wales & West	P225VCK	16625	North West	P352ASO	40052	East Scotland
P58XBO	33558	Wales & West	P226VCK	16626	North West	P352JND	31352	South Midlands
P59VTG	33559	Wales & West	P227VCK	16627	North West	P352NKH	40802	East Midlands
P61VTG	33561	Wales & West	P228VCK	16628	North West	P353JND	31353	South Midlands
P92URG	52392	Wales & West	P229VCK	16629	North West	P353NKH	40803	North East
P101HNH	32001	South Midlands	P230VCK	16630	North West	P354JND	31354	South Midlands
P102HNH	32002	South Midlands	P231VCK	16631	North West	P354NKH	40804	North East
P103HNH	32003	South Midlands	P232VCK	16632	North West	P355JND	31355	South Midlands
P104HNH	32004	South Midlands	P233VCK	16633	North West	P356JND	31356	South Midlands
P105HNH	32005	South Midlands	P234VCK	16634	North West	P357JND	31357	South Midlands
P107FRS	52397	Wales & West	P235VCK	16635	North West	P361DSA	31361	South Midlands
P108DCW	52408	North West	P255ASA	52355	West Scotland	P362DSA	31362	South Midlands
P108FRS	52398	East	P260VPN	16636	North West	P363DSA	31363	South Midlands
P109DCW	52409	North West	P260WPN	16260	South East	P364DSA	31364	South Midlands
P109FRS	52399	Wales & West	P261VPN	16637	North West	P365DSA	31365	South Midlands
P110DCW	52410	North West	P261WPN	16261	South East	P366DSA	31366	West Scotland
P110FRS	52400	Wales & West	P262VPN	16638	North West	P367DSA	31367	West Scotland
P112DCW	52412	North West	P262WPN	16262	South East	P368DSA	31368	West Scotland
P113DCW	52413	North West	P263VPN	16639	North West	P369DSA	31369	West Scotland
P114DCW	52414	North West	P263WPN	16263	South East	P370DSA	31370	West Scotland
P118XCN	20118	East Scotland	P264VPN	16264	South East	P371DSA	31371	West Scotland
P119XCN	20119	East Scotland	P265VPN	16265	South East	P372DSA	31372	West Scotland

Reg	No	Region	Reg	No	Region	Reg	No	Region
P373DSA	31373	West Scotland	P537HMP	16037	West Scotland	P568EFL	16568	East
P374DSA	31374	West Scotland	P537PNE	42537	Manchester	P568MSX	52361	East Scotland
P375DSA	31375	West Scotland	P538EFL	16538	East	P569EFL	16569	East
P376DSA	31376	West Scotland	P538ESA	20538	West Scotland	P569MSX	52362	East Scotland
P377DSA	31377	West Scotland	P538HMP	16038	West Scotland	P570EFL	16570	East
P378DSA	31378	West Scotland	P538PNE	42538	Manchester	P571EFL	16571	East
P379DSA	31379	West Scotland	P539EFL	16539	East	P572EFL	16572	East
P380DSA	31380	West Scotland	P539ESA	20539	West Scotland	P573EFL	16573	East
P381DSA	31381	West Scotland	P539HMP	16039	West Scotland	P574EFL	16574	East
P382DSA	31382	West Scotland	P539PNE	42539	Manchester	P575EFL	16575	East
P383DSA	31383	West Scotland	P540EFL	16540	East	P576EFL	16576	East
P384DSA	31384	West Scotland	P540ESA	20540	North West	P577EFL	16577	East
P385DSA	31385	West Scotland	P540HMP	16040	West Scotland	P578EFL	16578	East
P386DSA	31386	West Scotland	P540PNE	42540	Manchester	P579EFL	16579	East
P390LPS	32390	West Scotland	P541EFL	16541	East	P601JBU	21101	North East
P391LPS	32391	West Scotland	P541ESA	20541	North West	P602JBU	21102	North East
P392LPS	32392	West Scotland	P541HMP	16041	London	P603JBU	21103	North East
P393LPS	32393	West Scotland	P541PNE	42541	Manchester	P604JBU	21104	North East
P394LPS	32394	West Scotland	P542EFL	16542	East	P605JBU	21105	North East
P395BRS	32395	West Scotland	P542ESA	20542	North West	P606CMS	32206	East Scotland
P396BRS	32396	West Scotland	P542HMP	16042	London	P607CMS	32207	East Scotland
P397BRS	32397	West Scotland	P542PNE	42542	Manchester	P608CMS	32208	East Scotland
P398BRS	32398	West Scotland	P543EFL	16543	East	P609CMS	32209	East Scotland
P418KWF	32818	East Midlands	P543ESA	20543	North West	P610CMS	32210	East Scotland
P419KWF	32819	East Midlands	P543HMP	16043	London	P611CMS	32211	East Scotland
P420KWF	32820	East Midlands	P543PNE	42543	Manchester	P612CMS	32212	East Scotland
P426AYJ	33036	South East	P544EFL	16544	East	P613CMS	32213	East Scotland
P434AYJ	33034	South East	P544ESA	20544	North West	P615PGP	32615	North East
P435AYJ	33035	South East	P544PNE	42544	Manchester	P616PGP	32616	North East
P450KRP	32006	South Midlands	P545EFL	16545	East	P617PGP	32617	North East
P451KRP	32007	South Midlands	P545ESA	20545	North West	P618PGP	32618	South West
P452KRP	32008	South Midlands	P545PNE	42545	Manchester	P619PGP	32619	South West
P455EEF	32655	North East	P546EFL	16546	East	P620PGP	32620	North East
P456EEF	32656	North East	P546ESA	20546	North West	P621PGP	32621	North East
P457AYJ	33037	South East	P546PNE	42546	Manchester	P622ESO	52382	East Scotland
P457EEF	32657	North East	P547EFL	16547	East	P622PGP	32622	North East
P458AYJ	33038	South East	P547ESA	20547	North West	P623PGP	32623	North East
P458EEF	32658	North East	P547PNE	42547	Manchester	P624PGP	32624	North East
P459EEF	32659	North East	P548EFL	16548	East	P625NSE	52385	East Scotland
P460EEF	32660	North East	P548ESA	20548	West Scotland	P625PGP	32625	South Midlands
P461EEF	32661	North East	P548PNE	42548	Manchester	P626NSE	52386	East Scotland
P466AYJ	33040	South East	P549EFL	16549	East	P626PGP	32626	South Midlands
P479AYJ	33039	South East	P549ESA	20549	West Scotland	P627ESO	52387	East Scotland
P491BRS	31491	East Scotland	P549PNE	42549	Manchester	P627PGP	32627	South Midlands
P492BRS	31492	East Scotland	P550EFL	16550	East	P628PGP	32628	South Midlands
P493BRS	31493	East Scotland	P550ESA	20550	North East	P629PGP	32629	South Midlands
P494BRS	31494	East Scotland	P550PNE	42550	Manchester	P630PGP	32630	South Midlands
P495BRS	31495	East Scotland	P551EFL	16551	East	P631PGP	32631	North East
P496BRS	31496	East Scotland	P551ESA	20551	North East	P632PGP	32632	North East
P497BRS	31497	East Scotland	P551PNE	42551	Manchester	P633PGP	32633	North East
P498BRS	31498	East Scotland	P552EFL	16552	East	P634PGP	32634	North East
P499BRS	31499	East Scotland	P552ESA	20552	North East	P636PGP	32636	South West
P526EFL	16555	East	P552PNE	42552	Manchester	P637PGP	32637	North East
P527EFL	16527	East	P553EFL	16553	East	P638PGP	32638	North East
P527HMP	16027	South Midlands	P553ESA	20553	North East	P639PGP	32639	South West
P528EFL	16528	East	P553PNE	42553	Manchester	P640PGP	32640	South West
P528HMP	16028	South Midlands	P554EFL	16554	East	P644SEV	16044	London
P529EFL	16529	East	P554ESA	20554	North East	P645SEV	16045	London
P529HMP	16029	South Midlands	P554PNE	42554	Manchester	P646SEV	16046	London
P530EFL	16530	East	P556EFL	16556	East	P660ESO	20560	South Midlands
P530ESA	20530	West Scotland	P556ESA	20556	West Scotland	P677NOJ	31333	South Midlands
P530HMP	16030	South Midlands	P556PNE	42556	Manchester	P686JBD	16686	East
P530PNE	42530	Manchester	P557EFL	16557	East	P687JBD	16687	East
P531EFL	16531	East	P557ESA	20557	South Midlands	P688JBD	16688	East
P531ESA	20531	West Scotland	P557PNE	42557	Manchester	P689JBD	16689	East
P531HMP	16031	South Midlands	P558EFL	16558	East	P690JBD	16690	East
P531PNE	42531	Manchester	P558ESA	20558	South Midlands	P691JBD	16691	East
P532EFL	16532	East	P558PNE	42558	Manchester	P692JBD	16692	East
P532ESA	20532	West Scotland	P559EFL	16559	East	P701BTA	31701	South West
P532HMP	16032	South Midlands	P559ESA	20559	South Midlands	P702BTA	31702	South West
P532PNE	42532	Manchester	P559PNE	42559	Manchester	P703BTA	31703	South West
P533EFL	16533	East	P561EFL	16561	East	P704BTA	31704	South West
P533ESA	20533	West Scotland	P562EFL	16562	East	P705BTA	31705	South West
P533HMP	16033	South Midlands	P562PNE	42562	Manchester	P706BTA	31706	South West
P533PNE	42533	Manchester	P563EFL	16563	East	P707BTA	31707	South West
P534EFL	16534	East	P563MSX	51063	South West	P708BTA	31708	South West
P534ESA	20534	West Scotland	P563PNE	42563	Manchester	P709BTA	31709	South West
P534HMP	16034	South Midlands	P564APM	33397	East	P710BTA	31710	South West
P534PNE	42534	Manchester	P564EFL	16564	East	P711BTA	31711	South West
P535EFL	16535	East	P564MSX	51064	South West	P712BTA	31712	South West
P535ESA	20535	West Scotland	P564PNE	42564	Manchester	P713BTA	31713	South West
P535HMP	16035	East Scotland	P565EFL	16565	East	P714BTA	31714	South West
P535PNE	42535	Manchester	P565MSX	52365	East Scotland	P716GND	16786	Manchester
P536EFL	16536	East	P565PNE	42565	Manchester	P717GND	16787	Manchester
P536ESA	20536	West Scotland	P566EFL	16566	East	P718GND	16788	Manchester
P536HMP	16036	East Scotland	P566MSX	52366	East Scotland	P719GND	16789	Manchester
P536PNE	42536	Manchester	P566PNE	42566	Manchester	P720GND	16790	Manchester
P537EFL	16537	East	P567EFL	16567	East	P721GND	16791	Manchester
P537ESA	20537	West Scotland	P567MSX	52367	East Scotland	P722GND	16792	Manchester

Registration	Code	Fleet
P723GND	16793	Manchester
P724GND	16794	Manchester
P725GND	16795	Manchester
P726GND	16796	Manchester
P727GND	16797	Manchester
P728GND	16798	Manchester
P729GND	16799	Manchester
P730GND	16800	Manchester
P758FOD	33158	South West
P760FOD	33160	South West
P762FOD	33159	South West
P771TTG	52401	Wales & West
P772TTG	52402	Wales & West
P773TTG	52403	Wales & West
P774TTG	52404	Wales & West
P780WCN	32780	North East
P781WCN	32781	North East
P782WCN	32782	North East
P783WCN	32783	North East
P784WCN	32784	North East
P785WCN	32785	North East
P786WVK	32786	North East
P787WVK	32787	North East
P788WVK	32788	North East
P789WVK	32789	North East
P790WVK	32790	North East
P791WVK	32791	North East
P792WVK	32792	North East
P793WVK	32793	North East
P801GMU	16001	London
P801NJN	33351	London
P801XTA	52341	South West
P802GMU	16002	London
P802NJN	33352	London
P802XTA	52342	South West
P803GMU	16003	London
P803NJN	33353	London
P803XTA	52343	South West
P804GMU	16004	East
P804NJN	33354	London
P804XTA	52344	South West
P805GMU	16005	East
P805NJN	33355	London
P805XTA	52345	South West
P806GMU	16006	East
P806NJN	33356	London
P806XTA	52346	South West
P807GMU	16007	East
P807NJN	33357	London
P808GMU	16008	East
P809GMU	16009	East
P810GMU	16010	East
P811GMU	16011	East
P812GMU	16012	East
P813GMU	16013	East
P814GMU	16014	East
P815GMU	16015	East
P816GMU	16016	South West
P817GMU	16017	South West
P818GMU	16018	East
P819GMU	16019	East
P819GNC	20819	Wales & West
P820GMU	16020	East
P820GNC	20820	Wales & West
P821FVU	20821	South Midlands
P821GMU	16021	East
P822FVU	20822	Wales & West
P822GMU	16022	East
P823FVU	20823	South Midlands
P823GMU	16023	East
P824FVU	20824	Wales & West
P824GMU	16024	East
P825FVU	20825	Wales & West
P825GMU	16025	East
P826FVU	20826	Wales & West
P826GMU	16026	East
P827FVU	20827	Wales & West
P828FEF	16828	North East
P828FVU	20828	Wales & West
P829FEF	16829	North East
P829FVU	20829	South East
P830FEF	16830	North East
P830FVU	20830	South East
P831FVU	20831	South East
P833FVU	20833	South East
P834FVU	20834	South East
P835FVU	20835	South East
P836GND	20836	South East
P837GND	20837	North East
P838GND	20838	North East
P839GND	20839	North East
P840GND	20840	North East
P841GND	20841	North East
P842GND	20842	North East
P843GND	20843	North East
P844GND	20844	North East
P845GND	20845	Manchester
P846GND	20846	Manchester
P847GND	20847	Manchester
P848GND	20848	Manchester
P849GND	20849	Manchester
P850GND	20850	Manchester
P851GND	20851	Manchester
P852GND	20852	Manchester
P852SMR	31852	South Midlands
P853GND	20853	Manchester
P853SMR	31853	South Midlands
P854GND	20854	Manchester
P854SMR	31854	South Midlands
P855GND	20855	Manchester
P856GND	20856	Manchester
P857GND	20857	Manchester
P858GND	20858	Manchester
P859GND	20859	Manchester
P860GND	20860	Manchester
P861GND	20861	Manchester
P862GND	20862	Manchester
P863GND	20863	Manchester
P864GND	20864	Manchester
P865GND	20865	Manchester
P866GND	20866	Manchester
P867GND	20867	Manchester
P868GND	20868	Manchester
P869MNE	20869	Wales & West
P870MNE	20870	Wales & West
P871MNE	20871	Wales & West
P872MNE	20872	Wales & West
P873MNE	20873	Wales & West
P874MNE	20874	Wales & West
P875MNE	20875	Manchester
P876MNE	20876	Manchester
P877MNE	20877	Manchester
P878MNE	20878	Manchester
P879MNE	20879	Manchester
P880MNE	20880	Manchester
P881MNE	20881	Manchester
P882MNE	20882	Manchester
P883MNE	20883	Wales & West
P884MNE	20884	Wales & West
P885MNE	20885	Wales & West
P886MNE	20886	Wales & West
P887MNE	20887	Wales & West
P889MNE	20889	Wales & West
P890MNE	20890	Wales & West
P891MNE	20891	Wales & West
P892MNE	20892	Wales & West
P893MNE	20893	Manchester
P894MNE	20894	Manchester
P901SMR	32901	Wales & West
P902SMR	32902	Wales & West
P903SMR	32903	Wales & West
P904SMR	33904	Wales & West
P905SMR	33905	Wales & West
P906SMR	33906	Wales & West
P907SMR	33907	Wales & West
P908SMR	33908	Wales & West
P909SMR	33909	Wales & West
P910SMR	33910	Wales & West
P911SMR	33911	Wales & West
P912SMR	33912	Wales & West
P913SMR	33913	Wales & West
P914SMR	33914	Wales & West
P969UKG	46271	Wales & West
P970UKG	46272	Wales & West
P971UKG	46273	Wales & West
P977UBV	52405	North West
P978UBV	52406	North West
P979UBV	52407	North West
PJI4316	59037	East Midlands
PO51WLF	47016	North West
PO51WLG	47017	North West
PO51WLH	47018	North West
PO51WLJ	47019	North West
PO51WLK	47020	North West
PO51WLL	47021	North West
PO51WLN	47022	North West
PO51WLP	47023	North West
PO51WLR	47024	North West
PRX189B	19917	North East
PS2743	52008	East Midlands
PSU443	52005	East Midlands
PSU764	52007	East Midlands
PSU787	59014	North West
PUK621R	25421	South Midlands
PUK622R	25422	South Midlands
PYE841Y	59087	East Midlands
R34AKV	52434	South Midlands
R35AKV	52435	South Midlands
R36AKV	52436	South Midlands
R36LSO	42000	North West
R37AKV	52437	South Midlands
R38AKV	52438	South Midlands
R39AKV	52439	South Midlands
R63UFC	32163	South Midlands
R64UFC	32164	South Midlands
R65UFC	32165	South Midlands
R71NPN	31051	South East
R82SEF	52462	East Scotland
R82XNO	16082	London
R83SEF	52463	East Scotland
R83XNO	16083	London
R84SEF	52464	West Scotland
R84XNO	16084	London
R85SEF	52465	West Scotland
R85XNO	16085	London
R86XNO	16086	London
R87XNO	16087	London
R89XNO	16089	London
R91XNO	16091	London
R92XNO	16092	London
R93XNO	16093	London
R94XNO	16094	London
R95NPN	31045	South East
R95XNO	16095	London
R96XNO	16096	London
R97XNO	16097	London
R98XNO	16098	London
R101KRG	33101	North East
R101NTA	42101	South West
R101XNO	16101	London
R102KRG	33102	North East
R102NTA	42102	South West
R102XNO	16102	London
R103KRG	33103	North East
R103LSO	52425	West Scotland
R103NTA	42103	South West
R103XNO	16103	London
R104KRG	33104	North East
R104LSO	52426	West Scotland
R104NTA	42104	South West
R104XNO	16104	London
R105KRG	33105	North East
R105LSO	52427	West Scotland
R105NTA	42105	South West
R105XNO	16105	London
R107KRG	33107	North East
R107NTA	42107	South West
R107XNO	16107	London
R108KRG	33108	North East
R108NTA	42108	South West
R108XNO	16108	London
R109KRG	33109	North East
R109NTA	42109	South West
R109XNO	16109	London
R110KRG	33110	North East
R110NTA	42110	South West
R112KRG	33112	North East
R112NTA	42112	South West
R112OPS	52422	East Scotland
R112XNO	16112	London
R113KRG	33113	North East
R113NTA	42113	South West
R113OPS	52423	East Scotland
R113XNO	16113	London
R114KRG	33114	North East
R114NTA	42114	South West
R114OPS	52424	East Scotland
R114XNO	16114	London
R115KRG	33115	North East
R115NTA	42115	South West
R115OPS	52415	East
R115XNO	16115	London
R116KRG	33116	North East
R116NTA	42116	South West
R116OPS	52416	West Scotland
R116XNO	16116	London
R117KRG	33117	North East

Reg	No	Region	Reg	No	Region	Reg	No	Region
R117OPS	52417	Wales & West	R159HHK	16159	London	R246KRG	21146	North East
R117XNO	16117	London	R159VPU	16059	London	R246NBV	16646	North West
R118KRG	33118	North East	R160HHK	16160	London	R247KRG	21147	North East
R118OP3	52418	West Scotland	R160VPU	16060	London	H24/NBV	1664/	North West
R118XNO	16118	London	R161HHK	16161	London	R248KRG	21148	North East
R119KRG	33119	South East	R161VPU	16061	London	R248NBV	16648	North West
R119NPN	31049	South East	R162HHK	16162	London	R249KRG	21149	North East
R119OPS	52419	West Scotland	R162VPU	16062	London	R249NBV	16649	North West
R119XNO	16119	London	R163HHK	16163	London	R250KRG	21150	North East
R120KRG	33120	North East	R163VPU	16063	London	R250NBV	16650	North West
R120OPS	52420	East Scotland	R164HHK	16164	South West	R251KRG	21151	North East
R120VFR	52490	North West	R164VPU	16064	London	R251NBV	16651	North West
R120XNO	16120	London	R165HHK	16165	London	R252KRG	21152	North East
R121KRG	33121	North East	R165VPU	16065	London	R252NBV	16652	North West
R121OPS	52421	West Scotland	R166HHK	16166	London	R253KRG	21153	North East
R121VPU	34021	West Scotland	R166VPU	16066	London	R253NBV	16653	North West
R121XNO	16121	London	R167HHK	16167	London	R254KRG	21154	North East
R122EVX	16122	London	R167VPU	16067	London	R254NBV	16654	North West
R122KRG	33122	North East	R168HHK	16168	London	R255KRG	21155	North East
R122VPU	34022	London	R168VPU	16068	West Scotland	R255NBV	16655	North West
R123EVX	16123	London	R169HHK	16169	London	R256KRG	21156	North East
R123KRG	33123	North East	R169VPU	16069	London	R256NBV	16656	North West
R123VPU	34023	London	R170HHK	16170	London	R257KRG	21157	North East
R124EVX	16124	London	R170VPU	16070	London	R257NBV	16657	North West
R124KRG	33124	North East	R171HHK	16171	London	R258KRG	21158	North East
R124VPU	34024	London	R171VPU	16071	London	R258NBV	16658	North West
R125EVX	16125	London	R172HHK	16172	London	R259NBV	16659	North West
R125KRG	33125	North East	R172VPU	16072	London	R260NBV	16660	North West
R125VPU	34025	West Scotland	R173HHK	16173	London	R261NBV	16661	North West
R126EVX	16126	London	R173VPU	16073	London	R262NBV	16662	North West
R126KRG	33126	North East	R174DNH	52474	East	R263NBV	16663	North West
R126VPU	34026	West Scotland	R174HHK	16174	London	R264NBV	16664	North West
R127EVX	16127	London	R174VPU	16074	West Scotland	R265NBV	16665	North West
R127KRG	33127	North East	R175DNH	52475	East	R266NBV	16666	North West
R127VPU	34027	London	R175HHK	16175	London	R267NBV	16667	North West
R128EVX	16128	London	R175VPU	16075	London	R268NBV	16668	North West
R128KRG	33128	North East	R176DNH	52476	East	R270RPN	31050	South East
R128VPU	34028	London	R176HHK	16176	London	R276CBU	42567	Manchester
R129EVX	16129	London	R176VPU	16076	London	R277CBU	42568	Manchester
R129VPU	34029	London	R177DNH	52477	East	R291HCD	16291	South East
R130EVX	16130	London	R177HHK	16177	London	R292HCD	16292	South East
R131EVX	16131	London	R177NPN	31047	South East	R293HCD	16293	South East
R132EVX	16132	London	R177VPU	16077	London	R294HCD	16294	South East
R132NPN	31052	South East	R178DNH	52478	East	R295HCD	16295	South East
R133EVX	16133	London	R178HHK	16178	London	R296HCD	16296	South East
R133NPN	31043	South East	R178NPN	31048	South East	R297HCD	16297	South East
R134EVX	16134	London	R178VPU	16078	London	R298HCD	16298	South East
R135EVX	16135	London	R179DNH	52479	East	R299HCD	16299	South East
R136EVX	16136	London	R179VPU	16079	London	R301HCD	16301	South East
R137EVX	16137	London	R180DNH	52480	East	R311XNO	16111	London
R138EVX	16138	London	R180VPU	16080	London	R330HFS	20330	East Scotland
R139EVX	16139	London	R181DNH	52481	East	R331HFS	20331	East Scotland
R140EVX	16140	London	R181VPU	16081	London	R332HFS	20332	East Scotland
R141EVX	16141	London	R182DNH	52482	East	R334HFS	20334	East Scotland
R142EVX	16142	London	R183DNH	52483	East	R335HFS	20335	East Scotland
R143EVX	16143	London	R184DNH	52484	East	R336HFS	20336	East Scotland
R144EVX	16144	London	R185DNH	52485	East	R337HFS	20337	East Scotland
R144NPN	31044	South East	R186DNH	52486	East	R338HFS	20338	East Scotland
R145EVX	16145	London	R188XNO	16088	London	R339HFS	20339	East Scotland
R146EVX	16146	London	R190XNO	16090	London	R340HFS	20340	East Scotland
R147EVX	16147	London	R196NPN	31046	South East	R341HFS	20341	East Scotland
R148EVX	16148	London	R203DHB	16203	Wales & West	R342HFS	20342	East Scotland
R148VPU	16048	London	R204DHB	16204	Wales & West	R353LER	33393	East
R149HHK	16149	London	R205DHB	16205	Wales & West	R354LER	33394	East
R149VPU	16049	London	R206XNO	16106	London	R355LER	33395	East
R150CRW	33650	South Midlands	R207DHB	16207	Wales & West	R356LER	33396	East
R150HHK	16150	London	R207XNO	16099	London	R365JVA	33398	East
R150VPU	16050	London	R208DHB	16208	Wales & West	R366JVA	33399	East
R151CRW	33651	South Midlands	R208XNO	33358	London	R414XFC	16514	South Midlands
R151HHK	16151	London	R209XNO	33359	London	R415XFC	16515	South Midlands
R151VPU	16051	London	R210XNO	16100	London	R416XFC	16516	South Midlands
R152CRW	33652	South Midlands	R221CRW	20221	South Midlands	R417XFC	16517	South Midlands
R152HHK	16152	London	R223CRW	20223	South Midlands	R418XFC	16518	South Midlands
R152VPU	16052	London	R224CRW	20224	South Midlands	R419XFC	16519	South Midlands
R153CRW	33653	South Midlands	R225CRW	20225	South Midlands	R420XFC	16520	South Midlands
R153HHK	16153	London	R226CRW	20226	South Midlands	R421XFC	16521	South Midlands
R153VPU	16053	London	R227CRW	20227	South Midlands	R422XFC	16522	South Midlands
R154CRW	33654	South Midlands	R228CRW	20228	South Midlands	R423XFC	16523	South Midlands
R154HHK	16154	London	R236KRG	21136	North East	R424XFC	16524	South Midlands
R154VPU	16054	London	R237KRG	21137	North East	R425XFC	16525	South Midlands
R155CRW	33655	South Midlands	R238KRG	21138	North East	R426XFC	16526	South Midlands
R155HHK	16155	London	R239KRG	21139	North East	R446YNF	42569	Manchester
R155VPU	16055	London	R240KRG	21140	North East	R447YNF	42570	Manchester
R156HHK	16156	London	R241KRG	21141	North East	R451FVX	34051	London
R156VPU	16056	London	R242KRG	21142	North East	R452FVX	34052	London
R157HHK	16157	London	R243KRG	21143	North East	R453FCE	52447	South Midlands
R157VPU	16057	London	R244KRG	21144	North East	R453FVX	34053	London
R158HHK	16158	London	R245KRG	21145	North East	R454FCE	52444	South Midlands
R158VPU	16058	London				R454FVX	34054	London

184

Registration	Fleet	Region
R455FCE	52445	East
R455FVX	34055	London
R456FCE	52446	East
R456FVX	34056	London
R457FVX	34057	London
R458FVX	34058	London
R460LSO	33760	East Midlands
R461LSO	33761	East Midlands
R462LSO	33762	East Midlands
R462SEF	33482	North East
R463LSO	33763	South Midlands
R463SEF	33483	North East
R464LSO	33764	East Midlands
R464SEF	33484	North East
R465LSO	33765	East Midlands
R465SEF	33485	North East
R466LSO	33766	East Midlands
R466SEF	33486	North East
R467LSO	33767	East Midlands
R467SEF	33487	North East
R468LSO	33768	East Midlands
R468SEF	33488	North East
R469LSO	33769	East Midlands
R469MVN	33489	North East
R470LSO	33770	East Midlands
R470MVN	33490	North East
R471LSO	33771	North East
R471MVN	33491	North East
R472MVN	33492	North East
R473MCW	20473	North West
R474MCW	20474	North West
R475MCW	20475	North West
R476MCW	20476	North West
R477MCW	20477	North West
R478MCW	20478	North West
R479MCW	20479	South West
R480MCW	20480	South West
R481MCW	20481	South West
R482MCW	20482	South West
R501UWL	16501	Manchester
R501YWC	42001	London
R502KSA	20502	West Scotland
R502UWL	16502	Manchester
R502YWC	42002	Manchester
R503KSA	20503	West Scotland
R503UWL	16503	Manchester
R503YWC	42003	Manchester
R504KSA	20504	West Scotland
R504UWL	16504	Manchester
R504YWC	42004	Manchester
R505UWL	16505	Manchester
R505YWC	42005	London
R506UWL	16506	Manchester
R506YWC	42006	London
R507UWL	16507	Manchester
R507YWC	42007	London
R508UWL	16508	Manchester
R508YWC	42008	London
R509UWL	16509	Manchester
R509YWC	42009	London
R510UWL	16510	Manchester
R510YWC	42010	London
R511UWL	16511	Manchester
R511YWC	42011	London
R512UWL	16512	Manchester
R512YWC	42012	London
R513KSA	20513	West Scotland
R513UWL	16513	Manchester
R513YWC	42013	Manchester
R514KSA	20514	West Scotland
R514YWC	42014	Manchester
R515KSA	20515	West Scotland
R515YWC	42015	London
R516VSE	20516	West Scotland
R516YWC	42016	Manchester
R517VSE	20517	West Scotland
R517YWC	42017	Manchester
R518VSE	20518	West Scotland
R518YWC	42018	London
R519VSE	20519	West Scotland
R521VSE	20521	West Scotland
R522VSE	20522	West Scotland
R524VSE	20524	West Scotland
R526VSE	20526	West Scotland
R539GSF	52440	East Scotland
R541GSF	52441	East Scotland
R542GSF	52442	East Scotland
R543GSF	52443	East Scotland
R550JDF	52450	Wales & West
R551JDF	52451	Wales & West
R552JDF	52452	Wales & West
R553JDF	52453	Wales & West
R554JDF	52454	Wales & West
R554RPY	20264	North East
R556RPY	20256	North East
R557RPY	20257	North East
R558RPY	20258	North East
R560DRP	16210	East
R561DRP	16211	East
R562DRP	16212	East
R563DRP	16213	East
R564DRP	16214	East
R565DRP	16215	East
R566DRP	16216	East
R567DRP	16217	East
R568DRP	16218	East
R580JVA	16580	East
R581JVA	16581	East
R582JVA	16582	East
R583JVA	16583	East
R584JVA	16584	East
R585JVA	16585	East
R586JVA	16586	East
R595LSO	20595	West Scotland
R596LSO	20596	West Scotland
R601SWO	33601	Wales & West
R602KDD	46602	North West
R602SWO	33602	Wales & West
R603KDD	46603	North West
R603SWO	33603	Wales & West
R604KDD	46604	South West
R604SWO	33604	East
R606KDD	46606	Wales & West
R606SWO	33606	Wales & West
R607KDD	46607	Wales & West
R607SWO	33607	Wales & West
R608KDD	46608	South West
R608SWO	33608	Wales & West
R609KDD	46609	South West
R609SWO	33609	Wales & West
R610KDD	46610	Wales & West
R610SWO	33610	Wales & West
R611KDD	46611	South East
R611SWO	33611	Wales & West
R612KDD	46612	South East
R612SWO	33612	Wales & West
R613KDD	46613	South East
R613SWO	33613	Wales & West
R614GFS	33414	East Scotland
R614KDD	46614	South East
R614SWO	33614	Wales & West
R615KDD	46615	South East
R615SWO	33615	Wales & West
R616KDD	46616	South East
R616SWO	33616	Wales & West
R617RWO	46277	Wales & West
R617SWO	33617	Wales & West
R618SWO	33618	Wales & West
R619SWO	33619	Wales & West
R620SWO	33620	Wales & West
R621SWO	33621	Wales & West
R624CTX	42624	South Midlands
R636RSE	52456	West Scotland
R637RSE	52457	East Scotland
R638RSE	52458	East Scotland
R639RSE	52459	East Scotland
R640OVN	16840	North East
R640RSE	52460	East Scotland
R641LSO	20141	East Scotland
R642LSO	20142	East Scotland
R643LSO	20143	East Scotland
R644LSO	20144	East Scotland
R645LSO	20145	East Scotland
R646HCD	20646	South East
R646LSO	20146	East Scotland
R647HCD	20647	South East
R647LSO	20147	East Scotland
R648HCD	20648	South East
R648LSO	20148	East Scotland
R649HCD	20649	South East
R649LSO	20149	East Scotland
R650LSO	20150	East Scotland
R651VSE	20151	East Scotland
R652VSE	20152	East Scotland
R653HCD	20653	Manchester
R653RPY	20253	North East
R653VSE	20153	East Scotland
R654HCD	20654	South East
R654RPY	20254	North East
R654VSE	20154	East Scotland
R655RPY	20255	North East
R663TKU	52493	East Midlands
R664TKU	52494	East Midlands
R670LFV	42670	North West
R672LFV	42672	North West
R674HCD	20674	Manchester
R675HCD	20675	South East
R676HCD	20676	South East
R677HCD	20677	Manchester
R678HCD	20678	South East
R679HCD	20679	South East
R680HCD	20680	South East
R693DNH	16693	East
R694DNH	16694	East
R695DNH	16695	East
R696DNH	16696	East
R697DNH	16697	East
R698DNH	16698	East
R699DNH	16699	East
R701DNH	16221	East
R701DNJ	33001	North East
R701YWC	32351	Manchester
R702DNH	16222	East
R702DNJ	33002	South East
R702YWC	32352	Manchester
R703DNJ	33003	South East
R703YWC	32353	Manchester
R704DNJ	33004	South East
R704YWC	32354	Manchester
R705YWC	32355	Manchester
R706DNJ	33006	South East
R706YUD	33806	East
R706YWC	32356	Manchester
R707DNJ	33007	South East
R707YWC	32357	Manchester
R708DNJ	33008	South East
R708YWC	32358	Manchester
R709DNJ	33009	South East
R709YWC	32359	Manchester
R710DNJ	33010	South East
R710YWC	32360	Manchester
R711DNJ	33011	South East
R711YWC	32361	Manchester
R712YWC	32362	Manchester
R713YWC	32363	Manchester
R714YWC	32364	Manchester
R715YWC	32365	Manchester
R716YWC	32366	Manchester
R717YWC	32367	Manchester
R718YWC	32368	Manchester
R719RPY	20279	North East
R720RPY	20280	North East
R720YUD	33820	East
R721RPY	20281	North East
R722RPY	20282	North East
R723RPY	20283	North East
R724RPY	20284	North East
R725RPY	20285	North East
R726RPY	20286	North East
R744DRJ	16744	Manchester
R745DRJ	16745	Manchester
R746DRJ	16746	Manchester
R747DRJ	16747	Manchester
R747XAR	16047	London
R748DRJ	16748	Manchester
R749DRJ	16749	Manchester
R751BDV	33751	South West
R751DRJ	16751	Manchester
R752DRJ	16752	Manchester
R753DRJ	16753	Manchester
R754DRJ	16754	Manchester
R755DRJ	16755	Manchester
R755RPY	20265	North East
R756DRJ	16756	Manchester
R757DRJ	16757	Manchester
R758DRJ	16758	Manchester
R759DRJ	16759	Manchester
R760DRJ	16760	Manchester
R761DRJ	16761	Manchester
R762DRJ	16762	Manchester
R763DRJ	16763	Manchester
R765DRJ	16765	Manchester
R775CDW	52495	Wales & West
R776CDW	52496	Wales & West
R778CDW	52498	Wales & West
R779CDW	52499	Wales & West
R780CDW	52500	Wales & West

Reg	No	Region	Reg	No	Region	Reg	No	Region
R781CDW	52501	Wales & West	R908XVM	20908	Manchester	R970XVM	20970	Manchester
R782CDW	52502	Wales & West	R909XFC	20009	South Midlands	R971XVM	20971	Manchester
R783CDW	52503	Wales & West	R909XVM	20909	Manchester	R972XVM	20972	Manchester
H784CDW	52504	Wales & West	R910XFC	20010	South Midlands	R973XVM	20973	Manchester
R785DHB	20385	Wales & West	R910XVM	20910	Manchester	R974XVM	20974	Manchester
R787DHB	20387	Wales & West	R912XFC	20012	South Midlands	R975XVM	20975	Manchester
R788DHB	20388	Wales & West	R912XVM	20912	Manchester	R976XVM	20976	Manchester
R789DHB	20389	Wales & West	R913XVM	20913	Manchester	R977XVM	20977	Manchester
R790DHB	20390	Wales & West	R914XVM	20914	Manchester	R978XVM	20978	Manchester
R791DHB	20391	Wales & West	R915GMW	33915	Wales & West	R979XVM	20979	Manchester
R791PAO	52491	North West	R915XVM	20915	Manchester	R980XVM	20980	Manchester
R792DHB	20392	Wales & West	R916GMW	33916	Wales & West	R981XVM	20981	Manchester
R792PAO	52492	North West	R916XVM	20916	Manchester	R982XVM	20982	Manchester
R793URM	20793	North West	R917GMW	33917	Wales & West	R983XVM	20983	Manchester
R794URM	20794	North West	R917XVM	20917	Manchester	R984XVM	20984	Manchester
R795URM	20795	North West	R918GMW	33918	Wales & West	R985XVM	20985	Manchester
R801YUD	33801	South West	R918XVM	20918	Manchester	R986XVM	20986	Manchester
R802YUD	33802	East	R919XVM	20919	Manchester	R987XVM	20987	Manchester
R803YUD	33803	South West	R920XVM	20920	Manchester	R988XVM	20988	Manchester
R804YUD	33804	South West	R921XVM	20921	Manchester	R989XVM	20989	Manchester
R805YUD	33805	South West	R922XVM	20922	Manchester	R990XVM	20990	Manchester
R807JDV	20347	South West	R923XVM	20923	Manchester	R991XVM	20991	Manchester
R807YUD	33807	South West	R924XVM	20924	Manchester	R992XVM	20992	Manchester
R808YUD	33808	Wales & West	R925XVM	20925	Manchester	R993XVM	20993	Manchester
R809YUD	33809	Wales & West	R926XVM	20926	Manchester	R994XVM	20994	Manchester
R810YUD	33810	Wales & West	R927XVM	20927	Manchester	R995XVM	20995	Manchester
R811XFC	20011	South Midlands	R928XVM	20928	Manchester	R996XVM	20996	Manchester
R811YUD	33811	Wales & West	R929XVM	20929	Manchester	RBZ5459	48015	North West
R812YUD	33812	Wales & West	R930FOO	34030	London	RCS382	19982	West Scotland
R813HCD	33013	South East	R930XVM	20930	Manchester	RDZ6115	28615	London
R813YUD	33813	East	R931FOO	34031	London	RDZ6116	28616	London
R814HCD	33014	South East	R931XVM	20931	Manchester	RDZ6117	28617	London
R814YUD	33814	East	R932FOO	34032	London	RDZ6118	28618	London
R815HCD	33015	South East	R932XVM	20932	Manchester	RDZ6119	28619	London
R815YUD	33815	East	R933FOO	34033	London	RDZ6120	28620	London
R816HCD	33016	South East	R933XVM	20933	Manchester	RDZ6121	28621	London
R816YUD	33816	East	R934FOO	34034	London	RDZ6122	28622	London
R817HCD	33017	South East	R934XVM	20934	Manchester	RDZ6123	28623	London
R817YUD	33817	East	R935FOO	34035	London	RDZ6124	28624	London
R818HCD	33018	South East	R935XVM	20935	Manchester	RDZ6125	28625	London
R818YUD	33818	East	R936FOO	34036	London	RDZ6126	28626	London
R819HCD	33019	South East	R936XVM	20936	Manchester	RDZ6127	28627	London
R819YUD	33819	East	R937FOO	34037	Manchester	RDZ6128	28628	London
R821HCD	33021	South East	R937XVM	20937	Manchester	RDZ6129	28629	London
R821YUD	33821	South Midlands	R938FOO	34038	Manchester	RDZ6130	28630	London
R822HCD	33022	South East	R938XVM	20938	Manchester	RIB4309	11110	North West
R822YUD	33822	South Midlands	R939FOO	34039	London	RIL5085	48017	North West
R823HCD	33023	South East	R939XVM	20939	Manchester	RUT842	48066	North West
R823YUD	33823	South West	R940FOO	34040	London	RV52OGL	80001	Manchester
R824HCD	33024	South East	R940XVM	20940	Manchester	RYK819Y	10819	East Scotland
R824YUD	33824	South West	R941FOO	34041	Manchester	RYK820Y	10820	East Scotland
R825YUD	33825	North East	R941XVM	20941	Manchester	S101TRJ	22101	Manchester
R826YUD	33826	North East	R942FOO	34042	London	S101WHK	34101	London
R827YUD	33827	North East	R942XVM	20942	Manchester	S102TRJ	22102	Manchester
R828YUD	33828	North East	R943FOO	34043	London	S102WHK	34102	London
R829YUD	33829	North East	R943XVM	20943	Manchester	S103TRJ	22103	Manchester
R831OVN	16831	North East	R944FOO	34044	London	S103WHK	34103	London
R832OVN	16832	North East	R944XVM	20944	Manchester	S104TRJ	22104	Manchester
R833OVN	16833	North East	R945FOO	34045	London	S104WHK	34104	London
R834OVN	16834	North East	R945XVM	20945	Manchester	S105TRJ	22105	Manchester
R835OVN	16835	North East	R946FOO	34046	London	S105WHK	34105	London
R836OVN	16836	North East	R946XVM	20946	Manchester	S106TRJ	22106	Manchester
R837OVN	16837	North East	R947FOO	34047	Manchester	S106WHK	34106	London
R838OVN	16838	North East	R947XVM	20947	Manchester	S107TRJ	22107	Manchester
R839OVN	16839	North East	R948FOO	34048	London	S108TRJ	22108	Manchester
R895XVM	20895	Manchester	R948XVM	20948	Manchester	S109TRJ	22109	East Scotland
R896XVM	20896	Manchester	R949FOO	34049	London	S110SHJ	16110	London
R897XVM	20897	Manchester	R949XVM	20949	Manchester	S110TRJ	22110	East Scotland
R898AVM	42571	Manchester	R950FOO	34050	London	S112TRJ	22112	East Scotland
R898XVM	20898	Manchester	R950XVM	20950	Manchester	S113TRJ	22113	Manchester
R899AVM	42572	Manchester	R951XVM	20951	Manchester	S114TRJ	22114	Manchester
R899XVM	20899	Manchester	R952XVM	20952	Manchester	S115TRJ	22115	Manchester
R901AVM	42573	Manchester	R953XVM	20953	Manchester	S116TRJ	22116	Manchester
R901FDV	16601	South West	R954XVM	20954	Manchester	S117JFJ	42117	South West
R901XVM	20901	Manchester	R955XVM	20955	Manchester	S117TRJ	22117	Manchester
R902JDV	16602	South West	R956XVM	20956	Manchester	S118JFJ	42118	South West
R902XVM	20902	Manchester	R957XVM	20957	Manchester	S118TRJ	22118	Manchester
R903JDV	16603	South West	R958XVM	20958	Manchester	S119TRJ	22119	Manchester
R903XVM	20903	Manchester	R959XVM	20959	Manchester	S120TRJ	22120	Manchester
R904JDV	16604	South West	R960XVM	20960	Manchester	S121TRJ	22121	Manchester
R904XFC	20004	South Midlands	R961XVM	20961	Manchester	S122TRJ	22122	Manchester
R904XVM	20904	Manchester	R962XVM	20962	Manchester	S124TRJ	22124	Manchester
R905XFC	20005	South Midlands	R963XVM	20963	Manchester	S125TRJ	22125	Manchester
R905XVM	20905	Manchester	R964XVM	20964	Manchester	S126TRJ	22126	Manchester
R906XFC	20006	South Midlands	R965XVM	20965	Manchester	S127TRJ	22127	Manchester
R906XVM	20906	Manchester	R966XVM	20966	Manchester	S128TRJ	22128	Manchester
R907XFC	20007	South Midlands	R967XVM	20967	Manchester	S129TRJ	22129	Manchester
R907XVM	20907	Manchester	R968XVM	20968	Manchester	S130TRJ	22130	Manchester.
R908XFC	20008	South Midlands	R969XVM	20969	Manchester	S131TRJ	22131	Manchester

The 2003 Stagecoach Bus Handbook

Code	No.	Area	Code	No.	Area	Code	No.	Area
S132TRJ	22132	Manchester	S379DFC	42379	South Midlands	S615CSC	33415	East Scotland
S133KRM	52603	North West	S380DFC	42380	South Midlands	S616CSC	33416	East Scotland
S133TRJ	22133	Manchester	S381DFC	42381	South Midlands	S617CSC	33417	East Scotland
S134KRM	52604	North West	S382DFC	42382	South Midlands	S618CSC	33418	East Scotland
S134TRJ	22134	Manchester	S383DFC	42383	South Midlands	S619CSC	33419	East Scotland
S135TRJ	22135	Manchester	S401SDT	33404	East Midlands	S622TDW	33622	Wales & West
S136TRJ	22136	Manchester	S402SDT	33405	East Midlands	S623TDW	33623	Wales & West
S137TRJ	22137	Manchester	S403SDT	33406	East Midlands	S624TDW	33624	Wales & West
S138TRJ	22138	Manchester	S410TNO	33360	London	S625TDW	33625	Wales & West
S139TRJ	22139	Manchester	S411TNO	33361	London	S626TDW	33626	Wales & West
S140TRJ	22140	Manchester	S451OFT	22451	North East	S627TDW	33627	Wales & West
S141TRJ	22141	Manchester	S452OFT	22452	North East	S655JSE	52605	East Scotland
S142TRJ	22142	Manchester	S453CVV	33453	East	S656JSE	52606	East Scotland
S143TRJ	22143	Manchester	S453OFT	22453	North East	S657JSE	52607	East Scotland
S144TRJ	22144	Manchester	S454CVV	33454	East	S658JSE	52608	East Scotland
S145TRJ	22145	Manchester	S454OFT	22454	North East	S659JSE	52609	East Scotland
S146TRJ	22146	Manchester	S455CVV	33455	East	S660JSE	52610	East Scotland
S147TRJ	22147	Manchester	S455OFT	22455	North East	S661JSE	52611	East Scotland
S148TRJ	22148	Manchester	S456CVV	33456	East	S662JSE	52612	East Scotland
S149TRJ	22149	Manchester	S456OFT	22456	North East	S665SDT	52635	East Midlands
S150TRJ	22150	Manchester	S457BCE	52617	East	S670RWJ	52630	East Midlands
S151TRJ	22151	Manchester	S457CVV	33457	East	S671RWJ	52631	East Midlands
S152TRJ	22152	Manchester	S457OFT	22457	East	S672RWJ	52632	East Midlands
S153TRJ	22153	Manchester	S458BCE	52618	East	S673RWJ	52633	East Midlands
S154TRJ	22154	Manchester	S458CVV	33458	East	S753DRP	16223	East
S156TRJ	22156	Manchester	S458OFT	22458	East	S754DRP	16224	East
S157TRJ	22157	Manchester	S459BCE	52619	East	S755DRP	16225	East
S158TRJ	22158	Manchester	S459BWC	34059	London	S756DRP	16226	East
S159TRJ	22159	Manchester	S459CVV	33459	East	S757DRP	16227	East
S161RET	16461	East Midlands	S459OFT	22459	East	S758DRP	16228	East
S162RET	16462	East Midlands	S460BCE	52620	East	S759DRP	16229	East
S163RET	16463	East Midlands	S460BWC	34060	London	S760DRP	16230	East
S164RET	16464	East Midlands	S460CVV	33460	East	S761DRP	16231	East
S165RET	16465	East Midlands	S460OFT	22460	East	S762DRP	16232	East
S166RET	16466	East Midlands	S461CVV	33461	East	S764SVU	16764	Manchester
S167RET	16467	East Midlands	S462BWC	34062	London	S766SVU	16766	Manchester
S168RET	16468	East Midlands	S463BWC	34063	West Scotland	S767SVU	16767	Manchester
S169RET	16469	East Midlands	S464BWC	34064	London	S768SVU	16768	Manchester
S173JVK	52601	East Midlands	S465BWC	34065	London	S769RVU	16769	Manchester
S174JVK	52602	East Midlands	S466BWC	34066	London	S770RVU	16770	Manchester
S190RAO	42090	North West	S467BWC	34067	London	S771RVU	16771	Manchester
S191RAO	42091	North West	S468BWC	34068	London	S772RVU	16772	Manchester
S192RAO	42092	North West	S469BWC	34069	London	S773RVU	16773	Manchester
S193RAO	42093	North West	S470BWC	34070	London	S774RVU	16774	Manchester
S194RAO	42094	North West	S471BWC	34071	London	S775RVU	16775	Manchester
S195RAO	42095	North West	S472BWC	34072	London	S776RVU	16776	Manchester
S196RAO	42096	North West	S472JSE	33472	East Scotland	S778RVU	16778	Manchester
S269KHG	52613	North West	S473BWC	34073	London	S779RVU	16779	Manchester
S270CCD	16270	South East	S473JSE	33473	East Scotland	S780RVU	16780	Manchester
S270KHG	52614	North West	S474BWC	34074	London	S781RVU	16781	Manchester
S271CCD	16271	South East	S474JSE	33474	East Scotland	S782RVU	16782	Manchester
S272CCD	16272	South East	S475BWC	34075	London	S796KRM	52626	North West
S273CCD	16273	South East	S475JSE	33475	East Scotland	S797KRM	52627	North West
S274CCD	16274	South East	S476BWC	34076	London	S798KRM	52628	North West
S275CCD	16275	South East	S476JSE	33476	East Scotland	S799KRM	52629	North West
S302CCD	16302	South East	S477BWC	34077	London	S801BWC	17001	London
S303CCD	16303	South East	S477JSE	33477	East Scotland	S802BWC	17002	London
S304CCD	16304	South East	S478BWC	34078	London	S803BWC	17003	London
S305CCD	16305	South East	S478JSE	33478	East Scotland	S804BWC	17004	London
S306CCD	16306	South East	S479BWC	34079	London	S805BWC	17005	London
S307CCD	16307	South East	S479JSE	33479	East Scotland	S806BWC	17006	London
S308CCD	16308	South East	S480BWC	34080	London	S807BWC	17007	London
S309CCD	16309	South East	S481BWC	34081	London	S808BTT	52638	East Scotland
S310CCD	16310	South East	S482BWC	34082	London	S808BWC	17008	London
S311CCD	16311	South East	S483BWC	34083	London	S809BWC	17009	London
S312CCD	16312	South East	S484BWC	34084	London	S810BWC	17010	London
S313CCD	16313	South East	S485BWC	34085	London	S811BWC	17011	London
S314CCD	16314	South East	S486BWC	34086	London	S812BWC	17012	London
S315CCD	16315	South East	S487BWC	34087	London	S813BWC	17013	London
S316CCD	16316	South East	S488BWC	34088	London	S814BWC	17014	London
S317CCD	16317	South East	S489BWC	34089	London	S815BWC	17015	London
S318CCD	16318	South East	S490BWC	34090	London	S816BWC	17016	London
S319CCD	16319	South East	S491BWC	34091	London	S817BWC	17017	London
S320CCD	16320	South East	S492BWC	34092	London	S818BWC	17018	London
S322CCD	16322	South East	S493BWC	34093	London	S819BWC	17019	London
S323CCD	16323	South East	S494BWC	34094	London	S820BWC	17020	London
S324CCD	16324	South East	S495BWC	34095	London	S821BWC	17021	London
S355KEF	42355	North East	S496BWC	34096	London	S822BWC	17022	London
S356KEF	42356	North East	S497BWC	34097	London	S823BWC	17023	London
S357KEF	42357	North East	S498BWC	34098	London	S824BWC	17024	London
S358KEF	42358	North East	S499BWC	34099	London	S825BWC	17025	London
S371DFC	42371	South Midlands	S561BWC	34061	London	S826BWC	17026	London
S372DFC	42372	South Midlands	S587BCE	16587	East	S827BWC	17027	London
S373DFC	42373	South Midlands	S588BCE	16588	East	S828BWC	17028	London
S374DFC	42374	South Midlands	S589BCE	16589	East	S829BWC	17029	London
S375DFC	42375	South Midlands	S590BCE	16590	East	S830BWC	17030	London
S376DFC	42376	South Midlands	S591BCE	16591	East	S831BWC	17031	London
S377DFC	42377	South Midlands	S592BCE	16592	East	S832BWC	17032	London
S378DFC	42378	South Midlands	S593BCE	16593	East	S833BWC	17033	London

Reg	No	Area	Reg	No	Area	Reg	No	Area
S834BWC	17034	London	T35DFC	50035	South Midlands	T375FUG	17675	East Midlands
S835BWC	17035	London	T35VCS	33088	West Scotland	T376FUG	17676	East Midlands
S836BWC	17036	London	T36DFC	50036	South Midlands	T377FUG	17677	East Midlands
5837BWC	17037	London	T36VCS	33089	West Scotland	T402UCS	33772	West Scotland
S838BWC	17038	London	T37BBW	50037	South Midlands	T403UCS	33773	West Scotland
S839BWC	17039	London	T38BBW	50038	South Midlands	T404UCS	33774	South West
S860VAT	52510	West Scotland	T38PTG	42579	East Midlands	T461BNL	22461	East
S901CCD	52621	South East	T39DJO	50039	South Midlands	T462BNL	22462	North East
S902CCD	52622	North West	T40UBE	50040	South Midlands	T463BNL	22463	North East
S903CCD	52623	North West	T41BBW	50041	South Midlands	T464BNL	22464	North East
S903JHG	16669	North West	T42BBW	50042	South Midlands	T465BNL	22465	North East
S904JHG	16670	North West	T43BBW	50043	South Midlands	T466BNL	22466	North East
S905JHG	52615	North West	T44UBE	50044	South Midlands	T467BNL	22467	North East
S906JHG	52616	North West	T45BBW	50045	South Midlands	T468BNL	22468	North East
S913CFC	22913	South Midlands	T46BBW	50046	South Midlands	T469BNL	22469	North East
S914ANH	16614	South Midlands	T47BBW	50047	South Midlands	T469GPS	33469	East Scotland
S914CFC	22914	South Midlands	T48BBW	50048	South Midlands	T470BNL	22470	North East
S915ANH	16615	South Midlands	T49BBW	50049	South Midlands	T470GPS	33470	East Scotland
S915CFC	22915	South Midlands	T50UBE	50050	South Midlands	T471BNL	22471	North East
S916ANH	16616	South Midlands	T51BBW	50051	South Midlands	T471GPS	33471	East Scotland
S916CFC	22916	South Midlands	T52BBW	50052	South Midlands	T472BNL	22472	North East
S917ANH	16617	South Midlands	T53BBW	50053	South Midlands	T473BNL	22473	North East
S917CFC	22917	South Midlands	T54BBW	50054	South Midlands	T474BNL	22474	North East
S918ANH	16618	South Midlands	T55UBE	50055	South Midlands	T475BNL	22475	North East
S918CFC	22918	South Midlands	T56BBW	50056	South Midlands	T476BNL	22476	North East
S919ANH	16619	South Midlands	T56JKG	42576	East Midlands	T477BNL	22477	North East
S919CFC	22919	South Midlands	T57BBW	50057	South Midlands	T478BNL	22478	North East
S920ANH	16620	South Midlands	T57JKG	42577	East Midlands	T479BNL	22479	North East
S920CFC	22920	South Midlands	T58BBW	50058	South Midlands	T480BNL	22480	North East
S921CFC	22921	South Midlands	T58JKG	42578	East Midlands	T481BNL	22481	North East
S922CFC	22922	South Midlands	T59BBW	50059	South Midlands	T482BNL	22482	North East
S923CFC	22923	South Midlands	T60UBE	50060	South Midlands	T483BNL	22483	North East
S924CFC	22924	South Midlands	T95JHN	51095	West Scotland	T484BNL	22484	North East
S924PDD	33924	Wales & West	T96JHN	51096	North East	T485BNL	22485	North East
S925CFC	22925	South Midlands	T97JHN	51097	West Scotland	T486BNL	22486	North East
S925PDD	33925	Wales & West	T131MGB	33782	South West	T487BNL	22487	North East
S926CFC	22926	South Midlands	T132MGB	33783	South West	T488BNL	22488	North East
S926PDD	33926	Wales & West	T160MVM	22160	Manchester	T489BNL	22489	North East
S927CFC	22927	South Midlands	T161MVM	22161	Manchester	T490BNL	22490	North East
S927PDD	33927	Wales & West	T162MVM	22162	Manchester	T491BNL	22491	North East
S928CFC	22928	South Midlands	T163MVM	22163	Manchester	T492BNL	22492	North East
S928PDD	33928	Wales & West	T164MVM	22164	Manchester	T493BNL	22493	North East
S929CFC	22929	South Midlands	T165MVM	22165	Manchester	T494BNL	22494	North East
S929PDD	33929	Wales & West	T166MVM	22166	Manchester	T495BNL	22495	North East
S930CFC	22930	South Midlands	T167MVM	22167	Manchester	T575KGB	33781	South West
S930PDD	33930	Wales & West	T168MVM	22168	Manchester	T582SKG	42582	East Midlands
S931CFC	22931	South Midlands	T169MVM	22169	Manchester	T583SKG	42583	East Midlands
S932CFC	22932	South Midlands	T172MVM	22172	North East	T584SKG	42584	East Midlands
S933CFC	22933	South Midlands	T173MVM	22173	Manchester	T585SKG	42585	East Midlands
S934CFC	22934	South Midlands	T174MVM	22174	North East	T586SKG	42586	South Midlands
S935CFC	22935	South Midlands	T178MVM	22178	Manchester	T587SKG	42587	East Midlands
S936CFC	22936	South Midlands	T179MVM	22179	Manchester	T588SKG	42588	South Midlands
S937CFC	22937	South Midlands	T180MVM	22180	Manchester	T589SKG	42589	East Midlands
S938CFC	22938	South Midlands	T181MVM	22181	Manchester	T590SKG	42590	East Midlands
S940CFC	22940	South Midlands	T182MVM	22182	Manchester	T593CGT	33020	South East
S941CFC	22941	South Midlands	T183MVM	22183	Manchester	T612MNF	17612	Manchester
SAG517W	15917	North East	T184MVM	22184	Manchester	T613MNF	17613	Manchester
SCN249S	15824	North East	T185MVM	22185	Manchester	T640KCS	51092	West Scotland
SHE307Y	14307	East Midlands	T186MVM	22186	Manchester	T640KPU	17040	London
SHH124M	25704	North West	T187MVM	22187	Manchester	T641KCS	51093	West Scotland
SK52USN	17734	Devon	T188MVM	22188	Manchester	T641KPU	17041	London
SK52USO	17735	Devon	T189MVM	22189	Manchester	T642KCS	51094	West Scotland
SK52USP	17736	Devon	T190MVM	22190	North East	T642KPU	17042	London
SKY31Y	59035	East Midlands	T193MVM	22193	North East	T643KPU	17043	London
SKY32Y	52010	East Midlands	T195MVM	22195	North East	T644KPU	17044	London
SMK661F	12661	London	T196MVM	22196	North East	T645KPU	17045	London
SMK665F	12665	London	T197MVM	22197	North East	T646KPU	17046	London
SMK668F	12668	London	T198TND	22198	North East	T647KPU	17047	London
SMK670F	12670	London	T199TND	22199	North East	T648KPU	17048	London
SMK671F	12671	London	T201TND	22201	North East	T649KPU	17049	London
SMK696F	12696	London	T202TND	22202	North East	T650KPU	17050	London
SMK705F	12705	London	T203TND	22203	North East	T651KPU	17051	London
SMK709F	12709	London	T204TND	22204	North East	T652KPU	17052	London
SMK719F	12719	London	T205TND	22205	North East	T653KPU	17053	London
SMK723F	12723	London	T206TND	22206	North East	T654KPU	17054	London
SMK738F	12738	London	T207TND	22207	North East	T655KPU	17055	London
SMK743F	12743	London	T208TND	22208	North East	T656KPU	17056	London
SMK748F	12748	London	T209TND	22209	North East	T656OEF	22656	North East
SMK749F	12749	London	T210TND	22210	North East	T657KPU	17057	London
SMK760F	12760	London	T211TND	22211	North East	T657OEF	22657	North East
SND455X	15855	Manchester	T212TND	22212	Manchester	T658KPU	17058	London
SP51AMK	22278	East	T213TND	22213	Manchester	T658OEF	22658	North East
SP51AMO	22279	South Midlands	T214TND	22214	North East	T659KPU	17059	London
SSA2X	14402	North East	T215TND	22215	North East	T659OEF	22659	North East
SSA3X	14403	North East	T370FUG	17686	East Midlands	T660KPU	17060	London
SSA4X	14404	East Scotland	T371FUG	17687	East Midlands	T660OEF	22660	North East
SSA5X	14405	North East	T372FUG	17688	East Midlands	T661KPU	17061	London
SYC52	52217	London	T373FUG	17673	East Midlands	T661OBD	52641	South Midlands
T34DFC	50034	South Midlands	T374FUG	17674	East Midlands	T661OEF	22661	North East

Reg	No	Location	Reg	No	Location	Reg	No	Location
T662KPU	17062	London	UWW3X	14281	Wales & West	V151DFT	17651	Manchester
T662OBD	52642	South Midlands	UWW7X	14283	Wales & West	V151MEV	17151	London
T662OEF	22662	North East	V102MEV	17102	London	V151MVX	34151	London
T663KPU	17063	London	V103MEV	17103	London	V152DFT	17652	Manchester
T663OBD	52643	South Midlands	V104MEV	17104	London	V152MEV	17152	London
T663OEF	22663	North East	V105MEV	17105	London	V152MVX	34152	London
T664KPU	17064	London	V106MEV	17106	London	V153DFT	17653	Manchester
T664OEF	22664	North East	V107MEV	17107	London	V153MEV	17153	London
T665KPU	17065	London	V107MVX	34107	London	V153MVX	34153	London
T665OEF	22665	North East	V108MEV	17108	London	V154DFT	17654	Manchester
T667KPU	17067	London	V108MVX	34108	London	V154MEV	17154	London
T667XTV	52647	East Scotland	V109MEV	17109	London	V154MVX	34154	London
T668KPU	17068	London	V109MVX	34109	London	V155DFT	17655	Manchester
T668XTV	52648	East Midlands	V110MVX	34110	London	V155MEV	17155	London
T669KPU	17069	London	V112MEV	17112	London	V155MVX	34155	London
T669XTV	52649	East Midlands	V112MVX	34112	London	V156DFT	17656	Manchester
T670KPU	17070	London	V113MEV	17113	London	V156MEV	17156	London
T671KPU	17071	London	V113MVX	34113	London	V156MVX	34156	London
T672KPU	17072	London	V114MEV	17114	London	V157DFT	17657	Manchester
T673KPU	17073	London	V114MVX	34114	London	V157MEV	17157	London
T675KPU	17075	London	V115MEV	17115	London	V157MVX	34157	London
T676KPU	17076	London	V115MVX	34115	London	V158DFT	17658	Manchester
T677KPU	17077	London	V116MEV	17116	London	V158MEV	17158	London
T678KPU	17078	London	V116MVX	34116	London	V158MVX	34158	London
T679KPU	17079	London	V117MEV	17117	London	V159DFT	17659	Manchester
T680KPU	17080	London	V117MVX	34117	London	V159MEV	17159	London
T681KPU	17081	London	V118MEV	17118	London	V159MVX	34159	London
T682KPU	17082	London	V118MVX	34118	London	V160DFT	17660	Manchester
T683KPU	17083	London	V119MEV	17119	London	V160MEV	17160	London
T684KPU	17084	London	V119MVX	34119	London	V160MVX	34160	London
T685KPU	17085	London	V120MEV	17120	London	V161DFT	17661	Manchester
T686KPU	17086	London	V120MVX	34120	London	V161MEV	17161	London
T687KPU	17087	London	V121MVX	34121	London	V161MVX	34161	London
T688KPU	17088	London	V122MEV	17122	London	V162DFT	17662	Manchester
T689KPU	17089	London	V122MVX	34122	London	V162MEV	17162	London
T690KPU	17090	London	V124MEV	17124	London	V162MVX	34162	London
T691KPU	17091	London	V124MVX	34124	London	V163DFT	17663	Manchester
T692KPU	17092	London	V125MEV	17125	London	V163MEV	17163	London
T693KPU	17093	London	V125MVX	34125	London	V163MVX	34163	London
T694KPU	17094	London	V126MEV	17126	London	V164DFT	17664	Manchester
T695KPU	17095	London	V126MVX	34126	London	V164MEV	17164	London
T696KPU	17096	London	V127MEV	17127	London	V164MVX	34164	London
T697KPU	17097	London	V127MVX	34127	London	V165DFT	17665	Manchester
T698KPU	17098	London	V128MEV	17128	London	V165MEV	17165	London
T699KVX	17066	London	V128MVX	34128	London	V165MVX	34165	London
T727OEF	22727	North East	V129MEV	17129	London	V166DEF	22666	North East
T728OEF	22728	North East	V129MVX	34129	London	V166DFT	17666	Manchester
T729OEF	22729	North East	V130MEV	17130	London	V166MEV	17166	London
T730OEF	22730	North East	V130MVX	34130	London	V166MVX	34166	London
T731OEF	22731	North East	V131MEV	17131	London	V167DFT	17667	Manchester
T732OEF	22732	North East	V131MVX	34131	London	V167MEV	17167	London
T733OEF	22733	North East	V132MEV	17132	London	V167MVX	34167	London
T734OEF	22734	North East	V132MVX	34132	London	V168DFT	17668	Manchester
T735OEF	22735	North East	V133MEV	17133	London	V168MEV	17168	London
T736FVN	22736	North East	V133MVX	34133	London	V168MVX	34168	London
T801OHL	33401	East Midlands	V134MEV	17134	London	V169DFT	17669	Manchester
T802OHL	33402	East Midlands	V134MVX	34134	London	V169MEV	17169	London
T803OHL	33403	East Midlands	V135MEV	17135	London	V169MVX	34169	London
T905XCD	33407	South East	V135MVX	34135	London	V170DFT	17670	Manchester
THX401S	10001	London	V136MEV	17136	London	V170MEV	17170	London
TOF710S	25410	South Midlands	V136MVX	34136	London	V170MVX	34170	London
TSJ71S	25771	West Scotland	V137MEV	17137	London	V171DFT	17671	Manchester
TSJ80S	25780	West Scotland	V137MVX	34137	London	V171MEV	17171	London
TSJ85S	25785	Manchester	V138MEV	17138	London	V171MVX	34171	London
TSO23X	14423	West Scotland	V138MVX	34138	London	V172DFT	17672	Manchester
TSU638	52090	Wales & West	V139MEV	17139	London	V172MEV	17172	London
TSU639	52113	East	V139MVX	34139	London	V172MVX	34172	London
TSU640	52114	East	V140MEV	17140	London	V173MEV	17173	London
TSU641	52118	East Scotland	V140MVX	34140	London	V173MVX	34111	London
TSU642	52119	East Scotland	V141MEV	17141	London	V174MEV	17174	London
TSV718	52131	East Scotland	V141MVX	34141	London	V175MEV	17175	London
TSV719	52132	East Scotland	V142MEV	17142	London	V175MVX	34123	London
TSV720	52133	North West	V142MVX	34142	London	V176MEV	17176	London
TSV721	52134	East Scotland	V143MEV	17143	London	V177MEV	17177	London
TSV722	52135	East Scotland	V143MVX	34143	London	V178MEV	17178	London
TSV778	52228	East Scotland	V144MEV	17144	London	V179MEV	17179	London
TSV779	52229	East Scotland	V144MVX	34144	London	V181MEV	17181	London
TSV780	52230	East Scotland	V145MEV	17145	London	V182MEV	17182	London
TSV781	52231	East Scotland	V145MVX	34145	London	V183MEV	17183	London
UCS659	19959	West Scotland	V146MEV	17146	London	V184MEV	17184	London
UF4813	19913	South East	V146MVX	34146	London	V185MEV	17185	London
UIB3076	25476	West Scotland	V147MEV	17147	London	V186MEV	17186	London
UIB3543	51071	West Scotland	V147MVX	34147	London	V188MEV	17188	London
UM7681	52097	West Scotland	V148MEV	17148	London	V189MEV	17189	London
UOT648	52171	East Scotland	V148MVX	34148	London	V190MEV	17190	London
URM801Y	14241	North West	V149MEV	17149	London	V191MEV	17191	London
URM802Y	14242	North West	V149MVX	34149	London	V192MEV	17192	London
USK625	12080	London	V150MEV	17150	London	V193MEV	17193	London
UWP105	52096	West Scotland	V150MVX	34150	London	V194MEV	17194	London

Registration	Fleet No	Region
V195MEV	17195	London
V196MEV	17196	London
V197MEV	17197	London
V198MEV	17198	London
V199MEV	17199	London
V201MEV	17201	London
V202MEV	17202	London
V203MEV	17203	London
V204MEV	17204	London
V205MEV	17205	London
V206MEV	17206	London
V207MEV	17207	London
V208MEV	17208	London
V209MEV	17209	London
V210MEV	17210	London
V211MEV	17211	London
V212MEV	17212	London
V213MEV	17213	London
V214MEV	17214	London
V215MEV	17215	London
V216MEV	17216	London
V217MEV	17217	London
V218MEV	17218	London
V219MEV	17219	London
V220MEV	17220	London
V221MEV	17221	London
V252ESX	22252	East Scotland
V253ESX	22253	East Scotland
V254ESX	22254	East Scotland
V255ESX	22255	East Scotland
V256ESX	22256	East Scotland
V257ESX	22257	East Scotland
V258ESX	22258	East Scotland
V259ESX	22259	East Scotland
V260ESX	22260	East Scotland
V261ESX	22261	East Scotland
V262ESX	22262	East Scotland
V263ESX	22263	East Scotland
V264ESX	22264	East Scotland
V265ESX	22265	East Scotland
V266ESX	22266	East Scotland
V267ESX	22267	East Scotland
V268ESX	22268	East Scotland
V362OWC	17187	London
V363OWC	17200	London
V364OWC	17222	London
V378EWE	17678	East Midlands
V379EWE	17679	East Midlands
V380EWE	17680	East Midlands
V381EWE	17681	East Midlands
V382EWE	17682	East Midlands
V383EWE	17683	East Midlands
V384EWE	17684	East Midlands
V385EWE	17685	East Midlands
V462TVV	33462	East
V463TVV	33463	East
V464TVV	33464	East
V476KJN	17110	London
V477KJN	17111	London
V478KJN	17121	London
V479KJN	17123	London
V601GCS	22601	West Scotland
V602GCS	22602	West Scotland
V603GCS	22603	West Scotland
V604GCS	22604	West Scotland
V605GCS	22605	West Scotland
V606GCS	22606	West Scotland
V614DJA	17614	Manchester
V615DJA	17615	Manchester
V616DJA	17616	Manchester
V617DJA	17617	Manchester
V618DJA	17618	Manchester
V619DJA	17619	Manchester
V620DJA	17620	Manchester
V621DJA	17621	Manchester
V622DJA	17622	Manchester
V623DJA	17623	Manchester
V624DJA	17624	Manchester
V667DDC	22667	North East
V668DDC	22668	North East
V669DDC	22669	North East
V670DDC	22670	North East
V671DDC	22671	North East
V672DDC	22672	North East
V673DDC	22673	North East
V674DDC	22674	North East
V675DDC	22675	North East
V701DSA	22701	East Scotland
V702DSA	22702	East Scotland
V703DSA	22703	East Scotland
V704DSA	22704	East Scotland
V705DSA	22705	East Scotland
V706DSA	22706	East Scotland
V707DSA	22707	East Scotland
V708DSA	22708	East Scotland
V709DSA	22709	East Scotland
V710DSA	22710	East Scotland
V711DSA	22711	East Scotland
V712DSA	22712	East Scotland
V713DSA	22713	East Scotland
V801DFV	22801	North West
V802DFV	22802	North West
V803DFV	22803	North West
V804DFV	22804	North West
V806DFV	22806	North West
V807DFV	22807	North West
V808DFV	22808	North West
V809DFV	22809	North West
V811DFV	22811	North West
V812DFV	22812	North West
V904DPN	52654	South East
V905DPN	52655	South East
V906DPN	52656	South East
V907DDY	52657	South East
V908DDY	52658	South East
V909DDY	52659	South East
V938DFH	33938	Wales & West
V939DFH	33939	Wales & West
V940DFH	33940	Wales & West
V941DFH	33941	Wales & West
V942DFH	33942	Wales & West
V943DFH	33943	Wales & West
V944DFH	33944	Wales & West
V945DFH	33945	Wales & West
V946DFH	33946	Wales & West
V947DFH	33947	Wales & West
V948DDG	33948	Wales & West
V949DDG	33949	Wales & West
V950DDG	33950	Wales & West
V951DDG	33951	Wales & West
V952DDG	33952	Wales & West
V953DDG	33953	Wales & West
V954DDG	33954	Wales & West
V955DDG	33955	Wales & West
V956DDG	33956	Wales & West
V957DDG	33957	Wales & West
V958DDG	33958	Wales & West
V959DDG	33959	Wales & West
V960DDG	33960	Wales & West
V961DFH	33961	Wales & West
V962DFH	33962	Wales & West
VCS376	52080	West Scotland
VCS391	51062	West Scotland
VKB708	52002	North West
VLF578	48067	North West
VLT14	17099	London
VLT37	51074	West Scotland
VLT54	52103	East Scotland
VLT154	52168	East Scotland
VLT245	52140	East Scotland
VLT255	16431	East
VLT272	52139	East Scotland
VRN829Y	14129	North West
VX51NXR	33978	Wales & West
VX51NXS	33979	Wales & West
VX51NXT	33980	Wales & West
W66BBW	50066	South Midlands
W102PMS	33200	South West
W173DNO	34173	London
W174DNO	34174	London
W176DNO	34176	London
W177DNO	34177	London
W178DNO	34178	London
W181DNO	34181	London
W182DNO	34182	London
W183DNO	34183	London
W184DNO	34184	London
W185DNO	34185	London
W186DNO	34186	London
W187CNO	17180	London
W187DNO	34187	London
W188DNO	34188	London
W189DNO	34189	London
W191DNO	34191	London
W192DNO	34192	London
W193DNO	34193	London
W194DNO	34194	London
W195DNO	34195	London
W196DNO	34196	London
W197DNO	34197	London
W198DNO	34198	London
W199DNO	34199	London
W201DNO	34201	London
W202DNO	34202	London
W203DNO	34203	London
W204DNO	34204	London
W207DNO	34207	London
W208DNO	34208	London
W209DNO	34209	London
W211DNO	34211	London
W212DNO	34212	London
W213DNO	34213	London
W214DNO	34214	London
W215DNO	34215	London
W216DNO	34216	London
W218DNO	34218	London
W219DNO	34219	London
W221DNO	34221	London
W223DNO	34223	London
W224DNO	34175	London
W226DNO	34179	London
W227DNO	34180	London
W228DNO	34205	London
W229DNO	34206	London
W231DNO	34190	London
W232DNO	34210	London
W233DNO	34200	London
W234DNO	34217	London
W235DNO	34220	London
W236DNO	34222	London
W501VDD	33501	Wales & West
W504VDD	33504	Wales & West
W508VDD	33508	Wales & West
W509VDD	33509	Wales & West
W626RND	17626	Manchester
W627RND	17627	Manchester
W628RND	17628	Manchester
W629RND	17629	Manchester
W631RND	17631	Manchester
W632RND	17632	Manchester
W633RND	17633	Manchester
W634RND	17634	Manchester
W635RND	17635	Manchester
W636RND	17636	Manchester
W637RND	17637	Manchester
W638RND	17638	Manchester
W639RND	17639	Manchester
W641RND	17641	Manchester
W642RND	17642	Manchester
W643RND	17643	Manchester
W644RND	17644	Manchester
W645RND	17645	Manchester
W646RND	17646	Manchester
W647RND	17647	Manchester
W805VDD	33505	Wales & West
WA51OSE	33201	South West
WA51OSF	33202	South West
WAO645Y	59045	North West
WDA2T	52102	Wales & West
WFS138W	25738	Manchester
WLT415	52173	East Scotland
WLT416	52069	West Scotland
WLT439	20599	West Scotland
WLT447	52307	East Scotland
WLT461	17101	London
WLT491	17100	London
WLT512	16432	East
WLT526	52174	East Scotland
WLT528	16433	East
WLT538	20598	West Scotland
WLT546	25728	West Scotland
WLT575	17260	London
WLT613	12013	London
WLT682	16434	East
WLT720	51070	West Scotland
WLT774	20597	West Scotland
WLT809	51099	West Scotland
WLT830	52087	East Scotland
WLT874	52079	West Scotland
WLT878	12086	London
WLT890	52022	London
WLT898	34100	London
WLT908	16435	East
WLT978	51098	West Scotland
WLT980	52072	North West
WSU293	52031	South Midlands
WVT618	20618	South East

Reg	No	Area	Reg	No	Area	Reg	No	Area
WYV3T	10003	North East	X277XTS	22277	East Scotland	X392NNO	17328	London
WYV5T	10005	West Scotland	X278NNO	17278	London	X393NNO	17330	London
WYV29T	10029	West Scotland	X279NNO	17279	London	X394NNO	17333	London
WYV56T	10056	North West	X281NNO	17281	London	X395NNO	17340	London
X59XCS	33780	West Scotland	X282NNO	17282	London	X396NNO	17345	London
X216BNE	22216	Manchester	X283NNO	17283	London	X397NNO	17350	London
X217BNE	22217	Manchester	X284NNO	17284	London	X398NNO	17355	London
X218BNE	22218	Manchester	X285NNO	17285	London	X428NSE	33428	East Scotland
X219BNE	22219	Manchester	X286NNO	17286	London	X429NSE	33429	East Scotland
X221BNE	22220	Manchester	X287NNO	17287	London	X431NSE	33431	East Scotland
X223BNE	22223	Manchester	X288NNO	17288	London	X432NSE	33432	East Scotland
X224BNE	22224	Manchester	X289NNO	17289	London	X433NSE	33433	East Scotland
X224WNO	34224	London	X291NNO	17291	London	X434NSE	33434	East Scotland
X226BNE	22226	Manchester	X292NNO	17292	London	X435NSE	33435	East Scotland
X226WNO	34226	London	X293NNO	17293	London	X436NSE	33436	East Scotland
X227BNE	22227	Manchester	X294NNO	17294	London	X437NSE	33437	East Scotland
X227WNO	34227	London	X295NNO	17295	London	X438NSE	33438	East Scotland
X228BNE	22228	Manchester	X296NNO	17296	London	X439NSE	33439	East Scotland
X228WNO	34228	London	X297NNO	17297	London	X441NSE	33430	East Scotland
X229BNE	22229	Manchester	X298NNO	17298	London	X502ADF	33502	Wales & West
X229NNO	17229	London	X299NNO	17299	London	X503ADF	33503	Wales & West
X229WNO	34229	London	X301NNO	17301	London	X506ADF	33506	Wales & West
X231BNE	22231	Manchester	X302NNO	17302	London	X507ADF	33507	Wales & West
X231NNO	17231	London	X303NNO	17303	London	X510ADF	33510	Wales & West
X231WNO	34231	London	X304NNO	17304	London	X511ADF	33511	Wales & West
X232BNE	22232	Manchester	X307NNO	17307	London	X512ADF	33512	Wales & West
X232NNO	17232	London	X308NNO	17308	London	X513ADF	33513	Wales & West
X232WNO	34232	London	X309NNO	17309	London	X601VDY	17689	South East
X233BNE	22233	Manchester	X311NNO	17311	London	X602VDY	17690	South East
X233NNO	17233	London	X312NNO	17312	London	X604VDY	22004	South East
X233WNO	34233	London	X313NNO	17313	London	X605VDY	22005	South East
X234BNE	22234	Manchester	X314NNO	17314	London	X606VDY	22006	South East
X234NNO	17234	London	X315NNO	17315	London	X607VDY	22007	South East
X234WNO	34234	London	X317NNO	17317	London	X613JCS	33443	West Scotland
X235BNE	22235	Manchester	X319NNO	17319	London	X614JCS	33444	West Scotland
X235NNO	17235	London	X322NNO	17322	London	X615JCS	33445	West Scotland
X235WNO	34235	London	X324NNO	17324	London	X616JCS	33446	West Scotland
X236BNE	22236	Manchester	X326NNO	17326	London	X617JCS	33447	West Scotland
X236NNO	17236	London	X327NNO	17327	London	X676NSE	52666	East Scotland
X236WNO	34236	London	X329NNO	17329	London	X677NSE	52667	East Scotland
X237BNE	22237	Manchester	X331NNO	17331	London	X678NSE	52668	East Scotland
X237NNO	17237	London	X332NNO	17332	London	X679NSE	52669	East Scotland
X237WNO	34225	London	X334NNO	17334	London	X701JVV	17691	East
X238BNE	22238	Manchester	X335NNO	17335	London	X702JVV	17692	East
X238NNO	17238	London	X336NNO	17336	London	X703JVV	17693	East
X238WNO	34230	London	X337NNO	17337	London	X704JVV	17694	East
X239BNE	22239	Manchester	X338NNO	17338	London	X705JVV	17695	East
X239NNO	17239	London	X339NNO	17339	London	X706JVV	17696	East
X241ATD	22241	Manchester	X341NNO	17341	London	X707JVV	17697	East
X241NNO	17241	London	X342NNO	17342	London	X714NSE	22714	East Scotland
X242ATD	22242	Manchester	X343NNO	17343	London	X715NSE	22715	East Scotland
X242NNO	17242	London	X344NNO	17344	London	X716NSE	22716	East Scotland
X243ATD	22243	Manchester	X346NNO	17346	London	X717NSE	22717	East Scotland
X243NNO	17243	London	X347NNO	17347	London	X718NSE	22718	East Scotland
X244ATD	22244	Manchester	X348NNO	17348	London	X719NSE	22719	East Scotland
X246ATD	22246	Manchester	X349NNO	17349	London	X721NSE	22721	North West
X246NNO	17246	London	X351NNO	17351	London	X722NSE	22722	East Scotland
X247NNO	17247	London	X352NNO	17352	London	X739JCS	33775	West Scotland
X248NNO	17248	London	X353NNO	17353	London	X741JCS	33776	West Scotland
X249NNO	17249	London	X354NNO	17354	London	X742JCS	33777	West Scotland
X251NNO	17251	London	X356NNO	17356	London	X743JCS	33778	West Scotland
X252NNO	17252	London	X357NNO	17357	London	X744JCS	33779	West Scotland
X253NNO	17253	London	X358NNO	17358	London	X805SRM	22805	North West
X254NNO	17254	London	X361NNO	17223	London	X813SRM	22813	North West
X256NNO	17256	London	X362NNO	17224	London	X814SRM	22814	North West
X257NNO	17257	London	X363NNO	17225	London	X815SRM	22815	North West
X258NNO	17258	London	X364NNO	17226	London	X816SRM	22816	North West
X259NNO	17259	London	X365NNO	17227	London	X817SRM	22817	North West
X261NNO	17261	London	X366NNO	17228	London	X818SRM	22818	North West
X262NNO	17262	London	X367NNO	17230	London	X819SRM	22819	North West
X263NNO	17263	London	X368NNO	17240	London	X821SRM	22821	North West
X264NNO	17264	London	X369NNO	17244	London	X822SRM	22822	North West
X265NNO	17265	London	X371NNO	17245	London	X823SRM	22823	North West
X266NNO	17266	London	X372NNO	17250	London	X824SRM	22824	North West
X267NNO	17267	London	X373NNO	17255	London	X825SRM	22825	North West
X268NNO	17268	London	X376NNO	17270	London	X826SRM	22826	North West
X269NNO	17269	London	X377NNO	17275	London	X827SRM	22827	North West
X269XTS	22269	East Scotland	X378NNO	17280	London	X827AKW	33847	East Midlands
X271NNO	17271	London	X379NNO	17290	London	X828AKW	33848	East Midlands
X271XTS	22271	East Scotland	X381NNO	17300	London	X829AKW	33849	East Midlands
X272NNO	17272	London	X382NNO	17305	London	X831AKW	33831	East Midlands
X272XTS	22272	East Scotland	X383NNO	17306	London	X832AKW	33832	East Midlands
X273NNO	17273	London	X384NNO	17310	London	X833AKW	33833	East Midlands
X273XTS	22273	East Scotland	X385NNO	17316	London	X834AKW	33834	East Midlands
X274NNO	17274	London	X386NNO	17318	London	X835AKW	33835	East Midlands
X274XTS	22274	East Scotland	X387NNO	17320	London	X836AKW	33836	East Midlands
X276NNO	17276	London	X388NNO	17321	London	X837AKW	33837	East Midlands
X276XTS	22276	East Scotland	X389NNO	17323	London	X838HHE	33838	East Midlands
X277NNO	17277	London	X391NNO	17325	London	X839HHE	33839	East Midlands

X840HHE	33840	East Midlands	Y274FJN	34274	London	Y389NHK	17389	London
X841HHE	33841	East Midlands	Y276FJN	34276	London	Y391NHK	17391	London
X948XAP	22008	South East	Y277FJN	34277	London	Y392NHK	17392	London
X953VAP	33053	South East	Y279FJN	34279	London	Y393NHK	17393	London
X954VAP	33054	South East	Y281FJN	34281	London	Y395NHK	17395	London
X956VAP	33055	South East	Y282FJN	34282	London	Y397NHK	17397	London
X957VAP	33056	South East	Y283FJN	34283	London	Y398NHK	17398	London
X958VAP	33057	South East	Y284FJN	34284	London	Y401NHK	17401	London
X959VAP	33058	South East	Y285FJN	34285	London	Y404NHK	17404	London
X961VAP	33061	South East	Y286FJN	34286	London	Y407NHK	17407	London
X962VAP	33062	South East	Y287FJN	34287	London	Y409NHK	17409	London
X963VAP	33063	South East	Y289FJN	34289	London	Y429NHK	17429	London
X964VAP	33064	South East	Y291FJN	34291	London	Y434NHK	17434	London
X965VAP	33065	South East	Y292FJN	34292	London	Y436NHK	17436	London
X966AFH	33966	Wales & West	Y293FJN	34293	London	Y437NHK	17437	London
X966VAP	33066	South East	Y294FJN	34294	London	Y438NHK	17438	London
X967AFH	33967	Wales & West	Y295FJN	34295	London	Y441NHK	17441	London
X967VAP	33067	South East	Y296FJN	34296	London	Y442NHK	17442	London
X968AFH	33968	Wales & West	Y297FJN	34297	London	Y443NHK	17443	London
X968VAP	33068	South East	Y298FJN	34298	London	Y445NHK	17445	London
X969AFH	33969	Wales & West	Y299FJN	34299	London	Y446NHK	17446	London
X969VAP	33069	South East	Y301FJN	34301	London	Y447NHK	17447	London
X971AFH	33971	Wales & West	Y302FJN	34302	London	Y448NHK	17448	London
X971VAP	33071	South East	Y329FJN	34329	London	Y449NHK	17449	London
X972AFH	33972	Wales & West	Y331FJN	34331	London	Y452NHK	17452	London
X972VAP	33072	South East	Y332FJN	34332	London	Y453NHK	17453	London
X973AFH	33973	Wales & West	Y334FJN	34334	London	Y454NHK	17454	London
X974AFH	33974	Wales & West	Y335FJN	34335	London	Y458NHK	17458	London
X975AFH	33975	Wales & West	Y336FJN	34336	London	Y462NHK	17462	London
X976AFH	33976	Wales & West	Y337FJN	34337	London	Y464NHK	17464	London
X977AFH	33977	Wales & West	Y338FJN	34338	London	Y508NHK	17360	London
X978AFH	33970	Wales & West	Y339FJN	34339	London	Y509NHK	17370	London
XFF813	12098	London	Y342FJN	34342	London	Y511NHK	17375	London
XFF814	12090	London	Y343FJN	34343	London	Y512NHK	17380	London
XIA857	25493	South West	Y344FJN	34344	London	Y514NHK	17400	London
XOV753T	25453	South Midlands	Y346FJN	34346	London	Y517NHK	17406	London
XRC487	52176	East Scotland	Y347FJN	34240	London	Y522NHK	17440	London
XSL596A	12189	London	Y348FJN	34245	London	Y524NHK	17450	London
XSU612	33012	South East	Y349FJN	34250	London	Y526NHK	17455	London
XSU682	20832	South East	Y351FJN	34255	London	Y527NHK	17456	London
XYK876	32719	South East	Y352FJN	34260	London	Y529NHK	17460	London
Y103GHC	17402	South East	Y353FJN	34270	London	Y531NHK	17470	London
Y237FJN	34237	London	Y354FJN	34275	London	Y671JSG	34288	London
Y238FJN	34238	London	Y356FJN	34280	London	YDG616	52056	North West
Y239FJN	34239	London	Y359NHK	17359	London	YEL4T	14714	South East
Y241FJN	34241	London	Y361NHK	17361	London	YL02FKY	47025	North East
Y242FJN	34242	London	Y362NHK	17362	London	YLJ332	30803	South East
Y243FJN	34243	London	Y363NHK	17363	London	YN51VHH	35000	East Midlands
Y244FJN	34244	London	Y364NHK	17364	London	YN51VHJ	35001	East Midlands
Y246FJN	34246	London	Y365NHK	17365	London	YN51VHK	35002	East Midlands
Y247FJN	34247	London	Y366NHK	17366	London	YN51VHL	35003	East Midlands
Y248FJN	34248	London	Y367NHK	17367	London	YN51VHM	35004	East Midlands
Y249FJN	34249	London	Y368NHK	17368	London	YN51VHO	35005	East Midlands
Y251FJN	34251	London	Y369NHK	17369	London	YN51VHP	35006	East Midlands
Y252FJN	34252	London	Y371FJN	34328	London	YN51VHR	35007	East Midlands
Y253FJN	34253	London	Y371NHK	17371	London	YN51VHT	35008	East Midlands
Y254FJN	34254	London	Y372FJN	34330	London	YN51VHU	35009	East Midlands
Y256FJN	34256	London	Y372NHK	17372	London	YN51VHV	35010	East Midlands
Y257FJN	34257	London	Y373FJN	34333	London	YN51VHW	35011	East Midlands
Y258FJN	34258	London	Y373NHK	17373	London	YN51VHX	35012	East Midlands
Y259FJN	34259	London	Y374FJN	34340	London	YN51VHY	35013	East Midlands
Y261FJN	34261	London	Y374NHK	17374	London	YN51VHZ	35014	East Midlands
Y262FJN	34262	London	Y376FJN	34345	London	YN51VJA	35015	East Midlands
Y263FJN	34263	London	Y376NHK	17376	London	YR02YRY	47801	South East
Y264FJN	34264	London	Y377NHK	17377	London	YR02YTA	47802	South East
Y265FJN	34265	London	Y378NHK	17378	London	YSD350L	59950	West Scotland
Y266FJN	34266	London	Y379NHK	17379	London	YSO34Y	14434	North East
Y267FJN	34267	London	Y381NHK	17381	London	YSO35Y	14435	North East
Y268FJN	34268	London	Y382NHK	17382	London	YSV730	51061	West Scotland
Y269FJN	34269	London	Y384NHK	17384	London	YSV735	52088	West Scotland
Y271FJN	34271	London	Y385NHK	17385	London	YTS820A	12199	London
Y272FJN	34272	London	Y386NHK	17386	London	YU02GRK	47803	North East
Y273FJN	34273	London	Y388NHK	17388	London	YU02GRX	47804	North East

ISBN 1 897990 83 9

© Published by *British Bus Publishing Ltd* , January 2003

British Bus Publishing Ltd, 16 St Margaret's Drive, Wellington, Telford, TF1 3PH
Telephone: 01952 255669 - Facsimile: 01952 222397

www.britishbuspublishing.co.uk - E-mail editorial@britishbuspublishing.co.uk